A STUDY OF
INTERPERSONAL RELATIONS

Also by Patrick Mullahy

OEDIPUS—MYTH AND COMPLEX

A Study of
Interpersonal Relations

NEW CONTRIBUTIONS TO PSYCHIATRY

Edited and with an introduction by

PATRICK MULLAHY

SCIENCE HOUSE, New York

TO
HARRY STACK SULLIVAN
1892–1949

ACKNOWLEDGEMENTS

I TAKE pleasure in expressing thanks and acknowledgement to the following for permission to use their contributions in this volume: Drs. Ernest Beaglehole, Hilde Bruch, Robert A. Cohen, Kingsley Davis, Frieda Fromm-Reichmann, Eliot Dole Hutchinson, Harold D. Lasswell, Talcott Parsons, Janet MacKenzie Rioch, Ernest G. Schachtel, Herbert Staveren, Harry Stack Sullivan, Clara Thompson, Sarah S. Tower.

In addition, it is a pleasure to give thanks and acknowledgement to Mr. Philip Sapir, executor of the late Dr. Edward Sapir, for permission to use the latter's paper, "Why Cultural Anthropology Needs the Psychiatrist," and to Dr. Margaret Mead, executor of the late Dr. Ruth Benedict, for the latter's paper, "Continuities and Discontinuities in Cultural Conditioning."

Finally, I wish to express my gratitude to the *Bulletin of the New York Academy of Medicine* for the use of Dr. Hilde Bruch's paper, "Psychological Aspects of Obesity," published in the *Bulletin*, February, 1948, Volume 24, Number 2, pages 73-86.

In the preparation of this volume, Mrs. Helen Swick Perry, formerly Managing Editor of *Psychiatry*, from which all papers in this volume are taken, has given freely of her assistance.

PATRICK MULLAHY

January, 1967

CONTENTS

ACKNOWLEDGEMENTS   xi

INTRODUCTION
Patrick Mullahy   xv

ON MEMORY AND CHILDHOOD AMNESIA
Ernest G. Schachtel   3

INTERPERSONAL THEORY AND SOCIAL PSYCHOLOGY
Ernest Beaglehole   50

THE TRANSFERENCE PHENOMENON IN PSYCHO-
ANALYTIC THERAPY
Janet MacKenzie Rioch   80

PSYCHIATRY: INTRODUCTION TO THE STUDY OF
INTERPERSONAL RELATIONS
Harry Stack Sullivan   98

RECENT ADVANCES IN PSYCHOANALYTIC THERAPY
Frieda Fromm-Reichmann   122

CULTURAL PRESSURES IN THE PSYCHOLOGY OF
WOMEN
Clara Thompson   130

THE ROLE OF WOMEN IN THIS CULTURE
Clara Thompson   147

REMARKS ON THE PHILOSOPHY OF MENTAL DISORDER
Frieda Fromm-Reichmann   162

NOTES ON INVESTIGATION, THERAPY, AND EDUCATION IN
PSYCHIATRY AND THEIR RELATIONS TO SCHIZOPHRENIA
Harry Stack Sullivan   192

CHANGING CONCEPTS OF HOMOSEXUALITY
Clara Thompson   211

PSYCHOLOGICAL ASPECTS OF OBESITY
    Hilde Bruch   223

WHY CULTURAL ANTHROPOLOGY NEEDS THE
PSYCHIATRIST
    Edward Sapir   239

CULTURAL COMPLEXITY AND PSYCHOLOGICAL
PROBLEMS
    Ernest Beaglehole   250

CERTAIN PRIMARY SOURCES AND PATTERNS OF AGGRES-
SION IN THE SOCIAL STRUCTURE OF THE WESTERN
WORLD
    Talcott Parsons   269

CONTINUITIES AND DISCONTINUITIES IN CULTURAL
CONDITIONING
    Ruth Benedict   297

PERSON, PERSONALITY, GROUP, CULTURE
    Harold D. Lasswell   309

MENTAL HYGIENE AND THE CLASS STRUCTURE
    Kingsley Davis   364

VARIETIES OF INSIGHT IN HUMANS
    Eliot Dole Hutchinson   386

THE PERIOD OF FRUSTRATION IN CREATIVE ENDEAVOR
    Eliot Dole Hutchinson   404

THE NATURE OF INSIGHT
    Eliot Dole Hutchinson   421

THERAPEUTIC INVESTIGATIONS IN SCHIZOPHRENIA
    Harry Stack Sullivan   446

SUGGESTED SPECIFICITY OF CERTAIN DYNAMISMS IN A
CASE OF SCHIZOPHRENIA
    Herbert Staveren   455

MANAGEMENT OF PARANOID TRENDS IN TREATMENT
OF A POST-PSYCHOTIC OBSESSIONAL CONDITION
    Sarah S. Tower   471

THE MANAGEMENT OF ANXIETY IN A CASE OF
PARANOID SCHIZOPHRENIA
    Robert A. Cohen   480

INTRODUCTION

INTRODUCTION
Patrick Mullahy

SEVENTEEN years have passed since this collection of papers on psychiatry, psychology, and social science was published in book form. But despite the progress made in those fields most of the papers in the collection remain as fresh, as exciting, and as valuable as they were in 1949. While not all of the authors explicitly adhere to an interpersonal orientation, the latter is the unifying principle or set of assumptions governing their thought, whether taken for granted or overtly avowed. It is a frame of reference which, in varying degrees of comprehensiveness and depth of insight, has been increasingly adopted as its significance has gradually dawned on the minds of a great number of students of human behavior. Even Freudian psychiatrists and psychologists, who still cling to the classical Freudian orientation, are gradually, though perhaps grudgingly, beginning to recognize the significance and power of an interpersonal orientation. But their work seems to me to have become unnecessarily limited because they still attribute extraordinary importance to "libidinal drives" or, more generally, to "instincts," which, in fact, take on definition and meaning only in interpersonal contexts. Hence the recent "ego psychology" of Freudian psychoanalysis seems to me a relatively ineffectual attempt to reconcile Freud's instinctual orientation with Sullivan's interpersonal orientation.

In Sullivan's psychology the "ego" or self is an outcome of social interaction, of interpersonal relations—a point of view originally formulated by Charles Horton Cooley and George Herbert Mead. The self develops and functions in order that the person may satisfy drives and maintain security (ward off anxiety). There is no single generic drive, such as the libido, to serve as a "motor," lying back of human behavior. However classified, the motives of human behavior are multiple. And they are originally labile to a high degree. From a

Sullivanian point of view, the greatest shortcoming of Freudian psychology lies in its overemphasis on sexual drives, to the relative neglect of interpersonal necessities and demands, which give character and direction to *all* drives, including what some psychologists call the striving for self-realization. From a Sullivanian point of view, it makes no sense to talk of a self and its strivings apart from interpersonal relations.[1]

Nevertheless Sullivan's "system" is not a wholesale repudiation of Freud's. The former, to a considerable extent, is a modified and expanded version of the central ideas of Freud, though reformulated in terms of interpersonal relations. However, lest anyone think I am not adequately recognizing Sullivan's originality, I suggest a comparison of his interpretations of obsessional neurosis and schizophrenia with Freud's. The differences are profound.

From time to time, a few psychiatrists have privately expressed puzzlement as to why Sullivan's orientation has not "swept the field." Perhaps if Sullivan, who died at the age of fifty-six, had lived another fifteen years it would have, though I am none too sure about that. Be that as it may, one can discern several factors which have hindered the understanding or acceptance of Sullivanian psychiatry at its true value. First of all, there is the familiar fact that traditional ideas and attitudes in any field usually die hard. Once one has adopted a systematic point of view—or perhaps any point of view whatsoever—it tends to act like blinders. Or, to put this in another way, given a point of view, it acts as a filter through which experience is seen and organized. The history of thought seems to testify to this statement. Until a rigorous method of analysis and testing of ideas emerges, human ingenuity can almost always find a stratagem for explaining away or making light of defects, overlooking negative instances, castigating the new as superficial or wrong-headed.

Not that the new is always and everywhere superior to the old. Not that the new always absolutely invalidates the old. A craving for novelty merely for the sake of novelty is at best a symptom of immaturity.

A second difficulty, often closely allied to the first, inheres in the prestige which often attaches itself to tradition. Within limits this is a good thing, for it tends to put a brake on any wholesale reaching

[1] *Conceptions of Modern Psychiatry* by Harry Stack Sullivan, The William Alanson White Psychiatric Foundation, Washington, D.C., 1947, p. 88.

for unconsidered and untested novelty. But when tradition for its own sake, or rather for the sake of its prestige, is adhered to unaltered it makes for fear and hostility to the new, however promising the latter might otherwise be. Something of this love of tradition clings to classical psychoanalytic schools, I think, despite the fact that Freud himself had to fight hard and long against received ideas and attitudes. When Freud began his famous collaboration with Breuer, psychiatry did not amount to much. In one generation Freud had perhaps accomplished as much for the new science as all the men who, since Aristotle, preceded him. Understandably the memory of Freud carries an afterglow. His ideas have often been adopted with an almost religious fervor. The prestige of classical psychoanalysis—though often obscurely understood—is enormous. Whether it can retain this prestige is somewhat doubtful in the light of current trends.

A third difficulty facing Sullivanian psychiatry pertains to the lack of any stable organization comparable to the Freudian psychoanalytic institute, which would serve as a center for teaching and "training" young psychiatrists in interpersonal psychology. Although Sullivan has been called a "charismatic personality," he could not hand on his charisma. He left behind him no band of devoted disciples who would explicate and carry on his teachings. A few students and colleagues, such as the late Frieda Fromm-Reichmann struggled to consolidate and enrich interpersonal theory, but with indifferent success. There is no genuinely Sullivanian institute.

Though there is now a very wide diffusion of the *language* of interpersonal psychiatry, the ideas which it conveys are, as a rule, very bland and superficial versions of the original. One can see this clearly in some of the articles which appear in *Psychiatry,* the journal which Sullivan was instrumental in founding, and which once served as an organ for the expression of Sullivanian conceptions and ideas from the social sciences congenial to interpersonal psychiatry. Another example can be found in the prestigious text, *The Theory and Practice of Psychiatry,* of Redlich and Freedman. To be sure these authors do not profess to be Sullivanian psychiatrists. But their interpretations of Sullivan are superficial, as any conscientious psychiatrist who will compare the ideas in Sullivan's lectures with Redlich's and Freedman's interpretations can see.

Finally, I should like to mention the current vogue of bio-chemical explanations and speculations. While no judgment of these trends can be made here, one wonders how their proponents will deal with what has long been regarded as functional mental illness. To illustrate, Sullivan taught that anxiety is a central explanatory concept in the evolution and functioning of various kinds or categories of mental illness. Anxiety, he thought, originates and operates only in interpersonal contexts, and *could not occur* in the absence of certain kinds of inadequate interpersonal relations. On this view anxiety is an experiential ("mental") occurrence. It is not caused by specific bio-chemical factors. It cannot be permanently removed by chemical agents alone since it is an outcome of interpersonal relations. More generally, "psychogenic" interpretations of mental illness seem, in the main, to contradict current attempts at bio-chemical explanations. The two contrasting and conflicting generic views regarding the nature and cure of mental illness certainly pose nice problems for future psychiatric researchers.

For the fuller understanding of this volume, we now present some of the basic principles of the theory of interpersonal relations. With the partial exception of mental disorder based on organic impairment or deficiency, mental illness is seen to be a product of a social order which is in some ways grossly inadequate for the development of healthy and happy human beings.

By and large, the field of psychiatry is located in the phenomena of interpersonal relations, of social relations. It is circumscribed by the processes which involve or go on between people. For practical purposes, the psychiatrist must often limit his activities to more or less well defined problems of living and to the elaboration of developing techniques of therapy. But in principle no phenomenon of human life is alien to the psychiatrist. Ideally at any rate he is a humanist in the best sense of that frequently debased concept. In theory he takes the whole human world for his province, and he must find out as much as he can about it. There is no science, no art, from which he cannot learn.

Hence, the great discoveries and brilliant therapeutic techniques of Freud are utilized to the full. This does not mean that Freudian theory and therapy are regarded as the last word, a final revelation of psychiatric science. Nevertheless, although much of Freudian theory is being modified by more recent investigators in the light of much more adequate data, the fundamental discoveries of Freud remain and are of enduring value. It is on the foundations which Freud, above everyone else, has laid that subsequent theory and therapy arise. There are common strains of agreement in the writings of all psychoanalytically oriented psychiatrists. Parenthetically, we may observe that it is not true that science in its historical progress discards one theory after another. This notion has been fostered by those who are hostile to science and who have some special axe to grind. The history of science shows an increasing refinement of theory along with the accumulation of more and more factual data. Of course not every hypothesis offered in any scientific field remains as the sciences progress. In psychiatry the case is essentially no different. Some of Freud's theories seem destined to suffer the fate of the phlogiston hypothesis—the libido theory, for example. But of course Freud's genuine discoveries and insights have been retained. His speculations are for the most part being abandoned by many.

It is on the basis of Freud's discoveries, among others, that men like Sullivan and Fromm have erected their theories. For example, they have abandoned Freud's concept of the libido. Thus, because of his libido theory Freud explained affection as a "sublimation" of libidinal or sexual energy. There are two things worth noting about this. First, as others have pointed out, the notion of sublimation is itself rather mysterious and needs an explanation. By what strange kind of alchemy can sexual energy be transformed into the phenomenon we call affection? *Prima facie* the experience of affection is rather different from the experience of sexual excitement, though the two may often go together. However, there is an added complication. Freud expanded the concept of libido to include almost any kind of pleasure. It became a pleasure-striving "force" or entity. The libido became a "bag," as someone put it, into which one could throw a variety of phenomena. It purported to explain everything from the sucking of the infant to the intensely pleasurable experience of sexual orgasm.

For this reason the concept of libido, instead of making direct experience more intelligible, often made it more opaque. In endeavoring to effect a transition from the libido concept to direct experience Freud sometimes had to resort to awkward and ultimately unintelligible explanations, like that of "sublimation."

In other words Freud became entrapped in the reductive fallacy. He "reduced" the experience of affection, for example, to something more elemental, namely, a libidinal striving or a sublimation of it. And if one asks what a libidinal striving is, the answer is, it is a pleasure-striving "force." Hence, various experiences, which as they are directly had, are rather disparate, in this way lose their distinctive character for the sake of a concept which by "explaining" so much explains nothing.

To be sure, there is much more to be said on this subject which we cannot discuss here.

On the other hand, Freud's concept of the unconscious has been retained, though with some modification. Certain traits of Freud's notion of the unconscious as he at one time used the term have been abandoned, such as its "topographical" aspect. Other aspects of the concept of the unconscious, however, have been preserved, for example, that various experiences occur outside conscious awareness and vitally influence thought, feeling and overt behavior.

Another contribution of Freud's which must be and is retained is the detailed discovery that the experiences of childhood are enormously important for the subsequent development of personality, whether sick or healthy. However many conceive the significance of childhood somewhat differently from Freud.

There are of course many more contributions which Freud has to his everlasting credit; but these examples may suffice as to how revision and modification as well as conservation of Freudian theory take place.

While Freud conceived the role of society as primarily suppressive and external to the person,[2] people like Sullivan and Fromm claim that the function of society is primarily creative and only secondarily suppressive. The social sciences have driven home the point that it is misleading and confusing to set up any kind of

[2] See, for example, *New Introductory Lectures On Psychoanalysis* by Sigmund Freud, W. W. Norton & Co., Inc., New York, 1933, Chapters 3 and 4.

fundamental opposition between the person and society. Mind and personality are products of acculturation.

However, due to a variety of historical circumstances we tend to think of ourselves as somehow physically and mentally disparate from the rest of the world. We have grown up in a culture which implicitly stresses a separation of subject and object, ego and external world. And we imbibe this notion until it becomes so much a part of our thinking that we scarcely ever stop to question it. Yet the more we reflect on the matter, the more we realize that we are indissolubly united with what is ordinarily called our environment, physical and social, as long as life continues. Subject and object, therefore, are distinctions which we have instituted; they are not predetermined separate entities *in rerum natura*. In other words, we live communally with and in our environment. We do not exist apart from it.

In regard to the physical environment, it is easier to show our intimate connection with it than with our social milieu. Yet the very "stuff" of our minds is socially inherited. Furthermore, what we inherit has been acquired from various significant people, at first the mother or nurse, then others, such as father, sisters and brothers, schoolmates, teachers. The form and content of our mental activity have been built from "interaction" with other human beings. Hence, our mental activity occurs in the form of an "interaction" with other people, whether they are real, or "fantastic" or a blend of both. It is almost as if our minds, our personalities, became a forum in which the influences, the behavior, the ideas and attitudes of various people with whom we have been somehow in close contact were again and again acted out and re-lived.

We said it is "almost" as if our minds became a forum because the human being is not a helpless, passive victim of influences coming from what is called the external world. One, at first depending on various vicissitudes of the environment, more or less willy-nilly "selects" as best he can from others what he needs in accordance with his organic constitution. But later the selection and modification of what has been handed down become more specifically determined. To be sure, in infancy there is not much the infant

xxiii

can do except experience the attitudes and behavior of significant others, although even here, from the beginning of life, there appears to be differential behavior.[3] He depends on the mother for his very life. At first he has no mind or personality in a distinctive sense. Hence, the child necessarily imbibes the attitudes of others, at first conveyed "empathically" according to Sullivan, by means of some kind of emotional communion between mother and child. As he develops, gestures, facial expressions, and words are added, which convey to him something of the way others feel about him and, as time goes on, what they expect from him. And so gradually the child learns the use of language. He becomes "educated." What he learns is select excerpts from the cultural heritage passed on by the parents, playmates and teachers.

The two all-inclusive goals which people strive for in life, according to Sullivan, are satisfactions and security. Satisfactions are more obviously related to man's somatic organization. The desire for food and drink, sleep and rest, for sexual gratification, result in performances which are said to be the pursuit of satisfactions. Loneliness is also included as a "middling example."

While the pursuit of satisfactions is more immediately related to man's somatic needs, the pursuit of security, which is the second all-inclusive goal, pertains more to man's cultural equipment, although both are intimately interconnected. All "those movements, actions, speech, thoughts, reveries and so on which pertain more to the culture which has been imbedded in a particular individual than to the organization of his tissues and glands, is apt to belong in this classification of the pursuit of security."[4]

The pursuit of satisfactions and security may be regarded as "integrating tendencies." These goals are what bring people together. They explain in very general terms why any situation in which man finds himself is an inter-personal situation.

It seems that every human being is born with "something" of a

[3] Sullivan, *op. cit.,* pp. 14-15. Compare *Personality, A Biosocial Approach to Origins and Structure* by Gardner Murphy, Harper & Brothers, New York, 1947, Chapters 3 and 8.

[4] Sullivan, *op. cit.,* p. 6.

power motive, a tendency to master or control or come to grips with the environment in some more or less self-satisfying fashion. It needs no elaborate demonstration to show that the infant is quite helpless. If unaided by people, his existence becomes very brief indeed. And so from the infant's discovery of his powerlessness there begins a vast development of "actions, thoughts, foresights, and so on, which are calculated to protect one from a feeling of insecurity and helplessness in the situation which confronts one. This accultural evolution begins thus, and when it succeeds, when one evolves successfully along this line, one respects oneself, and as one respects oneself so one can respect others." [5]

To have power in interpersonal relations means that one can obtain and maintain satisfactions and security.

For the infant, the achievement of satisfaction, if other factors to be mentioned below do not intervene, brings a feeling of well-being. It seems that tonic changes in the unstriped involuntary muscles of the internal organs of the body are always intimately connected with the felt needs for satisfaction. Hunger seems to be associated with heightened tone of the stomach wall; the occurrence of vigorous contractions of the tense muscles are said, in a manner of speaking, to give rise to the pangs of hunger. The ingestion of food leads to the relief of the excess tone and the contractions quiet down. "Throughout life the pursuit of satisfactions is physiologically provoked by increased tone in some unstriped muscles; and the receiving of the satisfactions is a relaxation of this tone, with a tendency towards the diminution of attention, alertness, and vigilance, and an approach to sleep." [6]

In regard to the pursuit of security, things are more complicated. We have hinted above that the offspring has a peculiar sensitivity to what goes on in his immediate environment. Thus if the mother manifests anger or hate toward him, according to theory, he feels intense discomfort; his feeling of well-being is markedly decreased. This feeling of discomfort, uneasiness, lack of a feeling of well-being, is the basis of what Sullivan calls anxiety. It is called out by

[5] Sullivan, *op. cit.*, pp. 6-7.
[6] Sullivan, *op. cit.*, p. 43.

"noxious emotional states" empathized from his personal environment. And this feeling of intense and painful discomfort is said to be one of the most terrible experiences that man undergoes. It is somewhat like a blow on the head.

On the other hand, the child experiences other attitudes and behavior which relieve discomfort and feelings of insecurity. These other experiences restore his sense of well-being.

At some time in the child's life, which will vary from culture to culture, the mother or her surrogate begins deliberate training. She begins to teach the child what is considered right and wrong and what is considered correct behavior in her society. Thus she trains him in the "proper" toilet habits, eating habits, speech behavior, and so on. When the child conforms to her wishes, she is, at least often, warmly approving. If he does not conform, she disapproves, and depending on her own personality, may even resort to stronger measures. At any rate, the child feels her varying attitudes. And he gradually catches on to what happens. He learns, for example, that when his sense of well-being, of security has been decreased due to the empathized disapproval or hostility of the mother, performances in certain desired ways restore it.

In the process of relieving discomfort, insecurity, anxiety, the striped skeletal muscles take on a new function. In the securing of satisfaction they were "of relatively instrumental value"—Sullivan does not say what that is. But in any case they gradually become associated with the experiencing of anxiety. Hence the "oral dynamism," which includes the respiratory apparatus and the food taking apparatus, is of the greatest significance. "The oral dynamism," according to Sullivan, "has been the channel for performances needed to appease hunger and pain and other discomforts. It may be presumed that its function in emitting the cry has been quite automatic. This may not have worked too well, and delayed response to the cry may be one of the first experiences that tend to focus alertness. But in any case, the oral dynamism is not now effective in securing relief from the discomfort set up by empathy; on some occasions, it is simply ineffectual, and on other occasions, its activity is accompanied by increase of the empathized discomfort. This leads gradually to a differentiation of empathized from other discomforts, and to the *inhibition* of the cry as a universal tool. The inhibiting of a complex pattern of behavior is not as simple as was its automatic initiation. Some of the movements are cut off, but the increase of tone in the appropriate muscles may not be inhibited. The experience of empathized hostility, or unfriendly prohibition, or, as it later comes to be observed, a forbidding gesture, becomes colored by and associated with heightened tone in some striped muscles—at first those concerned with the cry.

"The course of acculturation, in so far as it pertains to toilet habits, is also a learning to suffer increasing tension in the bladder and rectum, and to resist the automatic relaxation of the sphincter muscles concerned in retaining the urine and feces. Failures in this are often accompanied by empathized discomfort, and success is often the occasion of empathized comfort—which is added to the satisfaction from relief of the tension." [7]

The child gradually learns to focus his attention on performances which bring approval or disapproval in order that he may more easily and effectually win the one, which is associated with good feeling, euphoria, security, and avoid the other, now perceived to be connected with the experiences of painful discomfort and anxiety. Hence, the child pays less heed, if any, to those of his performances which do not involve marked approval or disapproval. The result is that those performances go on outside discriminated awareness; they are not carefully noted.

There is a gradual focusing of discriminating awareness of performances by the child himself and others which are connected with the increase or decrease of approval and rewards for "good" behavior. It is out of this focusing of awareness that the self is evolved. This process may be said to be analogous to the function of a microscope, which facilitates concentrated observation of some things and excludes observation of others.

The self is thus built up and circumscribed by experiences of reward and punishment, of approval and disapproval, of the people who are significant in the child's life: the parents, playmates, teach-

[7] Sullivan, *op. cit.*, p. 44.

ers, and so on. The self acquires a determinate direction, and by and large it maintains it throughout life, although subsequent experience may alter its direction somewhat or at least expand the field of discriminating awareness.[8]

Since the child has no data for appraising himself or his performances except what he learns from the significant others, he tends to accept their judgments as to his worth and their valuation of his performances. Hence, the self comes to be made up of reflected appraisals. One learns to appraise his own worth as it has been appraised by others, who are themselves conditioned and moulded by their own life experience. In the beginning there is nothing else the child can do; and when he grows older and perhaps catches on at least dimly to the fact that different people have different views as to his worth, the self has already been firmly established and is as a rule quite inhospitable toward the idea of change. One becomes "personified" in the early experiences with others. The type of performances and actions which did not come under approval or disapproval goes on outside of discriminated awareness, outside the operation of the self dynamism. These other performances are said to be *selectively inattended* or disassociated.[9]

It was the experience of painful discomfort, of anxiety which caused the child to focus his awareness on performances which brought approval or disapproval. Thus anxiety became an instrumentality by which discriminated awareness was given a certain direction, which determines the form and content of the self. So it comes about that anxiety operates so as to limit the self, by and large, to developing in the direction it took at the beginning. Whenever the person experiences anything which tends to enlarge the margin of the self, anxiety occurs. Then the self, so to speak, veers away from such anxiety-laden experience. The person does not clearly notice what goes on. Things are rather blurred; the meaning of such experiences is not observed in any discriminating fashion.

[8] Fortunate experience during the school years, for example, may modify the bad effects of unloving parents.

[9] Sullivan's *Conceptions,* Lecture II. Compare Murphy, *Personality,* chapters 20, 21, 22, 23.

In traditional language, one is unconscious of what is happening. For example, if a person has been brought up in an environment where the significant others are derogatory, he acquires a derogatory attitude toward himself. This derogatory attitude will then tend to persist through life, barring the intervention of extraordinary circumstances. Whenever such a person in later life meets with another friendly person who has a different non-derogatory attitude, the former will not notice it or he will discount it. There is nothing in his self-system which would make a non-derogatory attitude meaningful. In other words, his low self-appraisal prevents the other fellow's attitude from making sense. Or if there were, anxiety would intervene and blot out the conscious awareness of the other person's friendliness.

So anxiety interferes with observation and understanding, and with all kinds of experience, at least to some extent. Anxiety thus interferes with alertness to whatever factors in a situation are relevant to its occurrence. For this reason it interferes with or modifies action. Anxiety is likewise opposed to the achievement of satisfactions. A very anxious person may be unable to sleep, or rest properly, or gain sexual gratification. In other words the tension of anxiety, which is always generated by interpersonal, social experience, is directly opposed to the tension of somatic needs.

Now to the degree to which a person cannot achieve satisfactions and security, due to unfortunate life experience, he is mentally ill. This is what Sullivan means by mental illness.

As we have already observed, many actions occur outside the field of discriminating awareness, which by and large means outside the self. In ordinary language, the person does not know what he is doing, at least consciously, in regard to certain aspects of his behavior. Some things, however, which the self ordinarily is not aware of, may be made conscious, may be integrated into the self system, if, for example, a friend should call one's attention to them. Such processes are said to be *selectively inattended*.[10] However, there are other processes going on outside the self which it refuses to become discriminatingly aware of. In this case, should anyone try

[10] Sullivan, *op. cit.*, p. 131.

to point them out, the person manifesting them not only denies their existence but probably gets angry as well. In other words, he has been made anxious. Anger is a frequent device which people unconsciously resort to when they are made anxious. Such processes to which the self refuses discriminating awareness are said to be *disassociated*.

Hence the personality includes those processes which are selectively inattended or disassociated as well as those which occur, as we say, in the self system.

It is clear that because of the limitations of the self system and the limitations imposed on the entire personality because of the vicissitudes of the development of the self, our powers of observation, discrimination and understanding of what goes on in interpersonal relations are often grossly limited. Our relations with people not rarely tend to be befogged with all kinds of irrelevancies, causally determined, however, in large part by the distortions imposed on us by our early training. Often we meet current interpersonal situations in terms of past situations because of the threat to our self system. New situations may have characteristics with which our self system cannot deal. Hence we tend to become anxious and blot out of discriminating awareness whatever is novel in the situation. When this happens, the actual situation as it might reveal itself to an ideal observer is said to be parataxic.

In other words, we relate to people as if they were more or less identical with people who were significant in our past life. What we experience is a kind of caricature, a parataxic distortion of the real persons acting in the situation. They become, as Sullivan has more recently expressed it, "eidetic personalities." Disassociated elements in our personality and in those of others also overtly or subtly operate. From these factors result so much of the puzzlement, confusion, misunderstanding, "irrational" feeling in our dealings with people.

By and large, the biological or somatic conditions of human nature, for many purposes at least, may be taken as fairly constant. Hence the psychiatrist turns his attention (1) to the specific situations in which interpersonal processes occur, (2) to the historical development of a person's acculturation, and (3) to the social forms, the cultural patterns, of which select excerpts have been incorporated into the personality of the individual.[11]

We have attempted to show why mental activity is an interpersonal process. Nevertheless, human nature and behavior have been conceived as constituted by fixed, predetermined and isolated impulses, drives, or instincts, which are expressed or manifested in overt behavior in a rather mechanical fashion. Not only have human beings been conceived of atomistically, but human impulses have likewise been thought of as self-contained and essentially independent, in regard to quality and form of expression, of the environing world.

But the new viewpoint of psychiatry holds that we cannot regard people as existing in such fashion. Human experience and behavior occur in situations constituted by two or more people, "only one of whom need not be illusory." The other person may exist only in the imagination, or he may be a flesh and blood individual, or he may be part "real" and part illusory. Hence, we never observe persons acting in a self-isolated fashion. Nor do we ever observe—or experience in any fashion—isolated impulses and drives. We observe behavior, actions, including what we call mental activity, in interpersonal situations. In other words, we observe and participate in interpersonal situations.

Since several papers in this volume discuss the detailed phenomena of such situations, we need not labor the point. One of the most detailed papers on interpersonal situations is Sullivan's *Psychiatry: Introduction to the Study of Interpersonal Relations.* However, this paper is highly complicated and involved, so we recommend that anyone unfamiliar with interpersonal theory first read some of the other papers in this volume. As an introduction to the theory, the papers by Drs. Lasswell and Beaglehole will serve.

Since no one's relationships with people are entirely devoid of distorting elements from the past, a discussion of (1) above always has to take account of (2). To understand people, the genetic-functional approach is often, if not always, essential. We cannot

[11] Compare Sullivan, *op. cit.,* pp. 94, 95, 87.

understand a person solely in terms of the past, nor can we as a rule, if ever, entirely understand what goes on in the present situation without some knowledge—sometimes a great deal of knowledge—of the past. This fact is brought out very vividly by the paper on *Transference* by Dr. Rioch. She believes, following Fromm's interpretation, that what is curative in the psychoanalytic process is not, for example, a re-living of early traumatic experience, but "that in tending to reconstruct with the analyst that atmosphere which obtained in childhood, the patient actually achieves something new. He discovers that part of himself which had to be repressed at the time of the original experience. He can only do this in an interpersonal relationship with the analyst which is suitable to such a re-discovery."

In another way, the inter-related role of past and present is also brought out brilliantly by Dr. Schachtel's paper *On Memory and Childhood Amnesia*. He claims that the function of memory "can be understood only as a capacity for the organization and reconstruction of past experiences and impressions in the service of present needs, fears, and interests." Schachtel also holds that the modern Western world has no use for experiences of the quality and intensity typical of early childhood. The memory of a rich childhood experience "would explode the restrictive social order of this civilization."

Thus in order to understand the vicissitudes of (1) and (2) one is eventually led to (3). Several papers make this very clear. Dr. Thompson's paper *Cultural Pressures in the Psychology of Women* also is as explicit as any on this point.

Changes in theory, if they are not merely formal or dialectical, usually involve changes in practice. Consequently, along with the changes in the theory of personality and personality development, important changes in methods of therapy have occurred. Dr. Frieda Fromm-Reichmann, formerly a practitioner of "classical" psychoanalysis, in *Recent Advances in Psychoanalytic Therapy*, discusses some of the modifications of therapy brought about largely as a result of, or in conjunction with, changes in theory. In her *Remarks on the Philosophy of Mental Disorder*, Fromm-Reichmann holds, contrary to popular opinion, that one "can emerge from a severe mental disorder as an artist of rank."

Another advance in therapy and theory concerns homosexuality. Classical psychoanalysis, as Dr. Thompson points out in her paper *Changing Concepts of Homosexuality in Psychoanalysis*, has used it as "a kind of wastebasket into which are dumped all forms of relationships with one's own sex." According to classical psychoanalytic theory, there are latent homosexuality, repressed homosexuality, and overt homosexuality. In regard to overt homosexuality, Thompson holds it is not a clinical entity at all but a symptom, analogous, say, to a headache, with different meanings in different people. In other words overt homosexuality seems to be a symptom often, if not always, of disturbed and inadequate interpersonal relationships.

Dr. Hilde Bruch presents some striking data on obesity in her paper *Psychological Aspects of Obesity*. She observes that it is brought about, in most instances, through a combination of overeating and inactivity. Eating and exercise for obese people have an emotional meaning different from the normal. Bruch's analysis reveals that the locus of the problem of obesity is to be discovered in disturbed relationships with people and the derogatory attitude obese people often have toward themselves.

Without mentioning all of the papers contained in this collection, we want to call attention finally to Dr. Hutchinson's series of papers on *Insight*. They are especially remarkable in that they not only offer a noteworthy attempt to analyze the cycle of activities involved in the creative process but also the consequences often following failure to realize one's creative gifts. Hutchinson does not give much comfort to those who believe that in order to be creative one must be "neurotic." He claims that "in the long run the possibility of creation is the salvation of genius, the guarantee of health and effectiveness, not its undoing."

Many other excellent papers have appeared in *Psychiatry* over the years, but for obvious reasons we cannot include them in one volume. And we have been obliged to exclude papers which do not of themselves, without reference to other papers, form a coherent whole.

To conclude, the point of view which the writers in this volume represent indicates that fixed biological needs and drives and their frustration do not provide the locus of mental illness, that instead the social order itself is the ultimate matrix of functional mental disorder. Such a view is, in the genuine sense of the term, radical. It shows that if psychiatry is to be socially effective, it cannot willingly acquiesce in cheerful acceptance of the status quo. A reading of this volume may likewise convince one that the standards now prevailing in Western culture may no longer be considered as eternal and immutable criteria of mental health and mental illness. Once and for all the empirically minded anthropologists have effectively disposed of that notion. Hence, a perusal of this volume may very well instill a proper humility in regard to some of the values now flourishing in the Western world. Such a study may thus teach us a greater respect for other cultures and their mode of life.

I should like to emphasize that interpersonal psychiatry cannot get a fair hearing until it is thoroughly understood. I do not think it is thoroughly understood now. The reprinting of this collection of papers, many of them classics, will, I surmise, engender a deeper, more comprehensive interest in interpersonal psychiatry.

January, 1967

A STUDY OF
INTERPERSONAL RELATIONS

ON MEMORY AND
CHILDHOOD AMNESIA

Ernest G. Schachtel

G REEK mythology celebrates Mnemosyne, the goddess of memory, as the mother of all art. She bore the nine muses to Zeus.[1] Centuries after the origin of this myth Plato banned poetry, the child of memory, from his ideal state as being idle and seductive. While lawmakers, generals, and inventors were useful for the common good, the fact that Homer was nothing but a wandering minstrel without a home and without a following proved how useless he was.[2] In the Odyssey the voices of the Sirens tempt Ulysses.

> For never yet hath any man rowed past
> This isle in his black ship, till he hath heard
> The honeyed music of our lips, and goes
> His way delighted and a wiser man.
> For see, we know the whole tale of the travail
> That Greeks and Trojans suffered in wide Troy-land
> By heaven's behest; yea, and all things we know
> That come to pass upon the fruitful earth.

Their irresistible song, in evoking the past, promises a delight which will allow no future and will be the end of Ulysses' plans to return to an active life and to resume the rule of Ithaca. He prevents his

[1] The words "muse" and "mnemosyne" derive from the same root μεν or μαν. Preller, Ludwig, *Griechische Mythologie;* Berlin 1872; vol. 1, p. 399, footnote 1. In German, too, the words "Gedächtnis" (memory) and "Dichtung" (poetry) derive from the same root "denken" (think); compare also "gedenken" (remember).

[2] Plato, *Republic,* 599, 600.

shipmates from listening to the alluring voices by plugging their ears with wax, and he, too curious to renounce the pleasure, has himself chained to the ship's mast so that he will not be able to yield to their song and abandon the future.

This ambivalent attitude toward memory, especially toward its most potent form as embodied in the song, the epic, the tale, in poetry, music, fiction, and in all art, has accompanied the history of man. The modern, popular attitude, so widespread in the United States, the country of the most advanced industrial and techno-logical civilization—that all art and poetry is "sissy"—is the latter-day implementation of the Platonic taboo. But with this difference: the contemporaries of Plato, and before them the shipmates of Ulysses, were susceptible to the promise of happiness that the song of the Sirens and of the muses contains, so that Ulysses and Plato, concerned with planning and not with the past, had to prevent their listening forcefully. Today the masses have internalized the ancient fear and prohibition of this alluring song and, in their contempt for it, express and repress both their longing for and their fear of the unknown vistas to which it might open the doors.

The profound fascination of memory of past experience and the double aspect of this fascination—its irresistible lure into the past with its promise of happiness and pleasure, and its threat to the kind of activity, planning, and purposeful thought and behavior encouraged by modern Western civilization—have attracted the thought of two men in recent times who have made the most sig-nificant modern contribution to the ancient questions posed by the Greek myth: Sigmund Freud and Marcel Proust.

Both are aware of the antagonism inherent in memory, the con-flict between reviving the past and actively participating in the present life of society. Both illuminate the nature of this conflict from different angles. Proust, the poet of memory, is ready to re-nounce all that people usually consider as active life, to renounce activity, enjoyment of the present moment, concern with the future, friendship, social intercourse, for the sublime happiness and pro-found truth recaptured in the most elusive of all treasures that man has hunted for, the "Remembrance of Things Past." He pursues this conflict between activity and memory into its most subtle manifestations. He knows that, as the awakening dreamer may lose the memory of his dream when he moves his limbs, opens his eyes, changes the position of his body, so the slightest motion may endanger and dispel the deep pleasure of the vision of the time in Combray, recaptured by the flavor of the *madeleine,* or the image of Venice conjured up by the sensation and the posture which the unevenness of the pavement in the court of the Guermantes town house brought to him as the unevenness of the pavement of San Marco had years ago.[3] He does not dare to stir, for fear that the exhilarating vision may disappear. Bodily movement is the basic and simplest form of all activity endangering memory. Action itself, the attitude of activity, even the activity of enjoying the immediate present are seen by Proust as the antagonists, the incompatible alternative of memory.[4] From here it is only one step to the insight that the memory which reveals the true vision of something past, the memory celebrated by Proust, is very different from the voluntary, everyday memory, the useful instrument needed by man every hour and every minute to recall a word, a figure, a date, to recognize a person or an object, to think of his plans, tasks, intentions, the eminently utilitarian memory characterized by the very fact that it serves the purposes of active and conventionally organized life in society. Proust speaks of the artificiality and untruth of the pictures that this memory furnishes, of its flat and uniform quality which cannot do justice to the unique flavor and the true qualities of anything remembered.[5]

While for Proust the antagonism between society and memory of the significant past can be resolved only by renouncing either one or the other, Goethe seeks to reconcile the two. When, at a party, a toast was proposed to memory he objected vehemently with these words: "I do not recognize memory in the sense in which you mean it. Whatever we encounter that is great, beautiful, significant, need

[3] Marcel Proust, À *la recherche du temps perdu, VIII, Le temps retrouvé;* Librairie Gallimard, Editions de la Nouvelle Revue Française, Paris 1927; vol. 2, p. 8.
[4] Reference footnote 3; p. 14.
[5] Reference footnote 3; pp. 11-12.

not be remembered from outside, need not be hunted up and laid hold of as it were. Rather, from the beginning, it must be woven into the fabric of our inmost self, must become one with it, create a new and better self in us and thus live and become a productive force in ourselves. There is no past that one is allowed to long for. There is only the eternally new, growing from the enlarged elements of the past; and genuine longing always must be productive, must create something new and better." [6]

Freud, not unlike Proust, approaches the problem of memory not from wondering what, or how well, or how much man remembers, but how hard it is to remember, how much is forgotten and not to be recovered at all or only with the greatest difficulty, and how the period richest in experience, the period of early childhood, is the one which usually is forgotten entirely save for a few apparently meaningless memory fragments. He finds this surprising since "we are informed that during those years which have left nothing but a few incomprehensible memory fragments, we have vividly reacted to impressions, that we have manifested human pain and pleasure and that we have expressed love, jealousy and other passions as they then affected us." [7] The few incomprehensible memory fragments left over from childhood, he considers as "concealing memories," (Deckerinnerungen) [8] and his painstaking work to decipher their language bears more than a superficial resemblance to Proust's attempt to decipher the hieroglyphic characters of the images of a cloud, a triangle, a belfry, a flower, a pebble,—a most difficult undertaking, but the only way to the true memories enclosed in these signs which seemed to be only indifferent material objects or sensations. [9] It was Freud who made the discovery that

[6] Author's translation from Goethe's *Gespräche;* Herausgegeben von Flodoard Freiherr von Biedermann; Vol. 3, Leipzig 1910, p. 37, (November 4th, 1823). Compare with this Proust's *"Les vrais paradis sont les paradis qu'on a perdu."* Reference footnote 3; p. 13.

[7] Sigmund Freud, Three Contributions to the Theory of Sex. In *The Basic Writings of Sigmund Freud;* Random House, New York 1938; p. 581.

[8] Sigmund Freud, Psychopathology of Everyday Life; see reference footnote 7; pp. 62-65.

[9] Reference footnote 3; p. 24.

a conflict, leading to repression, is responsible for the difficulty of this work of deciphering and for the difficulty of remembering the past. His well-known explanation of infantile amnesia is that the forgetting of childhood experiences is due to progressive repression of infantile sexuality, which reaches the peak of its manifestations in the third and fourth years of life. This repression is brought about by the "psychic forces of loathing, shame, and moral and esthetic ideal demands." [10] These forces have the sanction of society, they are the product of society, they are part and serve the purposes of the same conventionally organized life of society which moulds the functions of all social activity and of that "uniform" memory in which Proust saw the irreconcilable antagonists of the true remembrance of things past.

It is the purpose of this essay to explore further the dynamics of this conflict in memory which leads to the striking phenomenon of childhood amnesia as well as to the difficulty, encountered by Proust though more hidden to the average eye, of recovering *any* true picture of past experience. To speak of a conflict in memory is a convenient abbreviation. Formulated more explicity and accurately, the intention of this presentation is to shed light on some of the factors and conflicts in man and his society which make it difficult if not impossible for him really to remember his past and especially his early childhood.

Obviously, the concept of memory which such an approach pre-

[10] Reference footnote 7; p. 583. Freud asserts that the development of these forces during the latency period is organically determined and that it "can occasionally be produced without the help of education." It is surprising that the man who discovered, explored, described, and emphasized over and over again the conflict between culture, society, and sexual instinct should have ascribed the ontogenetic origin of sexual inhibitions to organic factors as though he wanted to explain as natural those inhibitions which a culture, hostile to pleasure and to sex, has created, deepened, and strengthened in every imaginable way. The only explanation for such a strange and questionable hypothesis lies, to my mind, in Freud's and every great discoverer's tragic conflict between a powerful and lucid mind searching for truth and the person who never can entirely extricate himself from the thousand threads with which he is captured and tied to the prejudices, ideologies, falsehoods, and conventions of his time and society.

supposes cannot be the impersonal, artificial, isolated, and abstract concept implied by experimentation on the recall of digits, nonsense syllables, and similar material, a concept which seems more appropriate for the testing of the capacity of some mechanical apparatus than for the understanding of the functioning of memory in the living person. Nor is such a concept fundamentally changed when logically meaningful phrases or perceptually organized "Gestalten" are substituted for nonsense syllables and memory is investigated for its capacity to reproduce those, rather than meaningless material. Nobody doubts that it is easier to remember meaningful than meaningless material and that the function of memory has not developed in order to make possible the recall of nonsense. Memory as a function of the living personality can be understood only as a capacity for the organization and reconstruction of past experiences and impressions in the service of present needs, fears, and interests. It goes without saying that, just as there is no such thing as impersonal perception and impersonal experience, there is also no impersonal memory. Man perceives and remembers not as a camera reproduces on the film the objects before its lens; the scope and quality of his perceptions and experiences as well as of their reproduction by memory are determined by his individual needs, fears, and interests. This is the more apparent the more significant an experience has been for the person.

With this concept of memory in mind, the puzzling problem of childhood amnesia seems to become more transparent and accessible to understanding. No greater change in the needs of man occurs than that which takes place between early childhood and adulthood. Into this change have gone all the decisive formative influences of the culture transmitted by the parents, laying the fundament of the transformation into the grown-up, "useful" member of society from the little heathen, who is helpless but as yet sees nothing wrong with following the pleasure principle completely and immediately and who has an insatiable curiosity and capacity for experience. An explanation of childhood amnesia that takes into account these changes leads to the following tentative hypothesis:

The categories (or schemata) of adult memory are not suitable receptacles for early childhood experiences and therefore not fit to preserve these experiences and enable their recall. The functional capacity of the conscious, adult memory is usually limited to those types of experience which the adult consciously makes and is capable of making.

It is not merely the repression of a specific content, such as early sexual experience, that accounts for the general childhood amnesia; the biologically, culturally, and socially influenced process of memory organization results in the formation of categories (schemata) of memory which are not suitable vehicles to receive and reproduce experiences of the quality and intensity typical of early childhood. The world of modern Western civilization has no use for this type of experience. In fact, it cannot permit itself to have any use for it; it cannot permit the memory of it, because such memory, if universal, would explode the restrictive social order of this civilization. No doubt the hostility of Western civilization to pleasure, and to sexual pleasure as the strongest of all, is a most important factor operative in the transformation and education of the child into an adult who will be able to fulfill the role and the functions he has to take over in society and will be satisfied by them. Freud has not only called attention to the phenomenon of childhood amnesia but has also singled out a decisive factor in its genesis. I believe, however, that two points are important for a more adequate understanding of the phenomenon. First, it is not sufficiently clear why a repression of sexual experience should lead to a repression of all experience in early childhood. For this reason the assumption seems more likely that there must be something in the general quality of childhood experience which leads to the forgetting of that experience. Second, the phenomenon of childhood amnesia leads to a problem regarding the nature of repression, especially repression of childhood material. The term and concept of repression suggest that material which *per se* could be recalled is excluded from recall because of its traumatic nature. If the traumatic factor can be clarified and dissolved, the material is again accessible to recall. But even the most profound and prolonged psychoanalysis does not lead to a recovery of childhood memory; at best it unearths some incidents and feelings that had been forgotten. Childhood amnesia, then, may be due to a formation of the memory functions which makes them unsuitable to accommodate childhood experience, rather than exclusively to a censor repressing objectionable material which, without such repression, could and would be remembered. The adult is usually not capable of experiencing what the child experiences; more often than not he is not even capable of imagining what the child experiences. It would not be surprising, then, that he should be incapable of recalling his own childhood experiences since his whole mode of experiencing has changed. The person who remembers is the present person, a person who has changed considerably, whose interests, needs, fears, capacity for experience and emotion have changed. The two mechanisms of forgetting suggested here shade gradually and imperceptibly into one another. They are neither alternatives nor opposites, but rather the two ends of a continuous scale. It might be theoretically interesting to follow up this viewpoint to see how much it could clarify the much used but not too clear concept of repression and the processes underlying repression. However, this would lead too far away from the immediate problem of a more concrete understanding and testing of the suggested general theory of early childhood amnesia.

A closer examination and comparison of the content and quality of adult and childhood memories may be helpful for the purpose of such an understanding. Both Freud and Proust speak of the autobiographical memory, and it is only with regard to this memory that the striking phenomenon of childhood amnesia and the less obvious difficulty of recovering any past experience may be observed. There is no specific childhood amnesia as far as the remembrance of words learned and of objects and persons recognized is concerned. This type of material is remembered because, in contrast to the autobiographical past, it is constantly re-experienced and used and because it is essential for the orientation and adaptation of the growing child to his environment. In the recall of this type of material we have to deal with memory serving the immediate, practical use of knowledge and perception (recognition) mainly. The memory of the personal past—of one's past experiences, which also contain the material that has gone into the formation of one's character—is a much less efficient and reliable servant than the memory of learned material, on the whole, seems to be. Yet the separation of the "useful" from the "autobiographical" memory is, of course, an artificial abstraction. Actually this distinction of the content of remembered material is not clear-cut, and the two types of material indicated by it are continuously and everywhere interrelated.

The autobiographical memory shows indeed in most persons, if not in all, the amnesia for their early childhood from birth to approximately the fifth or sixth year. Of course, there are considerable gaps in the memory of many people for later periods of their lives also, probably more so for the period before than after puberty; but these gaps vary individually to a much greater extent than does the ubiquitous early childhood amnesia. Freud's observation of this amnesia has not stimulated others, as far as I can see, to significant investigations of the adult autobiographical memory. Yet it would seem that an awareness of the main differences between the type of material remembered from early childhood and that remembered from later life might help in an understanding of the phenomenon of childhood amnesia. If one believes Proust, life after childhood is not remembered either, save for the elusive flashes of a vision given only to the most sensitive and differentiated mind as the rare grace of a fortunate moment, which then the poet, with passionate devotion and patient labor, may try to transcribe and communicate.

Freud contrasts the presumable riches of childhood experience, the child's great capacity for impressions and experience, with the poverty or total lack of memory of such rich experience. If one looks closely at the average adult's memory of the periods of his life after childhood, such memory, it is true, usually shows no great temporal gaps. It is fairly continuous. But its formal continuity in time is offset by barrenness in content, by an incapacity to reproduce anything that resembles a really rich, full, rounded, and alive experience. Even the most "exciting" events are remembered as milestones rather than as moments filled with the concrete abundance

of life. Adult memory reflects life as a road with occasional signposts
and milestones rather than as the landscape through which this road
has led. The milestones are the measurements of time, the months
and years, the empty count of time gone by, so many years spent
here, so many years spent there, moving from one place to another,
so many birthdays, and so forth. The signposts represent the outstanding events to which they point—entering college, the first job,
marriage, birth of children, buying a house, a family celebration, a
trip. But it is not the events that are remembered as they really
happened and were experienced at the time. What is remembered
is usually, more or less, only the fact that such an event took place.
The signpost is remembered, not the place, the thing, the situation
to which it points. And even these signposts themselves do not
usually indicate the really significant moments in a person's life;
rather they point to the events that are conventionally supposed to
be significant, to the clichés which society has come to consider as
the main stations of life. Thus, the memories of the majority of
people come to resemble increasingly the stereotyped answers to a
questionnaire, in which life consists of time and place of birth, religious denomination, residence, educational degrees, job, marriage,
number and birthdates of children, income, sickness and death. The
average traveler, asked about his trip, will tell you how many miles
he has made (how many years he has lived); how fast he went
(how successful he was); what places he has visited—usually only
the well known ones, often he visits only those that one "simply
must have seen"—(the jobs he has held, the prestige he has
gained). He can tell you whether the driving was smooth or rough,
or whether somebody bumped his fender, but he will be quite unable to give you any real idea of the country through which he
went. So the average traveler through life remembers chiefly what
the road map or the guide book says, what he is supposed to remember because it is exactly what everybody else remembers too.

In the course of later childhood, adolescence, and adult life, perception and experience themselves develop increasingly into the
rubber stamps of conventional clichés. The capacity to see and feel
what is there gives way to the tendency to see and feel what one

expects to see and feel, which, in turn, is what one is expected to see and feel because everybody else does.[11] Experience increasingly assumes the form of the cliché under which it will be recalled because this cliché is what conventionally is remembered by others. This is not the remembered situation itself, but the words which are customarily used to indicate this situation and the reactions which it is supposed to evoke. While this ubiquitous and powerful tendency toward pseudo-experience in terms of conventional clichés usually takes place unnoticed, it is quite articulate in some people and is used widely in advertising. There are people who experience a party, a visit to the movies, a play, a concert, a trip in the very words in which they are going to tell their friends about it; in fact, quite often, they anticipate such experience in these words. The experience is predigested, as it were, even before they have tasted of it. Like the unfortunate Midas, whose touch turned everything into gold so that he could not eat or drink, these people turn the potential nourishment of the anticipated experience into the sterile currency of the conventional phrase which exhausts their experience because they have seen, heard, felt nothing but this phrase with which later they will report to their friends the "exciting time" they have had. The advertising business seems to be quite aware of this. It does not have to promise a good book, a well-written and well-performed play, an entertaining or amusing movie. It suffices to say that the book, the play, the movie will be the talk of the town, of the next party, of one's friends. To have been there, to be able to say that one has been present at the performance, to have read the book even when one is unable to have the slightest personal reaction to it, is quite sufficient. But while Midas suffered tortures of starvation, the people under whose eyes every experience turns into a barren cliché do not know that they starve. Their starvation

[11] Tolstoi gives a masterful description of how, in an adolescent girl during a visit to the opera, the experience of what happens on the stage changes from a genuine, naive, and fresh view to the conventional "appreciation" of the opera habitué. His account of her initial perceptions, by the way, is a surrealist description of opera more than half a century before surrealism. Tolstoi, *War and Peace,* part 8, chapters 9 and 10.

manifests itself merely in boredom or in restless activity and incapacity for any real enjoyment.

The burial and distortion of experience in the process of memory under the cliché of the conventionally accepted finds an interesting confirmation in Bartlett's experiments on memory.[12] In one of them he showed to his subjects, who were educated adults, five picture postcards, on each of which was the representation of the face of a naval or army officer or man. He asked them to look at each card for ten seconds "noting carefully as many of the characteristics of the faces as you can, so that later you may be able to describe the faces, and to answer questions about them." Half an hour after the exposure of the cards, each subject described them and answered questions about some of the details. This was repeated after a week and then after longer intervals. Reporting the outcome of this experiment, Bartlett says, among other things: "Obviously, complicating the perceptual pattern were all kinds of conventional notions about soldiers and sailors of a given rank. . . . A particular face often at once aroused a more or less conventional attitude appropriate to the given type. Thereupon, the attitude actively affected the detail of representation. Even in immediate memory the features of the face often tended to be made more conventional, while in subsequent recall they tended to approach yet more closely the conventional pattern." He summarizes the results of this experiment by saying that it "seems certain that attitudes may strongly influence recall and may tend in particular to produce stereotyped and conventional reproductions which adequately serve all normal needs, though they are very unfaithful to their originals."

In another experiment he used a North American Indian folk tale, "The War of the Ghosts." Each subject read the story twice. Then he reproduced it after 15 minutes and again, several times, after considerably longer intervals. In these reproductions a most important role is played by a factor which Bartlett calls "rationalisation"; the function which he attributes to it is "to render material

[12] Bartlett, F. C., *Remembering: A Study in Experimental and Social Psychology;* Cambridge University Press, Cambridge 1932; see especially pp. 53-54, 89, 125, 171-173.

acceptable, understandable, comfortable, straightforward; to rob it of all puzzling elements." With one of his subjects all mention of ghosts disappeared in the very first reproduction of the story "in spite of the fact that special attention was called to the title. The same thing occurred at some stage in *every* series obtained with this story as a starting point. This omission illustrates how any element of imported culture which finds very little background in the culture to which it comes must fail to be assimilated."

However, conventionalization affects not only elements of "imported culture," but everything recalled. Bartlett gave newspaper reports of a cricket game and a passage from a review of Tilden's book *The Art of Lawn Tennis* to Cambridge undergraduates for repeated reproduction. In still another experiment he used a passage, "The intellect is vagabond," from Emerson's essay, *Self-Reliance,* with entirely similar results. In one chain of reproductions of the latter "every bit of general reasoning had disappeared. The whole point of the original is lost. All that is left is a bald record of a personal incident, and one general opinion. This opinion is the exact opposite to the original from which it is derived, but is no doubt more in accord with common views." In his summary of the experiments using stories and similar material, Bartlett comes to the conclusion that "all the stories tend to be shorn of their individualising features, the descriptive passages lose most of the peculiarities of style and matter that they may possess, and the arguments tend to be reduced to a bald expression of conventional opinion. . . . Where the opinions expressed are individual they appear to tend to pass over into opposed conventional views; where the epithets are original they tend to become current, commonplace terms. The style gets flattened out and loses any pretensions it may have had to forcefulness and beauty."

The process of memory thus substitutes the conventional cliché for the actual experience. It is true that the original experience or perception usually is already, to a large extent, determined by conventional cliché, by what the person expected to see or hear, which means by what he has been taught to expect. However, everybody who has paid attention to these processes in himself and others can

observe that there is, especially at first, some awareness of the discrepancy between the experience itself and the thought or words
which articulate, preserve, and express it. The experience is always
fuller and richer than the articulate formula by which we try to be
aware of it or to recover it. As time passes, this formula comes to
replace more and more the original experience and, in addition, to
become itself increasingly flat and conventionalized. Memory, in
other words, is even more governed by the conventional patterns
than perception and experience are. One might say that, while all
human experience, perception, and thought are eminently social—
that is, determined by the socially prevailing ways of experiencing,
perceiving, and thinking—memory is even more socialized, to an
even higher degree dependent on the commonly accepted categories of what and how one remembers. Bartlett's experiments confirm this. As time passes, the remembered story loses more and
more of its original flavor until nothing remains of its essence and
a banal cliché is substituted for it. "Rationalization," as psychoanalytic theory knows it, is but one type of such transformation of actual
experience into individually and socially acceptable clichés. One
important reason why memory is even more susceptible than experience and perception to such conventionalization is that experience
and perception always are in *some*, however flimsy, immediate relation to the situation experienced, the object perceived, while memory is distant from it in time and space. The object of memory has
less chance than the objects of experience and perception have to
penetrate and do away with part of that glass, colored and ground
by the social mores and viewpoints, through which man sees everything or fails to see it. Memory is a distance sense, as it were, and—
to an even greater degree than the two other distance senses, vision
and hearing—less immediately related to its objects than the proximity senses of smell, taste, and touch, and more influenced and
moulded by the categories of the mind. Also like sight and hearing,
only more so, memory is a phylogenetically and ontogenetically
more differentiated, later, and more "spiritual" development than
smell, taste, and touch. All this predestines memory to lose contact
with actual experience and to substitute preformed, conventional

patterns of thought for it. And, as will be seen later, it has significant bearing especially on the problem of early childhood amnesia.

How well is the average highly conventionalized adult memory
equipped to contain and recall the time and the experiences of
early childhood? Very poorly or not at all. This will become more
apparent through consideration of the quality of early childhood
experience. The adult amnesia for this period prevents direct knowledge. Observation of little children and imagination are the only
means of learning something about this subject. It is safe to assume
that early childhood is the period of human life which is richest
in experience. Everything is new to the newborn child. His gradual
grasp of his environment and of the world around him are discoveries which, in experiential scope and quality, go far beyond any
discovery that the most adventurous and daring explorer will ever
make in his adult life. No Columbus, no Marco Polo has ever seen
stranger and more fascinating and thoroughly absorbing sights
than the child that learns to perceive, to taste, to smell, to touch,
to hear and see, and to use his body, his senses, and his mind.
No wonder that the child shows an insatiable curiosity. He has
the whole world to discover. Education and learning, while on
the one hand furthering this process of discovery, on the other hand
gradually brake and finally stop it completely. There are relatively
few adults who are fortunate enough to have retained something of
the child's curiosity, his capacity for questioning and for wondering.
The average adult "knows all the answers," which is exactly why he
will never know even a single answer. He has ceased to wonder, to
discover. He knows his way around, and it is indeed a way around
and around the same conventional pattern, in which everything is
familiar and nothing cause for wonder. It is this adult who answers
the child's questions and, in answering, fails to answer them but
instead acquaints the child with the conventional patterns of his
civilization, which effectively close up the asking mouth and shut
the wondering eye. Franz Kafka once formulated this aspect of education by saying that "probably all education is but two things, first,
parrying of the ignorant children's impetuous assault on the truth

and, second, gentle, imperceptible, step-by-step initiation of the humiliated children into the lie." [13]

Most children go through a period of endless questioning. While at first they desire an answer, gradually their search turns into an almost automatic repetition of the same seemingly senseless question or into the related ritual of countering every answer with a new question. It is as though the child no longer really expected or perhaps wanted to obtain information by this type of questioning, but expressed only the last stubborn assault against the unbroken wall of adult "answers." The child has already almost forgotten what he wanted to know, but he still knows *that* he wanted to know and did not receive an answer. The automatic questioning may have the unconscious purpose of driving this point home to the adult. It is chiefly during the period of early childhood that the quality of the world around him changes for the growing child from a place where everything is new and to be explored—to be tasted, smelled, touched and handled, wondered about and marveled at—to a place where everything either has received a name and a label or is potentially capable of being "explained" by such a label, a process which will be pursued systematically in school. No experience, no object perceived with the quality of freshness, newness, of something wonder-full, can be preserved and recalled by the conventional concept of that object as designated in its conventional name in language. Even if, in modern Western civilization, the capacity of such fresh experience has largely been deadened, most people, unless they have become complete automatons, have had glimpses of the exhilarating quality that makes fresh experience, unlabeled, so unique, concrete, and filled with life. They can realize, if their attention is called to it,

[13] In view of the inadequacy of the author's translation, the German text is given here: "Wie ja allerdings wahrscheinlich alle Erziehung nur zweierlei ist, einmal Abwehr des ungestuemen Angriffs der unwissenden Kinder auf die Wahrheit und dann sanfte unmerklich-allmähliche Einfuehrung der gedemuetigten Kinder in die Luege." Kafka, Franz, *Beschreibung eines Kampfes; Novellen, Skizzen, Aphorismen aus dem Nachlass;* Verlag Heinrich Mercy Sohn, Prag 1936; p. 317. The passage is taken from an earlier version of what probably was the last story Kafka wrote, "Forschungen eines Hundes" (Researches of a dog).

the great difference between such experience and one which merely registers the label of things seen, of the furniture of the room, the familiar faces, the houses on the street. Yet this difference is small when compared with the difference that separates the young child's fresh experience and discoveries from the adult's recognition of the familiar clichés into which the automatic labeling of perception and language has transformed the objects around him. Since adult memory functions predominantly in terms of recalling clichés, the conventional schemata of things and experiences rather than the things and experiences themselves, it becomes apparent how ill-equipped, in fact incapable, such conventionalized memory is to recall the experiences of early childhood in their freshness, in the real significance which they had at that time. The age of discovery, early childhood, is buried deep under the age of routine familiarity, adulthood.

The incompatibility of early childhood experience with the categories and the organization of adult memory is to a large extent due to what I call the conventionalization of the adult memory. Conventionalization is a particular form of what one might call schematization of memory. Voluntary memory recalls largely schemata of experience rather than experience. These schemata are mostly built along the lines of words and concepts of the culture. Also the so-called visual or the auditory memory reproduces schemata of visual or auditory impressions rather than the impressions themselves. Obviously the schemata of experience as well as of memory [14] are determined by the culture which has developed a certain view of the world and of life, a view which furnishes the schemata for all experience and all memory. But the range and differentiation of a culture like that of Greece, India, China, or modern Western civiliza-

[14] The term memory schemata is taken from Bartlett (reference footnote 12) but used in a somewhat different sense. Bartlett rightly emphasizes that remembering is "an affair of reconstruction rather than mere reproduction." According to him, this reconstruction serves as a justification of the present attitude toward past experience. Such reconstructions he calls schemata, and these are determined by sense differences, appetites, instincts, and interests. In this essay, however, the concept of memory schemata is used only to designate socially and culturally determined patterns of reconstruction of the past, as contrasted to individually determined patterns. Obviously the greater part of all individual memory schemata in Bartlett's sense are culturally determined.

tion is of considerable scope. It offers highly differentiated and subtle as well as very conventional, banal, and commonplace schemata. By conventionalization of the memory (and experience) schemata I understand those memory processes which are subject to the most conventional schematization and which, therefore, are not capable of reproducing individual experience, but can only reproduce what John Doe is supposed to have experienced according to the Joneses' and everybody else's ideas of what people experience. Every fresh and spontaneous experience transcends the capacity of the conventionalized memory schema and, to some degree, of any schema. That part of the experience which transcends the memory schema as preformed by the culture is in danger of being lost because there exists as yet no vessel, as it were, in which to preserve it. Even if the schemata of experience have not prevented the person from becoming aware of or sensing that quality of his experience which transcended these schemata, this quality, if it is to be preserved and to become a productive part of the personality, has to overcome the second handicap of the memory schemata, which tend, as time goes on, to supplant this fresh and new element of experience with some preformed notion and thus to bury it. The process of schematization and conventionalization and its effect on the raw material of experience, especially childhood experience, can be well observed in two of its specific developments which take place as the child learns to make use of his senses and to speak.

Language, in its articulating and its obscuring function, may be considered first since the adult, too, encounters the problem of the incompatibility of experience with language and the consequent forgetting of experience or its distortion by the cliché of language. The fact that language is adult language, the language of an adult civilization, and that the infant and small child is moulded only very gradually from its natural existence into a member of the civilization into which it is born makes the discrepancy between his precivilized, unschematized experience and the categories of civilized, conventional language much greater. Yet between this discrepancy and that existing between the adult's experience and his language, there is a difference of degree rather than of kind. Everyone who has honestly tried to describe some genuine experience exactly, however small and insignificant it may have seemed, knows how difficult if not impossible that is. One might well say that the greatest problem of the writer or the poet is the temptation of language. At every step a word beckons, it seems so convenient, so suitable, one has heard or read it so often in a similar context, it sounds so well, it makes the phrase flow so smoothly. If he follows the temptation of this word, he will perhaps describe something that many people recognize at once, that they already know, that follows a familiar pattern; but he will have missed the nuance that distinguishes his experience from others, that makes it his own. If he wants to communicate that elusive nuance which in some way, however small, will be his contribution, a widening or opening of the scope of articulate human experience at some point, he has to fight constantly against the easy flow of words that offer themselves. Like the search for truth, which never reaches its goal yet never can be abandoned, the endeavor to articulate, express, and communicate an experience can never succeed completely. It consists of an approach, step by step, toward that distant vantage point, that bend of the road from which one hopes to see the real experience in its entirety and from where it will become visible to others, —a point which is never reached. The lag, the discrepancy between experience and word is a productive force in man as long as he remains aware of it, as long as he knows and feels that his experience was in some way more than and different from what his concepts and words articulate. The awareness of this unexplored margin of experience, which may be its essential part, can turn into that productive energy which enables man to go one step closer to understanding and communicating his experience, and thus add to the scope of human insight. It is this awareness and the struggle and the ability to narrow the gap between experience and words which make the writer and the poet. The danger of the schemata of language, and especially of the worn currency of conventional language in vogue at the moment when the attempt is made to understand and describe an experience, is that the person making this attempt will overlook the discrepancy between experience and language cliché or that he will not be persistent enough in his attempt to eliminate this discrepancy. Once the conventional schema has replaced the experience in his mind, the significant quality of the experience is condemned to oblivion.

The discrepancy between concepts, language, and experience can be looked upon as a model and as part of the discrepancy between memory schemata and experience. This close relationship, of course, is not accidental since voluntary recall and communication of recalled experience are essentially dependent on conceptual thought and language. While there is also recall of experience without the vehicle of language, a great deal of what we recall, especially of what we recall voluntarily, is recalled already in terms of language and in concepts formed by language. This has considerable bearing on the problem of childhood amnesia. The infant and small child has to undergo and assimilate the comparatively greatest amount of new experience at a time when his language, his concepts, and his memory schemata are poorest or as yet entirely undeveloped. Only very gradually does he acquire the faculty of language, learn the conceptual schemata of his culture, and develop a memory and memory schemata. The experiences of the infant are inarticulate and complex. In a term coined by Sullivan, they are instantaneous records of total situations.[15] They are also as yet unformed and untainted by the experience schemata of the culture which, from the viewpoint of the culture, justifies Freud's remark that the small child is "polymorphous-perverse." He is a little animal, a little heathen, and his experiences are only gradually and increasingly forced into the Procrustean bed of the culturally prevalent experience schemata which allow for certain experiences, forbid others, and omit a great many for which the culture has either no frame of reference or only an unsuitable one. It is true that only by learning and developing the schemata of language, conceptual thought, experience, and memory prevalent in the culture can the child progress from the phase of complex and inarticulate experience to that of specific and articulate experience. It is true that the complex and inartic-

[15] Mullahy, Patrick, A Theory of Interpersonal Relations and the Evolution of Personality, PSYCHIATRY (1945) 8:177-205; p. 183.

ulate experience of infancy and early childhood, because of the very lack of schemata for detailed articulation, is often prevented from reaching awareness or else soon removed from awareness and forgotten. But, on the other hand, the schemata provided by the culture and gradually acquired by the growing child cannot accommodate his experience in its entirety, but will distort and bias it according to the patterns of the culture. Two major trends thus operate in the direction of the eventual outcome of early childhood amnesia. First, the schemata for articulate experience and for recall of such experience are relatively slow and late in developing. They are entirely lacking in the earliest period of life and one could say generally that as they develop, experience gradually loses its character of newness and acquires the quality of familiarity and recognition. The tremendous amount of experience which the small child undergoes does not, therefore, find a proportionate variety of suitable vessels (schemata) for its preservation. Second, the quality of early childhood experience does not fit into the developing schemata of experience, thought, and memory since these are fashioned by the adult culture and all its biases, emphases, and taboos.

Both these trends become even more apparent if one considers them in connection with the development of the *senses* in the child. Such a consideration also shows how closely biological and cultural factors are interwoven in the causation of early childhood amnesia and how difficult, if not impossible, it is to draw a clear borderline between the two. What might have been a cultural factor in man's prehistory may well seem to the present observer like a biological development. Phylogenetically as well as ontogenetically the distance senses, sight and hearing, attain their full development later than the proximity senses, smell, taste, and touch. Sight and hearing are more highly differentiated and more closely linked up with the human mind than smell, taste, and touch. The latter senses, especially smell and taste, are neglected and to a considerable extent even tabooed by Western civilization. They are the animalistic senses *par excellence.* Man, who has been engaged for thousands of years in a battle for control and mastery of nature outside and inside himself, especially Western man, does not want to be reminded that he is not only man but also nature, also animal. Because of the cultural taboo on smell and taste—smell even more than taste, but the two are inseparable—it is [not] even possible for the adult to realize clearly the effect which the discrepancy between experience on the one hand, and language and memory schemata, on the other hand, has on the capacity for recall, especially voluntary recall. English vocabulary, and equally the vocabulary of the other Western languages, is conspicuously poor in words for the description of smells and tastes. Even when it comes to the flavor of wine or of a dish, in spite of the great material and historical role of drinking and eating, language is quite incapable of expressing any but the crudest differences in taste. A wine is said to be dry, sweet, robust, fine, full and so on, but none of these words enables one to imagine the flavor and bouquet of the wine. Compared with this poverty of words, the vocabulary for the description of the visible world and its forms and colors is much richer. Even poetry has never succeeded in conjuring the flavor of a smell or taste, although it sometimes enables the imagination to evoke a visual image. For these reasons, the experience schemata for smell and taste sensations are relatively undeveloped. This is true even more of the memory schemata. A taste or a smell is usually remembered only involuntarily; that is, the former experience may be recognized by renewed encounter with the same stimulus. But it is difficult or impossible for most people to recall voluntarily the taste of a particular wine or the smell of a particular flower, animal, or person. In fact, most people are hardly aware of the differences in smell of different people.

Both pleasure and disgust are more intimately linked with the proximity senses than with the distance senses. The pleasure which a perfume, a taste, or a texture can give is much more of a bodily, physical one, hence also more akin to sexual pleasure, than is the more sublime pleasure aroused by sound and the least bodily of all pleasures, the sight of something beautiful. No other sense produces the emotion of disgust more easily and violently and provokes reactions of nausea and vomiting more readily than the olfactory sense. The infant is not disgusted by his feces; he quite likes their smell. Very many, if not most, adults do not have the reaction of disgust to the smell of their own excretions; many do not show it with regard to the body odor or the excretions of a beloved person. As everybody knows, animals, especially dogs, are best able to tell one person from another and one dog from another by body and excretion smell. The infant, long before he knows and remembers how his mother looks, knows how she smells and tastes. Very likely, angry or frightened mother tastes and smells rather different from good or comfortable mother to the infant, just as she will look very different to him as he grows older.[16] In his growing experience of the world around him, the proximity senses at first have primacy over the distance senses. He tastes and sniffs and touches earlier and better than he perceives with eye and ear. In order to get really acquainted with something or somebody, he has to touch it and to put it in his mouth as he first did with his mother's nipple. Only very gradually and slowly does the emphasis shift from the proximity to the distance senses. This partly biological and phylogenetically determined shift is helped along powerfully and the development of taste and smell discouraged by the stringent taboos of the significant adults, who do not want baby to take everything in his mouth and who drastically and persistently in cleanliness education show their disgust with the most important objects of smell, those of the body and its excretions, so that the child cannot but feel that he has to refrain not only from the pleasure given by body and excretion odors but even from the discriminating perception of them.[17] The proximity senses, which play

[16] Groddeck, speaking about the paramount importance of the sense of smell in infancy and early childhood, asserts that, even more than the dog, the child judges people and objects largely by their smell and, since the child is small or is being held on the lap, this means chiefly the smell of legs, lap, sexual and excretory organs. Groddeck, G., *The World of Man;* The C. W. Daniel Company, London 1934; p. 132.

[17] Freud links fetishism with a repressed coprophilic smell desire; feet and hair become fetishes after the now unpleasant sensation of smell has been renounced. Reference footnote 7; p. 567, footnote 3. On another occasion he suggests that the sense of smell which attracts the male to the menstruating female animal became the victim of organic repression as man started to walk erect and that this was the origin of the emotion of disgust. *Das Unbehagen in der Kultur;* Wien 1930; p. 62 footnote.

such a great role in relations between animals and, if not repressed, in the sexual relations of man, are otherwise tabooed in interpersonal relations the more a culture or a group tends to isolate people, to put distance between them, and to prevent spontaneous relationships and the "natural" animal-like expressions of such relations. The emphasis on distance and the taboo on smell in modern society is more outspoken in the ruling than in the laboring class, distance being also a means of domination and of imposing authority. Disgust arises where the repression has not succeeded completely and a powerful deterrent is needed in order to bolster it.[18]

Whatever the social and cultural reasons for the discouragement and neglect of the proximity senses, the shift from their initial predominance to that of the distance senses, which takes place progressively during infancy and early childhood and which is a result partly of these cultural factors and partly of biological and phylogenetical factors, necessarily entails for the child a far-reaching change in the whole way of perceiving and experiencing the people and the world around him, a change which the adult mind is quite unable to imagine concretely. Much less is the adult memory capable of recalling experience that had occurred before the shift in the organization of the senses was made, since this change altered the entire mode of perception and experience.

Together with and continuing after the shift in the organization of perception from the primacy of the proximity senses to that of the distance senses, a comprehensive development in the direction of specialization and differentiation takes place in the child's apparatus for experience. This, too, brings about considerable changes in the mode of experience. As ontogenetic development of the child from conception to adulthood repeats the phylogenetic development of man from his farthest ancestors in the most primitive living organisms to his present state, the development of consciousness is a relatively late stage in this process, beginning only some time after birth and continuing for a long period. Within the develop-

[18] Something of the importance of the deeply rooted taboo on smell in Western man comes to the surface in the vituperative and hateful use that is made of body odor in interracial conflicts.

ment of consciousness, the consciousness of self comes latest, and neither individually nor in the history of the race has man as yet ever reached anything approaching full consciousness of self. Memory, especially voluntary memory, is an important part of consciousness. It seems probable that in the infant and child the development of memory starts with a recognition of certain complex, undifferentiated states of his own body-feeling, primarily states of comfort, satisfaction and pleasure, and states of discomfort, tension and displeasure. Since the infant has as yet no cognition, one cannot properly speak of recognition either; rather one should speak of a re-sensing, a re-experiencing of certain complex and dim states of his own well-being or not well-being. The differentiation between body and mind, body and psyche, also develops gradually and becomes more accentuated in the course of time. The infant, at first, is probably not capable of distinguishing between himself and whatever persons or objects of his environment come sufficiently close to him to affect him.[19] The mother's breast is not, at first, part of "another person"; it belongs to the undifferentiated little world of the infant, is part of his "own cosmic entity," as Sullivan puts it.[20] The whole concept of self and others does not make sense at this earliest period, and nothing corresponding to this concept exists for the small infant. It is not chance, then, that much later in life those rare instances of a whole vision recalled by involuntary memory are often stimulated by some body-sensation, that is, by the resensing of a sensation of long ago. They are memories of the

[19] This was already the opinion of Descartes, who said: "In early life the mind was so closely bound to the body that it attended to nothing beyond the thoughts by which it perceived the objects that made impression on the body; nor as yet did it refer these thoughts to anything existing beyond itself, but simply felt pain when the body was hurt, or pleasure when anything beneficial to the body occurred. . . . And afterward when the machine of the body, which has been so fabricated by nature that it can of its own inherent power move itself in various ways, by turning itself at random on every side, followed after what was useful and avoided what was detrimental, the mind, which was closely connected with it, reflecting on the objects it pursued and avoided, remarked, for the first time, that they existed out of itself. . . ." Descartes, *Principia Philosophiae*, I, 71, John Veitch's translation.

[20] Sullivan, Harry Stack, Conceptions of Modern Psychiatry, PSYCHIATRY (1940) 3:1-117; p. 15.

body, as it were, or of the unexplored realm where body and psyche
are identical, and it is here that Proust's involuntary memory flashes,
occasioned by the taste of the *madeleine,* by the unevenness of the
pavement, have their earliest origin.[21] The perception of the environment as something separate, a changing configuration of various
objects, develops only very gradually in the infant and small child.
Objects can be handled and eventually controlled to some extent,
but life in the early stages of infancy as well as in the lower forms
of the fauna begins with a state in which the living organism is
merely affected by his environment and experiences this as a change
in his own bodily state, not—as the growing child and the adult
will perceive it later—as the actions of people and objects outside
himself. In this context it is significant that the olfactory sense, so
important in infancy, throughout life is least, practically not at all,
capable of objectifying stimuli, whereas the more spiritual and
later developed sense of vision cannot but objectify the stimuli by
which it is affected. In this respect also, the olfactory sense retains
more of an earlier stage of development, a closer, less alienated,
and less differentiated relationship to the environment than the
distance senses and even the sense of touch. As the specialization
and differentiation of the apparatus for experience continue—including the sensory apparatus and the slowly developing consciousness—the initial lack of distinction between organism and environment gives way more and more to the division that is of such
fundamental importance in the history of man, that of subject and
object, a division that comes about slowly and gradually, but one
that the adult mind cannot possibly discard even in phantasy, and
certainly not in perception and rational thinking. It becomes so
predominant that it completely blots out the earlier kind of experience and whatever remains subterraneously, as it were, of this early
way of experiencing the environment in later life. In the slow development of consciousness, the sharp differentiation between sleep
and being awake also comes about only gradually. Memory is a

[21] See also Schachtel, Ernest G. The Dynamic Perception and the Symbolism of Form: With Special Reference to the Rorschach Test, PSYCHIATRY
(1941) 4:79-96; p. 85 and footnote 16.

relatively late product of this whole process of differentiation and specialization. Autobiographical memory—that is, the ability for voluntary recall of one's past life—is one of the latest developments in childhood, which is not surprising since it is part of the awareness of self, a capacity found only in man, and even in adult man usually not very well developed. According to Stern,[22] memory up to the third year refers almost exclusively to the visible world of objects and events. The life of the small child is naturally oriented toward the present and the future, not toward the past. The concept of "I" hardly develops before the third year, which is but another expression of the fact that the division between subject and object is a gradual, relatively late development. Yet the significance of this division and its particular quality in a particular society, culture, and stage of historical development can hardly be overestimated. It partakes of and is determined by all the fundamental attitudes in the relation of man to his fellow men, to nature, and to his material environment as they have developed in a specific society and culture.

The late development of the autobiographical memory and of the concept of "I" or "self" as a subject preserving one's identity in time is but another aspect of early childhood amnesia. The child lives much more in the present moment than the average adult does. His life is so. much more filled with the exploration of the environment and of his own growing capacities that the past has not much interest for him. And even with the appearance of the first traces of autobiographical memory and of the concept "I" in the third year of life, the quality of childhood experience is still so different from that of the adult that the memory schemata of the adult cannot accommodate the greater part of this experience.

The fact that autobiographical memory develops so late in childhood should be considered also with the question in mind of its usefulness for life, and especially for life in Western civilization. Considered from this angle it becomes apparent that it is of much less immediate use for orientation in and adaptation to the environ-

---

[22] Stern, William, *Psychologie der frühen Kindheit bis zum sechsten Lebensjahre;* Quelle & Meyer, Leipzig 1914; p. 166.

ment than the development of the senses, of the mind, and of "useful" memory—that is, memory in the service of the recognition of objects, the learning of words, and similar functions important for survival. Biologically and culturally, autobiographical memory thus finds little encouragement. In a culture oriented toward efficient performance of profitable activities, a society in which everybody has to fit like a cog in a machine and where powerful pressure is exerted to make people equal, in the sense of uniform, autobiographical memory is discouraged in its development and predestined to atrophy. It is of no use for the reliable and efficient performance of the worker at the machine, the clerk at his desk, the surgeon at the operating table; in fact, it would interfere with their activities. It would stand in the way of the process of equalization and uniformity since its very function is to preserve individual experience rather than repeat cultural and conventional schemata of experience. If Ulysses gives in to the song of the Sirens, his active life will have reached its end and his plans will come to naught. The pseudo-memory of the adult, which reproduces not his real experience but the experience schemata furnished by the culture, is a more reliable and conservative servant of the culture than the true memory which would preserve the real experience before it has been filtered through the memory schemata of the culture and thus cleansed from all that transcends the ubiquitous pattern.

In one other area of life, namely in the realm of *dreams,* one finds a general amnesia, although it is not quite so pervasive as that pertaining to early childhood. A closer study of the recall of dreams and especially of the period of awakening from a dream, when quite often one can observe its disappearance from memory or its transformation or fragmentation, may therefore add to, disprove, or corroborate the hypotheses developed so far for the phenomenon of early childhood amnesia and of adult forgetting of trans-schematic experience. It is probable that the majority of dreams are not remembered at all. A great many others are recalled in fragments only. Of those that are still remembered at the time of awakening, very many are forgotten in the course of the day, quite often in the first few minutes or the first hour of beginning the daily activities of rising, getting dressed, and so on. The relatively small proportion of dreams surviving in memory undergo a rapid transformation and fragmentation and usually they, too, are forgotten after a few days. If they are not forgotten, they are transformed in a way which is rather analogous to the transformation of the Indian story in Bartlett's experiment. That is to say, they lose increasingly their peculiar dream quality, and the peculiar language of the dream changes in the direction of conventionalization and rationalization. Even persons sensitized to awareness and recall of their dreams, for example psychoanalytic patients, find it difficult or impossible to counteract this powerful tendency toward forgetting or conventionalizing the dream unless they record their dreams as soon as possible after awakening. The dreams that make such a profound impression on the dreamer that they survive all these obstacles, although not without some damage, are rare indeed. Thus the question arises: What are the causes of this usual, general *dream-amnesia?* Why does one forget by far the greater part of his mental life going on during sleep, a life that in most people, judging from the fragments recalled, seems to be far more original, interesting, spontaneous, and creative than their waking life? It shares these latter qualities with early childhood which, from all one can observe, seems to be the most fascinating, spontaneous, original, and creative period in the life of most or perhaps of all people. Is it because of these qualities that the conventionalized memory schemata cannot reproduce the great majority of dreams and their real character?

Freud devotes a whole section of *The Interpretation of Dreams* to the problem of the forgetting of dreams.[23] His purpose in this section is to defend the validity of dream interpretation against the objection that one does not really know his dreams because he either forgets or distorts them. Freud's answer to the problem is that the "forgetting of dreams depends far more on the resistance [to the dream thought] than on the mutually alien character of the waking and sleeping states" and that the distortion of the dream in recalling or recounting it is "the secondary and often misunder-

[23] Chapter VII, section A; reference footnote 7; pp. 470-485.

standing elaboration of the dream by the agency of normal thinking" and thus "no more than a part of the elaboration to which
dream thoughts are constantly subjected as a result of the dream-
censorship." [24] I think that the question should be raised whether
"resistance" and "mutually alien character of the waking and sleeping states" are really, as Freud seems to assume, mutually exclusive and contradictory explanations of dream amnesia and dream
distortion by waking thought. Or whether, as I believe, "resistance"
is operative in the awake person, not only against the dream
thought but against the whole quality and language of the dream,
a resistance, to be sure, of a somewhat different character, yet
fundamentally related to that which represses and censors those
dream thoughts which are intolerable for consciousness.

In sleep and dream, man's activity in the outer world is suspended, especially his motor activity. Attention and perception are
withdrawn from outer reality. The necessity to cope with the environment is interrupted for the duration of sleep. The stringent
rules of logic and reason subside,—rules which during waking life
are geared to useful, rational, adaptive, conventional control of
behavior and thought. The psyche receives leave, for the period of
sleep, from the demands of active life in society. As Freud expresses
it, endopsychic censorship is reduced. And the psyche makes good
use of this short leave from the demands of reality. Its productions,
seen from the usual, realistic viewpoint, seem utterly useless. It is
true that other, older civilizations did not always share this viewpoint, but attributed considerable importance to dreams, sometimes
greater importance than to waking thought. But measured with the
yardstick of modern Western civilization with its emphasis on useful, efficient production and work, dreams are really quite useless.

During sleep motor activity, most essential for dealing with the
outer reality of objects and people, is reduced to a minimum.
Movements are not performed actively. But in the dream a world
of movement is perceived. Rorschach has called attention to the
fact that dreams are primarily kinesthesias, that is kinesthetic pro-

[24] Reference footnote 23, pp. 476 and 472.

duction.[25] Even in waking life Rorschach's experiment has demonstrated that kinesthetic perception, that is the most creative factor
in perception, is invariably inhibited or made altogether impossible
by an attitude of cramped attention, by the straining of will-power
in the direction of control and good performance, and that it is
facilitated by an attitude of giving in to one's ideas, to what will
occur to one, without straining for ambitious performance. The
dream, of course, is a mental production without any conscious
effort and one in which the dreamer passively gives in to the
images evoked by his phantasy. In that sense the dream is the opposite of *work* as it is known to Western civilization, the opposite of
efficiency. When awakening, it is often possible to catch hold of a
dream, as Rorschach has pointed out, if one lies perfectly still and
does not open his eyes. But the first movement, especially an active
one like jumping out of bed, will very often chase the dream into
oblivion. In other words, the return to the outer world through
motor activity and reshifting of attention and perception to the
environment leads to forgetting of the dream. This process is a
quite general one and, as far as I have been able to observe, bears
no relation to specific dream content. Therefore it seems to stem
from the incompatibility of the extroversive attitude of waking with
the introversive attitude of dreaming, rather than from resistance
to specific strivings which are expressed in the dream thoughts. The
antagonism between motor activity and dream recall brings to
mind Proust's words, that he could recapture his former being only
"dehors de l'action, de la jouissance immédiate" [26] and that in such
a moment he did not dare to budge lest he lose the refound memory of the past.

But even without the described effect of the resumption of motor
activity on the voluntary recall of dreams, it seems obvious that

[25] Rorschach, Hermann, *Psychodiagnostics: A Diagnostic Test Based on
Perception* (English edition by Paul Lemkau and Bernard Kronenberg);
Berne, Switzerland, Hans Huber, 1942; p. 72. Since dreams are the most creative mental production of the average person, this sheds an interesting light
on one of Rorschach's significant findings, that of a close kinship between
kinesthesia and mental creativity, and seems to corroborate this finding.

[26] Reference footnote 3; p. 14.

the experience and memory schemata developed and formed by
man's life in his society are much less suitable to preserve the
phantastic world of the dream than to recall conventional waking
experience. The awakening mind has to cope again with outer
reality, and to this end has to remobilize all the patterns and
schemata useful for, and developed by, the conventional social
forms of life and work. Attention has to be paid to the environment.
And the attitude of attention is to the mind what purposeful motor
activity is to the body.

In the forgetting and distortion of dreams during waking life it
is important to distinguish between that which is due to the resistance to and repression of a specific dream thought or dream
content and that which is due to the incapacity of the conventional
memory schemata to retain the phantastic general quality and the
strange language of dreams. The distortion of a dream thought
which resistance wants to keep from awareness has to be distinguished from the process of conventionalization which, more or
less, *all* dream elements undergo because the medium of the dream
language is incompatible with the medium of the conventional
world of waking life. In the degree of this incompatibility there
are, of course, considerable variations between different people
and, even more so, between different cultures. But modern Western
civilization with its streamlined efficiency, uniform mass culture,
and emphasis on usefulness in terms of profitable, material production is particularly and strikingly at the opposite pole from the
world of dreams.[27]

Dream amnesia and early childhood amnesia are due to related
causes. Experience and thought transcending the conventional
schemata of the culture are found in relatively few people. Yet they
are universal in early childhood and in the dream: in early childhood because the spontaneity of the child has not yet been deadened or channelized into the conventional patterns of the culture;
in the dream because the hold of these conventional patterns, the
hold of reality, can be relaxed to some extent since the dreamer

---

[27] Concerning the peculiar language of the dream, compare also Erich
Fromm's forthcoming paper, The Meaning of Dreams.

temporarily is cut off from active commerce with outer reality by the suspension of perception and motor activity. It is the trans-schematic quality of early childhood experience as well as of dreams which makes it difficult or impossible for the memory schemata to preserve and recall voluntarily such experience. Yet it is also this quality in which potentialities of progress, of going beyond the conventional pattern, and of widening the scope of human life are forever present and waiting to be released.

The main subject of my considerations so far has been to discover the causes of the forgetting of early childhood and other transschematic experience. What, then, are the qualities of that relatively rare remembrance by which the individual past, the lost experience is recalled, and what are the conditions favoring such recall? The veil of amnesia which hides former experience under the memory schemata of voluntary recall is sometimes lifted and the lost experience recovered. A dream, already forgotten, is suddenly remembered. A scene from childhood, buried under layers of years of a conventional life, reappears as though it had been yesterday. The recent age regression experiments in hypno-analysis show in dramatic fashion how forgotten experiences of many years ago, secreted in the unconscious, are recalled and relived during hypnosis and again lost when amnesia returns after awakening from the trance. But this is a more striking demonstration only of the classical teaching of psychoanalysis about the memory traces of the unconscious which usually are immune to voluntary recall but may be approached by the special techniques of dream interpretation, free association, and recall under hypnosis or under the influence of resistance-reducing drugs.

The hidden quality of these lost memories, their separation from the rest of life, their inaccessibility, and their incompatibility with voluntary memory and with conventional, purposeful, daily activity are described lucidly by Proust. He compares the recesses of the lost memories to a thousand vases distributed on the various altitudes of the past years of one's life, filled with the particular atmosphere of that period of his life, and containing sometimes a gesture, a word, an insignificant act which, however, may be the key to the recapturing of the lost experiences, the lost past of his life. According to him, the very fact that the experience, the past time, has been *forgotten* and thus has remained isolated as at the bottom of a valley or on the peak of a summit, gives it an incomparable air of freshness and aliveness when it is recovered, *because it has not been able to form any link with the present.*[28] In other words, it has not been distorted by the memory schemata, by the needs and fears of the present, by the routine of daily life. Proust's view, here, is almost identical with that of Freud, whose theory of memory postulates that *only* that which is unconscious can leave a permanent memory trace and that "becoming conscious and leaving behind a memory trace are processes incompatible with each other in the same system."[29]

The memory trace that has been secluded from contact with conscious present life thereby often acquires in the isolation of the unconscious the character of *strangeness* to one's present life. Hence the surprise when it is recovered. Again, Proust makes an illuminating contribution to the understanding of this phenomenon. He describes how, in the library of the Prince de Guermantes, he finds a book, *François le Champi,* that his mother had read to him when he was a child. The memory is painful at first. In the shock of sudden recall of the forgotten childhood scene he asks himself angrily who causes him such pain, and in the same moment he discovers that he sees *himself* as a child, he is the stranger. In rereading the title of the book, *François le Champi,* he suddenly finds himself transposed into the remote past and he reads with the eyes of the child, of the person that he was then, with the same reveries and the same fear of the next day that he had felt then.[30] The reason for the strangeness of such sudden and vivid recollections of hitherto forgotten experience is that such experience is in contrast to and alien to one's present state and conscious preoccupations. The voluntary memory

[28] Reference footnote 3; pp. 12-13.

[29] Freud, *Beyond the Pleasure Principle;* The International Psycho-analytical Press, London 1922; p. 28. See also, The Interpretation of Dreams; reference footnote 7; pp. 488-491.

[30] Reference footnote 3; pp. 30-38.

schemata accommodate the familiar and the conventional only, in terms of the present life. The involuntary recovery of the forgotten past very often intrudes on this present life like a strange, alien element. The person that one was then, the child that Proust sees in the scene recalled, has long since been buried under the years of social routine, of changed needs and interests, of the preoccupations of the present. He has become a stranger. But this stranger may also assert a life and wishes which had been starved and suffocated by the time gone by and the pressures it brought.

In Proust's work the recovery of the forgotten past is characterized as the supreme satisfaction, carrying with it a sense of exhilarating happiness and constituting the very core of the work of art. This is not the place to discuss the profound meaning of his evaluation which, three thousand years after the Greek myth, again celebrates memory as the mother of art and poetry. Be it sufficient to say that in the conflict of modern society between efficient adaptation and activity, on the one hand, and the preservation and recovery of the total personality, which to him seems possible only by the fullest awareness of the individual past, Proust sides against his society and with the "lost paradises" of his own past. And it is true that each genuine recovery of forgotten experience and, with it, something of the person that one was when having the experience carries with it an element of enrichment, adds to the light of consciousness, and thus widens the conscious scope of one's life.

Such widening of the personality by the recovery of lost ground and its liberating and exhilarating effect has to be distinguished from what I propose to call the *possessive* attitude to memory, or to one's past, an attitude that occurs much more frequently than the instances of genuine recovery of the past. The possessive attitude to one's own past, particularly to past feelings, more often imagined than real, seems to me the essence of sentimentality. The person who has this attitude pats himself on the shoulder as it were and feels what a fine fellow he is for having had such feelings or such experience. It is the same attitude that leads also to a kind of proprietary satisfaction about one's character. Character, feelings, the past are looked upon as prized possessions enhancing the prestige of their owner. On closer analysis, it usually turns out that these treasures are spurious.[31] The possessive attitude toward the past prevents rather than furthers the gain in consciousness and the widening of the scope of life by the rediscovery of forgotten experience.

Since the lost experience is inaccessible to voluntary recall and incompatible with the conventional memory schemata, the question arises as to what the conditions are under which such forgotten experience may be recalled. Of course, a definite and complete catalogue of these conditions cannot be given. But it may be useful to consider some situations which typically favor the rediscovery of a past that has been forgotten. Proust attributes to bodily sensations and to perceptions the greatest importance, in fact exclusive importance, as carriers of such significant memories. The accidental recurrence of a bodily posture or of a sensory perception which he had experienced in the past, on some occasions brings with it the entire vision of that past, of the person he was then and of the way he saw things then. It is a sensation—feeling of a body posture or sensation of the perceptive apparatus,—not a thought, as in willed recall, which revives the past. In Proust's account visual sensations are far outnumbered as carriers of such memories by those of the other, less spiritual, more bodily senses, such as the feeling of his own body in a particular posture, the touch of a napkin, the smell and taste of a flavor, the hearing of a sound—noise or melody, *not* the sound of words. All these sensations are far from conceptual thought, language, or conventional memory schemata. They renew a state of the psychosomatic entity, in some respect, that this entity had experienced before, felt before. It is as though they touched directly the unconscious memory trace, the record left behind by a total situation out of the past, whereas voluntary recall tries to approach and construct this past indirectly, coached and deflected by

[31] The possessive attitude toward the (pseudo-) remembered past is closely related to and finds its counterpart in the acquisitive anticipation of (pseudo-) experience, already described, in which not some event is experienced, not some object perceived, but instead the motions are gone through and a preconceived cliché replaces actual experience because the performance of such pseudo-experience promises an increase in prestige.

all those ideas, wishes, and needs which tell the present person how the past could, should, or might have been. Just as the infant's recall probably starts out as an automatic recognition or, rather, resensation of a certain state of his body—pleasurable or unpleasurable, satisfied or needy, comfortable or tense—and not as conscious recall of former experience, such resensation, more differentiated than in early infancy, seems to be one basis and one condition of involuntary recall of forgotten experience. By revival of a former sensation the attitude of the former self that first had this sensation is remobilized. And thus recall is made possible of the objects and feelings closely connected with the former sensation,—objects and feelings which the present self would otherwise not perceive or experience in the same manner since it thinks, feels, behaves differently and since, therefore, the conscious memory schemata are not prepared for the ready reproduction of material stemming from a historical past in which the person was different, moved by needs, interests, and fears different from those that move him now, especially from those of which he is aware at present. But all experience leaves a record behind, as it were, a memory trace, inaccessible, as a rule, to the consciously, purposefully searching mind, revealed sometimes by the repetition of a sensation that had occurred at the time when the record was first made.

This hypothesis of one type of involuntary recall of forgotten experience seems to fit in with two data from psychoanalytic theory and therapy. One of them concerns Freud's "screen" or "concealing" memories ("Deckerinnerungen") from early childhood; the other, therapeutic findings of Wilhelm Reich. Freud calls attention to the "fact that the earliest recollections of a person often seemed to preserve the unimportant and accidental, whereas . . . not a trace is found in the adult memory of the weighty and affective impressions of this period." [32] He distinguishes regressive, encroaching, and contemporaneous or contiguous concealing memories. The indifferent, unimportant recollection, according to Freud, conceals the forgotten, significant emotional experience. If the image recalled has preceded the significant experience, he speaks of a regressive conceal-

[32] Freud, Psychopathology of Everyday Life; reference footnote 7; p. 62.

ing memory; if it has succeeded the experience, he terms it an encroaching memory; if they belong to the same time, the concealing memory is a contemporaneous or contiguous one. To simplify matters I shall speak only of the contiguous screen memory. The question relevant for the problems presented in this essay concerns the nature of the associative connection between screen memory and forgotten, significant emotional experience. It is my impression that usually, if not always, this connection is very similar to the one described by Proust between the taste of the *madeleine* and the recall of his childhood, the sensation of uneven pavement and the recall of Venice, and all the other instances in which a seemingly quite indifferent object arouses most significant forgotten memories. In the analysis of such seemingly indifferent memories, such as the recall of a piece of furniture, a corridor, a stove in the parental home, of a piece of apparel worn by the child or by his parents, I have often found that it is possible, not only to rediscover the forgotten emotion "behind" this screen memory, but that what seemed merely a screen, an indifferent object, was not so indifferent after all. Quite often the feelings with which this particular object was seen, the perceptive "aura" of the object was a condensation of significant emotions in the interpersonal relations of the child at that time. There was a time, in other words, when the way in which the now indifferent object was perceived, contained in a complex, condensed, inarticulate manner the essence of the life of the child at that time. That a simple perception should contain such condensed material is not as astonishing as it may seem. Rorschach's psychodiagnostic test is based on the fact that the way in which a person sees *is* the person and that it is possible to reach significant conclusions as to structure and conflicts of a personality by analyzing the processes of his visual perception. In many, possibly in all, cases of contiguous screen memories, the indifferent object is not so much the significant element as the perceptive aura of this object in childhood,—the perception itself, its individual qualities and characteristics which contain the child, as it were, that once saw this object, the little stranger of whom the adult Proust speaks when the perception of the book *François le Champi* suddenly brings with it the whole atmosphere of the time when this book was read to him by his mother. In the course of growing up, the language label and the corresponding conventional memory schema replace the living perception of the object. Thus the significant individual perception is lost, the object loses its aura, and only its name remains; and its indifferent, conventional cliché or picture may be recalled voluntarily by the conventional memory schemata. But sometimes it is possible, by insisting, to revive the former alive perception, the childhood aura of the object, and in this way to arrive also at the significant emotional experiences of that time which endowed the object with its unique aura. Once the cliché quality of the object or scene recalled consciously in the screen memory is discarded, one can penetrate to the memory trace left behind by the living sensation, the individual perception of this object as experienced by this person in his past. The memory of the conscious, conventionalized mind thus gives way to the memory of the body, of the psychosomatic entity in which the old sensation left a record not only of this object but of the total emotional configuration in which the object was seen and which gave to it the aura that made it peculiarly fit to become a symbol for the period and event to which it refers.

The subjective element in perception, the individual perspective under which the seemingly indifferent object once was seen, thus turns out to be the associative link between screen memory and significant experience. From this viewpoint, the screen memory loses its seemingly indifferent and accidental character. The object of the screen memory and the significant emotional experience belong together. The significant experience constituted the atmosphere in which the object was perceived and which thus became part of that object. Significant experience and "accidental" object are no longer separate; they belong together and often shade imperceptibly into one another. The perceptive attitude was closely akin to, or identical with, the general attitude of the child in his experiences.

If the screen memories show how this attitude may be recovered by reviving the former unschematic perception of the object and by reviving therewith the attitude of the child at that time, Reich's vegetotherapeutic technique has shown how, starting not from an object recalled, but from the bodily residua and encrustations of childhood attitudes in posture, expression, and muscular armor, one can recover forgotten experience.[33] Reich has found that "the dissolution of a muscular rigidity . . . brings back into memory the very infantile situation in which the repression had taken place." According to him, the repressed affect and the defense against this affect produce muscular fixations and changes in the vegetative behavior. By analysing and dissolving the muscular rigidity, it is possible to revive and bring to awareness the defense against the repressed affect, the affect itself and the memory of the experience which had originally produced the affect. In other words, the body remembers as it were what the mind has forgotten and repressed.

The discussed instances of recall of previously forgotten or repressed material have in common that they all point to a "location" of involuntary memory, not in the conscious, purposefully remembering mind and its memory schemata, but in a sphere which is more adequately if vaguely described as memory of the body or, rather, of the psychosomatic entity. The forgotten experience is revived by the recurrence of a sensation which has left a record, a trace behind; or it is revived by the understanding and reliving of the bodily attitudes, muscular and vegetative, which the forgotten experience produced.

Another condition favorable for the recovery of forgotten experience which the conscious mind is unable to recall voluntarily is furnished by the psychoanalytic situation of free association. The relevant factor of this situation is indicated by the word "free." Three components may be distinguished in the freedom of association. One is the attempt, never entirely successful, to follow the fundamental rule of psychoanalysis: to eliminate rational, logical, and conventional control and censorship of one's thoughts in communicating them and to give in to whatever thought or feeling occurs. How well or how poorly one succeeds in this attempt is dependent chiefly on the two other factors important in free association, the general inner freedom of the person associating and the

---

[33] Wilhelm Reich, *The Function of the Orgasm;* Orgone Institute Press, New York 1942; see especially chapter VIII, pp. 266-325.

interpersonal relationship between him and the analyst. The more rigid, controlled, and automaton-like a person is, the more all his thinking is under the grip of the conventional schemata of thought, experience, and feeling, the less will he be able to associate freely, and the more difficult will it be for him to recover any experience that does not fit into the conventional patterns which govern his life. The same is true if he cannot relax from the purposeful, "useful" pursuit of some activity or thought and let his thoughts wander. In other words, the more a person is dependent on and a prisoner of the socially prevalent pattern of useful efficient activity—from which the usual highly uniform leisure-time pursuits are distinguished more by the fact that they are not profitable than by a fundamental difference of attitude—and the more his experiences and mode of living are conditioned by the conventional experience schemata of the culture, the less will he be able to escape the hold of these schemata, to relax and approach that state of relative freedom in which a forgotten experience may break through the armor of his conventionalized thought processes and memory schemata. As Alexander has pointed out, the recovery of memories is not the cause, but the result of therapeutic progress.[34] The loosening of rigid control and of defenses, the greater inner freedom brought about by the therapeutic process, gives the repressed and forgotten material a chance to reappear because the conventional thought and memory schemata have no longer such exclusive predominance in the mental life of the patient.

Freedom, which the psychoanalytic situation seeks to establish by controlled, purposeful procedure, is an essential condition for the possibility of true, that is nonschematic, recall of experience. This freedom may be brought about in different ways. The relaxation of censorship in sleep brings greater freedom. The memory schemata, which so largely govern voluntary recall in a state of wakefulness, lose their hold and relax their function during sleep, so that in

[34] Alexander, Franz, Concerning the Genesis of the Castration Complex; *Psychoanalytic Rev.* (1935) 22:49-52. See also Alexander, Franz, and French, Thomas M., *Psychoanalytic Therapy;* The Ronald Press Company, New York 1946; pp. 20, 163.

dreams experiences which otherwise have been forgotten may be recalled, usually in somewhat changed and distorted or in symbolic form. The artist, the writer, the poet, if they have any real claim to their vocation, must be capable of nonschematic experience. They must be perceptive; that is, they must experience, see, hear, feel things in a way which somewhere transcends the cultural, conventional experience schemata. The relative freedom from these experience schemata is also freedom, to whatever extent, from the conventional memory schemata. And memory, the Greek myth tells us, is the mother of the muses.

Memory and forgetting partake of the nature of man, who is both a biological and a cultural, social, historical being. In memory and forgetting the conflicts between nature and society, as well as the dynamics and antagonisms of society, play a determining role. To investigate abstract memory phenomena is to investigate an artifact, something that does not exist. This has become apparent at each step of these considerations, which now have led to a point where it is possible to formulate their main results.

Early childhood amnesia may be considered a *normal* amnesia. It shares this quality with most, though not all, of dream amnesia and with the constant forgetting of those parts and aspects of experience which do not fit into the ready patterns of language and culture,—trans-schematic experience. Normal amnesia is both akin to and different from pathological amnesia. Their likeness consists in their causation by a conflict between nature and culture or by intercultural conflict. Their difference consists chiefly in the fact that the conflicts causing normal amnesia are ubiquitous in a culture and their solution is part of the development of the personality in that culture; whereas in pathological amnesia, by and large, the conflict is due to individual traumatic experience which, although caused too by the stresses and conflicts operative in the culture, has become traumatic because of the particular history of the individual person. One might say that the normal amnesia, that which people usually are unable to recall, is an illuminating index to the quality of any given culture and society. It is that which does not serve the purposes of that society and would interfere with the pattern of the culture, that which would be traumatic to the culture because it would break up or transcend the conventions and mores of that culture. Early childhood amnesia is the most striking and dramatic expression merely of a dynamism operative throughout the life of people: the distortion or forgetting of trans-schematic experience, that is of experience for which the culture provides no pattern and no schema.

Cultures vary in the degree to which they impose clichés on experience and memory. The more a society develops in the direction of mass conformism, whether such development be achieved by a totalitarian pattern or within a democratic framework by means of the employment market, education, the patterns of social life, advertising, press, radio, movies, best-sellers, and so on, the more stringent becomes the rule of the conventional experience and memory schemata in the lives of the members of that society. In the history of the last hundred years of Western civilization the conventional schematization of experience and memory has become increasingly prevalent at an accelerating pace.

Even within a culture the degree to which in different *groups* conventional schemata of experience and memory prevent the recall of actual experience may show marked differences. Such a difference seems to exist, for example, between European men and women. There is some reason to assume that European men usually show a more extensive and pervasive amnesia for their early childhood than women.[35] A plausible hypothesis for the explanation of this difference would have to take into account the marked difference in the social status of the two sexes in Europe and, specifically, the difference in what one might call the social self-ideal of man versus that of woman. This idea of what the grown-up person, the respectable citizen, ought to be emphasizes the cleft between child-

---

[35] Oral communication by *Ruth Benedict*. In interviewing a number of European men and women Benedict found consistently that the women recalled quite a few details of their lives before they had reached the age of 6 while the men hardly recalled anything. The people interviewed by her did not constitute a representative sample of the population, yet the consistency of the phenomenon in all the people interviewed seemed indicative of its more general significance.

hood and adulthood much more in men than in women. All things pertaining to the rearing of children and to the home are the domain of the women and the average man would consider it beneath his "dignity" to know much about them or to be much concerned with them. Hence, to recall details of early childhood would be consistent with the social self-ideal of women whose interests are supposed to center around children, kitchen, and home. But to a man these things are not supposed to be sufficiently "important" to deserve much attention. To approximate the social self-ideal is important for his self-esteem; and the further removed from, and opposed to, the image of childhood the grown-up man's social self-ideal is the more difficult will it be for him to recall experiences showing that once he was an infant and little boy. In general, more extensive childhood amnesias are to be expected in those groups, cultures, and historical epochs which emphasize the belief that childhood is radically different from adulthood, than one is likely to find where the continuity between childhood and adult life is emphasized.[36]

Mankind's belief in a lost paradise is repeated in the belief, held by most people, in the individual myth of their happy childhood. Like most myths this one contains elements of both truth and illusion, is woven out of wishes, hopes, remembrance and sorrow, and hence has more than one meaning. One finds this belief even in people who have undergone cruel experiences as children and who had, without being or remaining aware of it, a childhood with hardly any love and affection from their parents. No doubt, one reason for the myth of happy childhood is that it bolsters parental authority and maintains a conventional prop of the authority of the family by asserting that one's parents were good and benevolent people who did everything for the good of their children, however much they may have done against it. And disappointed and suffering people, people without hope, want to believe that at least once there was a time in their life when they were happy. But the myth

[36] For the general significance of continuity and discontinuity between childhood and adulthood, see Benedict, Ruth, Continuities and Discontinuities in Cultural Conditioning, PSYCHIATRY (1938) 1:161-167. [Editor's Note: This paper is included in the present volume.]

of happy childhood reflects also the truth that, as in the myth of paradise lost, there was a time before animalistic innocence was lost, before pleasure-seeking nature and pleasure-forbidding culture clashed in the battle called education, a battle in which the child always is the loser. At no time is life so exclusively and directly governed by the pleasure principle as it is in early infancy; at no other time is man, especially civilized man, capable of abandoning himself so completely to pleasure and satisfaction. The myth of happy childhood takes the place of the lost memory of the actual riches, spontaneity, freshness of childhood experience, an experience which has been forgotten because there is no place for it in the adult memory schemata.

Childhood amnesia covers those aspects and experiences of the former personality which are incompatible with the culture. If they were remembered, man would demand that society affirm and accept the total personality with all its potentialities. In a society based on partial suppression of the personality such a demand, even the mere existence of a really free personality, would constitute a threat to the society. Hence it becomes necessary for the society that the remembrance of a time in which the potentialities of a fuller, freer, and more spontaneous life were strongly present and alive be extinguished. In memory's service of this purpose one may distinguish two processes which overlap and shade into one another. One process leaves the culturally unacceptable or unusable experiences and the memory thereof to starvation by the expedient of providing no linguistic, conceptual, and memory schemata for them and by channeling later experience into the experience schemata of the culture. As the person, in the process of education, gradually comes to live more and more exclusively within the framework of the culturally and conventionally provided experience schemata, there is less and less to remind him of the possibility of trans-schematic experience. As his memory schemata develop in accordance with the schematized experience, they become unfit to preserve and recall trans-schematic experience. Only if a person has escaped to some extent this process of schematization of experience and memory, only if he is more differentiated and more free than the average person, will he be in a position to break, at some point, the hold that the memory and experience schemata have on his life and his perceptiveness. But usually it needs special, fortunate circumstances to make possible the escape from the memory schemata and the recall of trans-schematic experience. In a highly developed culture this process resulting in amnesia for culturally undesirable or unacknowledged experience by means of providing memory schemata only for culturally acceptable experience is exceedingly complex, flexible, subtle, and all-pervading.

Compared with this process, the dynamism of the taboo and of repression of individually or culturally tabooed experience and strivings is like the nightstick of the policeman compared with the gradual, slow, insinuating process of education in which some things are just not mentioned and others said to be for the best of the child. But the dynamism active in normal amnesia is even more subtle than what is usually called education. It is an education of which the educators are not aware and of which the child is too helpless and too inarticulate to have more than the vaguest feeling that something is happening to him. On the other hand, those strivings, qualities, and potentialities of the child which are too strong to be left behind to die by the side of the road of education and which endanger the current social and cultural pattern have to be battled by the more drastic means of taboo and repression. In this sphere sexuality and the conflict with parental authority play central roles. One might say that taboo and repression are the psychological cannons of society against the child and against man, whereas in normal amnesia society uses the method of blockade and slow starvation against those experiences and memories which do not fit into the cultural pattern and which do not equip man for his role in the social process. The two methods of warfare supplement each other and, in the siege conducted by society against the human potentialities and inclinations which transcend the cultural pattern, the cannon helps to maintain the blockade, and the blockade and ensuing starvation make it less necessary to use the cannon.

Hesiod tells us that Lethe (Forgetting) is the daughter of Eris (Strife).[37] Amnesia, normal and pathological, is indeed the daughter of conflict, the conflict between nature and society and the conflict in society, the conflict between society and man and the conflict within man. Lethe is the stream of the underworld, of forgetting, the stream which constantly flows and never retains. In the realm of Lethe dwell the Danaïdes, who are condemned eternally to pour water into a leaking vessel. Plato interprets this as the punishment of those unwise souls who leak, who cannot remember and are therefore always empty.[38] But Mnemosyne is an older and more powerful goddess than Lethe. According to Hesiod she was one of the six Titanesses from whom all gods stem. And it was one of the world-founding deeds of Zeus that he begot the muses on her. Memory cannot be entirely extinguished in man, his capacity for experience cannot be entirely suppressed by schematization. It is in those experiences which transcend the cultural schemata, in those memories of experience which transcend the conventional memory schemata, that every new insight and every true work of art have their origin, and that the hope of progress, of a widening of the scope of human endeavor and human life, is founded.

[37] Hesiod, *Theogony*, 227.

[38] Plato, *Gorgias*, 493 c 2. For the mythology of Mnemosyne and Lethe, see Kerényi, Karl, Mnemosyne-Lesmosyne, in *Die Geburt der Helena*; Rhein Verlag, Zuerich 1945.

INTERPERSONAL THEORY
AND SOCIAL PSYCHOLOGY

Ernest Beaglehole

I N THE group of disciplines that make up collectively
the science of psychology none has offered more
problems of definition than that of social psychology. The boundaries of the field that social psychology has marked out as its own
have been in the past shifting and uncertain. The social psychologist
has shuttled uneasily between data derived from "straight" psychology, sociology, anthropology, abnormal psychology, and recently, psychoanalysis, seeking eagerly for some all-embracing conceptualization that would give focus, a point of view, and some
respectability to his often-times motley collection of data.

On the surface his problem should not have proved difficult. The
reasoning would go something like this: psychology is the study of the
behavior of man in so far as this behavior is mentally conditioned.
Some aspects of this behavior can be abstracted in a laboratory
and successfully studied without paying attention to the fact that
man is a social animal. These and related aspects of behavior make
up the field of "straight" psychology. Other aspects of behavior
cannot be thus abstracted from the flux of social events. These are
the province of social psychology. Sociology studies the behavior
of the individual as affected by, and impinging on, these social
events.

Now, the trouble with this sort of formulation is that facts, data,
human beings, do not fit the scheme. As long as the psychologist's
horizon was bounded by an ethno-centric concentration on the data
of his own culture, the psychologist could study perception or

memory, learning or stimulus-response situations relatively indifferent to the fact that all these aspects of human behavior were shot through and through with meanings and forms derived from cultural conditionings. The abnormal psychologist could proceed to formulate concepts of non-normal psychological functioning and feel fairly clear in his mind that he was dealing with almost eternal verities. The social psychologist, similarly, could follow the lead of the theorists and decide, according to wastebasket analogies, that everything not considered by experimental or abnormal psychologists must be his own field of study. Upon this neat scheme, a sudden and growing awareness of some of the disturbing results of modern anthropological studies made disorganizing impact. If, as anthropology suggested, consideration of the all-pervasive influence of culture in conditioning and socializing the lives of the neonata born into any society showed that these influences were tremendously important in turning the human animal into the human being, then either there was little excuse left for "straight" psychology or there was no legitimate field for social psychology. From the viewpoint of social psychologists, experimental psychology dissolved into physiology and all that was non-physiology became the province of social psychology. Even so, the matter was disturbing and difficult to digest according to established categories of psychological study.

For a time it has been possible for the social psychologist in his rôle of research student to neglect such problems as being of academic significance only—that is, of significance to the social psychologist only in his rôle of teacher. He has been able to say, and rightly enough, that his concern is with problems. If the problem which interests him leads him far afield in the collection of data which seem relevant to the solution of this problem, then he has been content to follow the empirical leads irrespective of whether this has meant straying over the boundaries of social psychology or not. If he is interested, for example, in problems of coöperation and competition, he finds before long that he is studying anthropological materials as well as seeking to analyze operationally a farmers' coöperative. This is all to the good, methodologically speaking. In dealing with social life, there is no reason why social or group life should fall neatly into categories previously established for the study of such life. The influence of the problem point of view has been both salutary and, one must confess, a little chastening, for the research worker. He possesses, as always, a point of view, but he now finds that this must be trained on ever widening bodies of data if his studies are to have perspective and his solutions or explanations are to be coherent and logical. This means, one suspects, that social psychology is rapidly becoming reorientated in terms of a newer social science and the social psychologist is becoming transformed into a new kind of social scientist.

This reorientation is one far other than a mere substitution of names or terms. It means that for the social psychologist as research worker, study boundaries are being dissolved, and that previous limitations based plausibly on inadequate data from this field or that can no longer be taken into account. The social psychologist who is interested in one out of half a hundred problems ranging from the structure of children's group life to problems of leadership, from the social manifestations of emotion to the dynamics of personality, now finds himself a scientist of the human group—and sometimes the animal group as well—wherever and however it manifests itself, among the Eskimo of Alaska or the monks of Mount Athos, in children's gangs of South African natives or in the contemporary natives of modern Germany. He finds himself joining hands with anthropologist and economist and psycho-analyst on the common basis of an interest in problems whose wide-ranging implications must inevitably lead him to take the whole province of social life into consideration.

As a research worker interested in his own problem or particular series of inter-related problems, the social psychologist can afford to say that discussions of boundaries and fields are purely academic. As a teacher, however, the social psychologist feels that such discussions have more than a passing relevance to one of his chief jobs; the job, that is, of training would-be scientists in his chosen field, and the correlative job of passing on to students a coherent and logical understanding of what a particular study of human nature has to say about the nature of this human nature. Here the teacher, if he is at all alive to modern trends, realizes the significance of data from all the social sciences. He is coming to realize that he is a social scientist first and foremost, a social psychologist only by a somewhat out-of-date reckoning!

For both teacher and researcher, however, there is one major problem that should be solved if both teaching and research are to be orientated in terms of a realistically empirical study and not merely by grace of a playing with pseudo-problems which, like certain questions, are quite unanswerable because they should never have been raised in the first instance. This major problem may be formulated in several ways. But in essence it is the problem of formulating an over-arching conceptualization of this wide and new field of study which will make the specific virtues of the psychological attack on social problems valuable and useful. Speaking with some hesitancy because one is never sure whether one's own views in a matter like this are merely short-sighted and not "insighted," I would suggest that the ground of this conceptualization may be found in the idea of interpersonal relations, the implications of which seem to be far-reaching and give promise for a fruitful reformulation for some at least of the major problems of social psychology.

DEFINITION

What is meant by interpersonal relations has been suggested by Sullivan in a series of papers which have also shown the implications of this formulation for psychiatry and sociology.[1] All that one can do here is to show rather briefly and crudely the insight that this conceptualization gives when it is applied to the point of view of the social scientist in general. One starts from the fact that man is both a human *animal* and a *human* animal. As an organism he takes his place in that realm of nature which it is the job of the biologist, physiologist and chemist, among others, to study and clarify. One thinks in this connection of Huxley's old tag: "Man's

[1] See also Beaglehole, Ernest, Notes on Interpersonal Theory. PSYCHIATRY (1940) 3:511-526.

place in nature and Nature's place in man." The study of this aspect
of man belongs to the biological and physical sciences. In so far,
however, as man is also a *human* animal, he lives in groups and in
social aggregates. That is the one fundamental meaning of the term
"human" about which all men agree. This also means that man the
animal is subjected to a certain conditioning process that is cultural and socializing. Despite statements to the contrary about
group minds and super-organicism, one suspects that culture is the
result of, and depends upon, the formulated relations between individuals or persons. These formulated ways of doing, thinking
and feeling which are characteristic of a social aggregate which has
a certain continuity in time and space, are embodied in a tradition
and are passed on from one generation to the next in that process
of socialization whereby the animal organism becomes specifically
human. There is no need to consider this process of socialization in
detail except to note that it deals with living persons, that it takes
place between persons, that there is some sort of modification or
learning among all concerned. In this learning process, typical of the
socialization process as a whole with its frustrations and satisfactions,[2] interpersonal relations are paramount: two or more persons
come to define an integrated situation—or in other terms, constitute
a field—which is ultimately resolved according to other cultural and
personal factors. The simplest structurally, but perhaps the most
complex functionally, of all groups is the interpersonal situation
made up of two individuals.

In absorbing or taking over the culture of the group into which
he is born, however, the individual does not merely absorb like a
sponge. He tends to give to this cultural material a set of personal,
private or idiomatic meanings which perhaps are more often noticeable in feeling relationships than in other types. These private
meanings are again the outcome or residue of interpersonal relations.
At their most normal they represent slight changes of accent, of

---

[2] Reference may be made here to Murdoch's statement of the seven basic
assumptions which, it is suggested, are fundamental in the organization of all
cultures everywhere: Murdoch, George P., The Cross-Cultural Survey. *Amer.
Sociol. Rev.* (1940) 5:361-370—in particular, pp. 366-369.

emphasis, of distortion, as compared with what most take to be the statistical norm of meaning for any particular pattern of behavior. In their more abnormal forms they represent those profound changes of meaning in which there is no point of contact between one private world and another: private worlds, in other words, represented by psychotic disturbance. These idiomatic relationships, then, vary all the way from slight personal idiosyncrasies of meaning to great, almost qualitative changes. Their basis must presumably be looked for, on a psychological level of understanding at any rate, in peculiarities of interpersonal relations between the child and the parents, teachers or friends who have been mainly instrumental in passing on the various aspects of the cultural heritage in which all persons of a specific culture more or less equally participate.

Many of these private meanings, validated for the individuals in terms of private person-symbolisms or person-surrogates as opposed to meanings that are consensually validated, are of great significance for the social psychologist in his task of explaining the dynamic factors of group life because they usually tend to exert a parataxic influence in group situations. By parataxic is meant that type of situation-integration in which one or both members are striving to integrate with the group in terms of a meaning that is private and personal to this or the other individual alone. There is a primary group integration in terms of ostensibly understood meaning that derives from supposedly understood cultural forms or meanings. At the same time there are other concomitant integrations—parataxes, secondary only in the sense of not being clearly understood by any member of the group, which may lead to the resolution of a situation in a manner that none could foresee if primary or obvious integrations only were considered. A clear and simple example of this sort of parataxic situation is one given by Sullivan where he analyzes the case of a woman patient of his who burst into his consulting room one day and said in great excitement that she had just discovered for the first time after some three hundred consultations that the psychiatrist was neither fat nor old and white-haired—the way in which she previously always "saw" her doctor. For many months this patient had been parataxically integrating a situation on the basis of a private, idiomatic meaning whereas the psychiatrist had been trying to integrate a social situation with quite another field of reference.[3]

Admittedly this example refers to an "abnormal" case. But reflection will probably suggest parataxes of a similar, though perhaps not of such extreme, form in one's own life—very normal, of course! A committee meeting, for instance, may be integrated at one level of meaning in terms of a group of people meeting together to get some job done. Each committee member, however, may be interpreting this situation by means of a tremendous variety of personal, parataxic meanings, all of them differing in personal acceptability to the subject, in degree of acknowledged verbalism and the like. Some of these meanings the individual, if he has some amount of self-honesty, may occasionally admit—meanings based on ambition or accrued prestige, for example; others may be quite unverbalized —objecting to a motion before the committee because the chairman or the proposer possesses a certain obnoxious type of personality. Without some knowledge of the ostensible as well as the parataxic, private meaning that each brings to the meetings and work of such a committee, one has hardly begun the job of analyzing the social psychology involved. Other examples come to mind quite readily: the psychology of a political convention, a political meeting or a faculty meeting; the influence of a leader in welding a group together; the rôle of a reader in being influenced by propaganda or advertising.

Or, to take another deceptively simple question: why do people go to church?—more generally, why do people participate in institutionalized group activity that we call religious? If the answer is, because people are religious, then what does "being religious" mean? There are certain obvious answers at the obvious level of interpersonal relations, answers which make use of such explana-

[3] For Sullivan's illuminating discussion of this case, see Sullivan, Harry Stack, Conceptions of Modern Psychiatry. PSYCHIATRY (1940) 3:1-117; pp. 101-103. Further analysis of the nature of parataxic integrations is given in the same lectures, pp. 45-58.

tions as tradition, social pressure, ambition, prestige, "keeping up with the Joneses," dependency, insecurity, love of God, and the like. But one suspects that the private, individual meanings of religion and the associated symbolism are as yet very incompletely known. Until we know them, however, we are far from being able to say what religion means to individual members of a church and why in consequence some people in our society go to church and why some people do not. Or again, what is the meaning of privacy? How much privacy is necessary in the life of the individual and of what kind? Does the individual suffer lack of satisfactions when deprived of privacy or when he has privacy? One thinks of under-privileged slum-dwellers and prisoners in solitary confinement, of hermits and certain primitive peoples, of psychotics and salesmen, the privy, the beach latrine, the one-roomed house and the palace. What privacy means in all these cases one cannot tell. It has obvious cultural meanings and obvious cultural satisfactions. Its meaning in terms of private personal symbolism and the manner in which this private world of meaning influences interpersonal relations is still largely an unknown chapter in the psychology of group life.

At this point then certain rather blunt statements—subject to refinement in the next section—can perhaps be made: in any group, no matter what its length of temporal existence—mob, crowd, group, institutional order such as a church, the behavior of the individual member has to be understood and explained on the basis of two sets of meanings; one, a cultural, consensually validated meaning; two, a private, parataxic meaning. Similarly, the behavior of the group which results from the impact of one individual upon another may be described and analyzed quite simply and behavioristically—"the mob looted broken-windowed shops. . . ." The dynamic quality and meaning of such acts can be understood only in terms of the interaction of obvious and parataxic meanings that come from the previous life history of each individual member of the group.

This type of conceptualization, of course, throws the psychologist fairly and squarely back on the study of the individual in inter-personal situations, with a two-fold emphasis that embraces both the individual as a unique product of past experience on the one hand, and as a product also of the interpersonal situation in which he is currently, at the moment of study, participating. The interpersonal situation, *qua* situation, becomes a field influencing and being influenced by the dynamic qualities of the individual who serves as the means for the expression of one of the integrating elements in this situation. The psychologist, therefore, has first the job of classifying his group situations according to whatever structural rubric seems desirable for the purpose in hand—or he may take over from the sociologists whatever type of formal group classification he finds convenient for the study of his problem. His own unique contribution to the solution of the problem comes from his attempt to understand the dynamics of the individual participating in the group, the manner in which varying and different meanings are given to the group situation by each individual concerned, the way in which group action is influenced and controlled by these meanings.

IMPLICATION

At this stage of the discussion it might perhaps be well to express in greater detail the implications of what has just been said for a definition of research problems and methodology in this newly orientated social psychology. One has to do this in a rather summary fashion, The result may appear in places to verge on dogmatic expression. It should be clear, however, that I am not interested in dogmatic or *ex cathedra* statements. My aim is to give rather a brief statement of what I take to be the rough blueprint of a theoretical structure that is capable of giving a certain order and coherency to what at present seems something of an unordered and confused field of inquiry. It should be obvious that I claim no personal originality in this attempt. Sullivan has explored the confines of interpersonal theory with an uncommonly brilliant mind. All that I can try to do here is to draw attention to a major extension of this interpersonal theory of human relations.

The most general statement of the task of social psychology is that it is concerned with the dynamic explanation of group behavior in terms of the psychological motivations of individuals integrated into interpersonal situations. These motivations are expressed in a series of *me-and-you* conceptions or configurations. The social psychologist has the job of recording and analyzing these *me-you* configurations in order to establish the underlying integration that forms the structure of the interpersonal situation. The almost infinite variety of interpersonal situations makes up what we know as group or social life.

It is obvious that in order to study group life we may begin with an analysis either of larger collectivities of individuals in interaction—the church, the nation, the state, the mob, the crowd and the like—or we may begin our investigation of smaller groups composed of two or three individuals and of the situations in which these individuals are integrated. For reasons presently to be made clear, it seems methodologically the wiser course to begin a consideration of social life with the attempt to understand two- or three-person group integrations. Membership in wider collectivities gives certain gross reference points whereby the meaning of a situation may be clearly defined. Once these gross reference points are established, however, we may concentrate on the more immediate task of establishing the structure and meaning of the more intimate groups. Later, we may follow the trail of meaning back to these larger groupings and thus try to establish the wider significance of membership in a nation, state, class or caste organization.

The unit, then, of social psychological study is the interpersonal situation. How may this interpersonal situation be defined? We may well follow Sullivan in his statement that "whenever two people are collaborating towards the achievement of a common goal they and their interpersonal relations make up, compose, and are integrated into a *personal* situation. Factors in this two-group which improve the collaboration, which increase the probability of achieving the goal, are constructive; factors which hinder the collaboration, diminish the probability, are destructive—with reference to the personal situation." [4]

[4] Sullivan, Harry Stack, Psychiatry: Introduction to the Study of Interpersonal Relations. PSYCHIATRY (1938) 1:121-134—this quotation is from p. 125, italics are Sullivan's. [Editor's Note: This paper is included in the present volume.]

The interpersonal situation, in other words, includes two or three individuals. The unit of study is the relations between these individuals. All but one of the individuals may be more or less completely illusory—as in dream states—but generally the individuals are real and perceived by the senses. The relations making up the situation are directed toward the other individual as perceived or imagined. They may be coöperative or antagonistic relations. The time span during which the interpersonal situation continues to exist is a function of the interplay of the integrating and disintegrating tendencies implicit in this situation. The integrating tendencies are generally on the surface level of the situation and are reinforced by such factors as habit, etiquette, politeness, self-interest, ambition, prestige and the like. The tendencies producing a disintegration of the situation are generally the relatively less powerful parataxic concomitants. In the behavior of the members of the interpersonal integration there are explicit—usually implicit, as well—conceptions or configurations of the "me" individual and of the "you" or "other" individual or individuals. These "me-you" conceptions provide the rationale of the behavior which integrates the situation. Hence the study of any interpersonal context is directed towards the analysis of the "me-you" configuration that controls the integration and time span of the situation under review.[5]

From the viewpoint of interpersonal study it is legitimate to think of *a society* as a collection of individuals united by a series of interpersonal relations which mark these individuals off from other individuals who do not participate in any of these relations. Society in general, on the other hand, represents a series of relations that are universal, pervasive, with no defined boundaries or limits. The smallest unit of interpersonal study, therefore, is constituted by a two- or three-individual group; the largest unit is *a* society. A society in this sense may be validly conceived as a collection of "two-groups and three-groups, real or illusory or a blend, and of larger, less durable integrations of two-groups and three-groups,

[5] For an excellent description of the manner in which these *me-you* conceptions function in the integration of a social situation, reference may be made to Sullivan, reference footnote 4, pp. 123-132.

having members in common." [6] The whole tissue of human inter-relations making up a society has a durable quality which is a function of the lives of the individuals composing these smaller face-to-face groups.

The social psychologist may thus start his study of interpersonal relations with the small two- or three-person group. On the basis of his knowledge of these groups he may then proceed to study larger social groups—a committee, a political rally, a lynching mob and the like. These larger groups are composed of integrations of smaller groups brought about by mutual common memberships in the small groups, the whole being given additional integrations through the interpersonal relations that tie the group members to the nominal, real or illusory leader of this larger integration of individuals.

To further the more exact study of interpersonal situations, it is convenient to establish a conceptual frame which will enable us to classify the ideal behavior patterns that set the obvious limits for the integration of any specific situation. The frame may well be the socio-psychological concept of status and rôle. [7] A status may be defined in Linton's words as a "polar position in a series of patterns of reciprocal behavior." It is a collection of rights and duties which governs at one level of integration the actual interpersonal behavior of individuals cognizant with the status of those functioning in the situational context. A rôle, on the other hand, is the status in action. It is the individual interpretation of the status patterns as the individuals concerned in an interpersonal relation work out the *me-you* configurations that govern the situation-integration. Statuses, to follow Linton's analysis, may be of two kinds. Achieved statuses are those which the individual wins for himself through struggle and competition. Ascribed statuses are those in which an individual participates because of the over-arched functioning of

[6] Sullivan, Harry Stack, A Note on the Implications of Psychiatry. . . . for Investigations in the Social Sciences. *Amer. J. Sociol.* (1937) 42:848-861—the quotation is from pp. 858-859.

[7] See Linton, Ralph, *The Study of Man;* New York, Appleton-Century, 1936 (viii and 503 pp.)—in particular Chapter 8, Status and Rôle, Chapter 15, Social Systems, and Chapter 26, Culture and Personality.

such reference points as age, sex, biological and kinship relationships, class, caste, racial minority relationships, occupations, and
associations. These are some—not all—of the reference points that
block in for the individual, integrated into an interpersonal situation, the major contours of attitude and behavior that govern the
pattern-development of some of the more customary situational
contexts.

The first step then in a social psychological analysis is to outline
these major statuses that set the stage for the formal analysis of the
situation. One may take such status relations as parents-children,
husband-wife, teacher-student, politician-voter, foreman-worker,
business executive-foreman, friend-friend, sibling-sibling, store-
keeper-customer, doctor-patient, lawyer-client, white-negro—to
name but some that come to mind—and for each of these, map out
the ideal or formal behavior patterns that govern two- or three-
group interpersonal situations on this level of status behavior. For
each of these situations and governing status one must naturally
consider the complicating factors of relative age, sex, class and
caste, in so far as they exert a determining influence on the *me-you*
configurations for each context. Knowledge of status patterns tells
us what individuals should do, what they often attempt to do to
the best of their ability just because of their knowledge that each
situation is controlled by this set of status patterns that present
expectancy attitudes and potentialities of behavior to each member of the interpersonal situation.

The second step in the analysis is the examination of the *actual*
patterns of behavior, not the ideal ones, which individuals follow
out as they seek to give an obvious meaning-integration to the
functioning interpersonal contexts in which they find themselves.
The cultural anthropologist is already familiar with this distinction
—the distinction between ideal cultural norms and what the individual primitive does as he tries to follow out, or reacts away from,
these ideal norms. One's behavior likewise in any interpersonal
situation is determined not only by one's knowledge of what one's
status demands but also by the personal, idiomatic interpretations
of this status as one tries to work out a rôle in the hurly-burly, give-

and-take of actual interpersonal situations. These personal, idiomatic interpretations may be made at a rather obvious level of
meaning integration. One would hardly expect a Rotarian business
man, for instance, rigidly to observe the Rotarian code if he wished
to stay in business; nor does one expect to find in even one's most
formal friends a too rigid adherence to the laws of Emily Post
etiquette. One is prepared for, and usually finds, deviations from
the standards that are justified with rather artificial rationalizations
that no one takes with any great seriousness.

But this brings us to the third step in the analysis. This step involves a consideration of the more intimately personal, often
private and symbolic meanings given by each individual to the
me-you configurations. "Two Crows denies this" must be our slo-
gan in this stage of investigation. We must not only be keenly on
the look-out for Two Crows in every interpersonal situation but we
must ask why he is prepared to deny this or that meaning and what
sort of integration he brings to the situation under review to replace the status or rôle integration. In his excellent theoretical summary of the manner in which different aspects of culture may be
interpreted by the individual on the basis of idea and behavior
systems which have private symbolic values for specific individuals,
Sapir distinguished between what he termed the generalized potency, the specialized potency, and the marginal or referential
potency of culture patterns. The distinction is based on the psychological emphases placed on the elements and implications of culture content. It is this specialized potency of status patterns that
should yield to analysis at this third stage of our inquiry.[8]

The final stage in the social psychological analysis of any interpersonal situation occurs when the attempt is made to elucidate
the parataxic concomitants which play an important rôle in the
collaborative or disintegrative tendencies upon which the very
existence of the situation studied is predicated. Previous stages in

[8] See Sapir, Edward, Cultural Anthropology and Psychiatry. *J. Abnormal
and Social Psychol.* (1932) 27:229-242—in particular, pp. 235-239. The reference to Two Crows comes from Sapir, Edward, Why Cultural Anthropology
Needs the Psychiatrist. Psychiatry (1938) 1:7-12. [Editor's Note: Included
in the present volume.]

the investigation will have laid bare the more obvious meanings and integrations of the interpersonal situation. They will have established the *me-you* configurations which, more or less coinciding in each individual concerned—or better, more or less acceptable to each individual—have given a rationale to the whole interpersonal situation. Now, in study of the parataxic integrations, an analysis is made of the other, illusory, *me-you* patterns that are outside of, or marginal to, the awareness of each individual concerned, but which, nonetheless, may, and often do, play a wholly determining rôle in the situation-integration.

Two further points may be noted here. First, that many situations are obviously integrated at a primary level in terms of universal motivational patterns which in a manner subsume the very status patterns which are an indirect derivation of these major motivations. Further consideration of these universal motivations may be left until the attempt is made to evaluate the concept of human nature for an interpersonal social psychology. The second point is that study of any interpersonal situation, particularly in our own society, is rendered more difficult by the impact of science and its physical and technological consequences upon the relations which individuals direct towards each other.[9] Examples of this impact are not difficult to find, though the influence of the impact on specific status situations may prove difficult to define. One thinks here, for instance, of the influence of the automobile on the courtship patterns of the lover-lover situation, with the apparent concomitant changes in the significance of interpersonal relations based on acquaintance and those based on intimacy. Or of the influence of the increasing use of contraceptives—some relatively efficient, some not so efficient—on the interpersonal relations of husband and wife. Or again, of the complicated modern apparatus in the physician's office that turns many of the doctor-patient relations into others more nearly integrated on the status basis of magician-cum-conjuror on the one hand, and suspicious-but-helpless-layman on the

---

[9] For a good general statement of the nature of this scientific impact, see Dewey, John, *Freedom and Culture;* New York, Putnam, 1939 (176 pp.)—in particular, Chapter 6, Science and Free Culture.

other. Or finally, one may recall the influence of technological improvements in industry with its speed-up, lay-offs, and assembly line on the interpersonal relations of worker with worker, worker with foreman—insecurity of job, anti-unionism, labor spies, and the like. This impact of science has played an important part in the splitting up into numerous sub-cultures of a once relatively uniform western European culture. It therefore complicates in great degree the problem of drawing generalizations from the specific interpersonal situations that come within the range of social psychological study.

In terms of the four-fold analysis which interpersonal theory might suggest as the basic problem of the social psychologist, a general note might well be added here on the applicability of basic techniques for the study of the interpersonal situation at each level of analysis. The various statistical and quantitative methods would seem to have a valid place in the determination of ideal and actual status patterns. Studies already made of conforming and non-conforming behavior may point the way to a more refined analysis of what is demanded by the status and what is given by the person living out his rôle. As yet, however, one sees hardly even a limited use, if any at all, for quantification when the attempt is made to explore the realm of personal and idiomatic symbolism. On the other hand, a carefully controlled use of questionnaire and experimental techniques often brings to light a surprisingly large number of private meanings that are of material aid in analyzing behavior in interpersonal contexts.[10] For analysis, however, of interpersonal situations at both the third and fourth levels of integration, more is to be expected from some of the so-called projective methods of personality study. One is not thinking here of the use of these methods for personality diagnoses, prognosis or therapy, but more generally of their use—as experimental in

[10] One has in mind here such research as Sapir, Edward, A Study of Phonetic Symbolism. *J. Exper. Psychol.* (1929) 12:225-239; Newman, Stanley S., Further Experiments in Phonetic Symbolism. *Amer. J. Psychol.* (1933) 45:53-75; Following a lead suggested by Sapir, I have been collecting for some time material on tobacco smoking in our own society which shows very clearly the significance of private, idiomatic meanings attached to this habit. This research is as yet unpublished.

the broadest sense—for the elaboration of an interpersonal situation under roughly controllable conditions. Moreno's psychodramatic techniques, Levy's test situations and Erikson's play configuration methods might well be used in this connection as an aid to the more refined qualitative analyses made possible by participant observers using one or the other of the more usual psychiatric interview techniques. Any subject, for instance, whether child, adolescent or adult, who uses, under defined conditions, a set of blocks and toys to tell a dramatic event or story is inevitably driven by the logic of the play context to formulate an interpersonal situation or a series of such impinging situations in which toy people, animals, houses, furniture, automobiles and the like, are made to fit together into a configuration that may be evaluated both for private meaning and symbolism and also for the parataxic concomitants which skilled interpretation is able to discover on the basis of the specific space configuration that is constructed with the toys at hand. At present, the play configuration technique, if one interprets Erikson's work correctly, is of particular interest in the present context of discussion because it not only gives leads for the discovery of parataxes that might otherwise be discovered more slowly by an interview technique, but also because it leads back to those parataxes based upon the patient's infantile reactions to his own body and its functions that have escaped verbalization and thus are doubly difficult of analysis by the interview.

It is important in this connection to stress the point that analysis of any interpersonal situation for deeper lying integrations must inevitably lead to analysis of the life histories of the individuals composing the interpersonal situation. Social psychology, as one defines it here, is both a situational and an individual historical study. It is not, and cannot be, in terms of interpersonal theory, an a-historical discipline. A quotation from Sullivan may be given to show how explicitly he views the historical conditions of *any* interpersonal situation. Thus, Sullivan writes: "An understanding of interpersonal relations requires a clear grasp of the serial order of development through the successive stages—infancy, childhood, the juvenile era, preadolescence, and the several stages of adolescence—to some point in which the motives (integrating tendencies) manifesting in any given situation have been evolved." And again: "If it were not for the parataxic concomitance of unresolved personal situations of the chronological past that survive in and complicate temporally present interpersonal situations, the study of human relations would be much less recondite than it is." [11]

These two quotations should make it quite clear that much as the social psychologist requires that quality which Stanley Hall called the power of "presentification," equally clearly he must face up to the situation that both past traumatic experience as well as run-of-the-mill historical happenings play an important rôle in fixing the outlines of a contemporary interpersonal relation. And after all, this is neither strange nor unexpected. Whatever else they may be, it is manifestly true that although interpersonal situations may be arbitrarily isolated by the scientist for the purposes of completer study, these interpersonal situations, by their very nature, are situations involving persons and personalities. Both of these have a determinable life history in which the latest experience is the outcome of all the host of innumerable experiences that have gone before. We can never thoroughly understand all aspects of a contemporary interpersonal situation without reference to the historical past of the individuals participating in this situation. Incidentally, in this attitude to the past, one finds one of the major differences between the field theory of social psychology, associated with the names of Lewin and Brown, and the application of interpersonal theory to the generalized study of situational contexts.

This further word of amplification, however, may perhaps be needed. Because interpersonal social psychology can never be anything but historical in one of its two major emphases, one does not need to conceive of the social psychologist as forever on the hunt for striking, exciting, or proving-all traumatic experiences that, magic-like, give the immediate and only key to an understanding of present behavior. The social psychologist, rather, has a dual task. One of these is to analyze the present situational context, seeking

---

[11] See Sullivan, reference footnote 6. The first quotation is from p. 853, fn. 4, the second from p. 860 of the article referred to.

to describe and understand it in all of its interpersonal facets. His second task leads him back to an understanding of the personal symbolism, the idiomatic meaning, the parataxic overtones, which may well be, in many cases, if not in all, the vital basis for the integrating tendencies that have brought the very interpersonal situation itself into temporal existence. This deeper understanding can come only from a consideration of the life history as it is laid bare in all its meagerness or its detail by the various techniques that the psychologist can employ for his purpose. In this sense, therefore, social psychology must be historically minded as well as situation minded. Those who object to this dual task on the basis of some personalized reading of the lessons of scientific methodology must be content to reap their whirlwind in the form of a lessened understanding of the richness of human experience.

Yet it certainly must be admitted that in spite of the distinguished research at present being devoted to the problem, we are not yet in a position adequately, efficiently and easily to collect and study life histories with the end in view of applying them to an increased understanding of the present situational context. We have been given by Dollard the criteria which such life histories should fulfill if they are to be considered at all efficient in providing us with a powerful instrument of explanation and understanding. The problem still remains of how to collect such histories without the expenditure of what now seems to be a disproportionate amount of time and energy. This latter problem is all-important for the newer social psychology here visualized. Without a solution for it the range of the psychologist's realistic understanding of the dynamics of interpersonal relations will be severely limited. He will simply be unable to cover the range and variety of interpersonal situations with the fullness that is necessary for adequate appreciation of the manifold generic and particular factors involved in such situations.

The problem, of course, is much more complex than, say, the determination of a relatively simple set of questions which would allow us to highlight the life history of a person admitted to the psychotic wards of a mental hospital. Whatever his interest in so-called abnormal persons, the social psychologist, one takes it, is primarily interested in the reactions, in the interpersonal context, of the more or less normal individual with no necessarily striking or bizarre behavior activities. For such persons, in such situations, we need a sort of time scale which will enable us to clarify the principal factors and situations which, in the past, have so formed the invariant reactive patterns of personality that the present interpersonal behavior could be none other than it is at the moment of observation. In another, non-academic context, it may be noted in passing, this same problem of an efficient, life-history understanding is of more than theoretical significance. It is generally conceded that an efficient psychiatric examination of draftees—not merely a psychometric examination—would conduce immeasurably to a more efficient performance of army duties. But such a psychiatric examination cannot, from the nature of the case, be a leisurely, time-consuming matter. What, then, are the important factors in individual experience that must be discovered and evaluated with quickness and ease in order that a relatively reliable judgment may be made of a particular individual's ability to adapt to the wide variety of interpersonal situations inherent in conscription and emergency conditions? To ask the question is to realize that we have as yet no sure answer, no ready means of finding an answer. Yet an answer would enable us immeasurably to reduce the human wastage and inefficiency now inevitably inherent in large-scale civilian army organizations.[12] The dictator can perhaps well afford to neglect such problems of human wastage. An army of a democracy cannot afford to do this without at the same time forfeiting its right to be an army of democracy.

Implicit in all that we have been saying about life histories is the attitude that the social psychologist must frankly admit his interest in the problems connected with the development of personality as observed and studied in the lives of specific individuals.

---

[12] See the Memorandum . . . on the Utilization of Psychiatry in the Promotion of National Security. PSYCHIATRY (1940) 3:483-492—in particular, p. 489. Chassell's Experience Variables Record seems an important adjunct in the task of rapidly securing a fair sample of an individual's life-history experience. See Chassell, Joseph, A Clinical Revision of the Experience Variables Record. PSYCHIATRY (1938) 1:67-77.

As a sort of hangover from nineteenth century scientific formulations there has developed among some social scientists a fear of studying the individual.[13] They have attempted to reach beyond the individual by a variety of techniques, most of them having in common some sort of statistical treatment of behavior. The results of these techniques have been supposed to high-light individual differences. But freely to paraphrase Frank, all that they have done is to show, not individual differences, but degrees of individual conformity to established—established for whatever purpose—cultural standards when these standards are broken down in terms of sex, age, educational background, home experience and the like. The individual, however, may be studied by various newly developed psychological and psychiatric techniques without the psychologist's becoming unscientific on the one hand, nor the individual cut up into nice bundles of traits on the other. In this type of individual personality study the social psychologist can also participate without feeling that he is neglecting the search for all-embracing uniformities of behavior. This does not mean that he become literary-minded, or vague or mystical about human nature. It does mean that he recognize the existence of individuals who interact to establish social situations and that these situations cannot be understood in fundamental terms save in the life experience of such individuals and their interaction.

In point of fact, it is just this very emphasis upon an interpersonal viewpoint in the study of personality development that enables the study of the person to be carried out in a legitimate fashion. It is also this emphasis which enables us to break down false methodological distinctions between the physical, or natural, sciences on the one hand, and the social sciences on the other. As long as the social sciences, social psychology included, were concerned to direct their energies to the study of forces and attributes —love of power, or acquisitiveness, for instance—explanation had to go in circles because explanation simply consisted in reifying

[13] See Frank, Lawrence K., Projective Methods for the Study of Personality. *J. Psychol.* (1939) 8:389-413. Frank shows very convincingly in this paper that, if we think in terms of twentieth century methodology, nothing is more scientific than the study of the individual, even if he is regarded as typical only of himself.

what had to be explained. When interpersonal relations become the focus, however, attention can be specifically directed to the observation and definition of the manner in which personalities react to each other in concrete situations. Thus the social sciences can be aligned, from the viewpoint of method, alongside the physical sciences where study of concrete relational situations has taken the place of a former explanation in terms of forces.[14]

As a final comment on the social psychological study of personality I would add that, so far, analysis seems to suggest the fact that the interpersonal situations which appear to have the most influence on personality-pattern development are certainly affected by given cultural conditions in the large, but that, within a given culture, these situations are cross-class in their generality and not specifically influenced by the gross reference points of class and caste. Class and caste references undoubtedly have great significance in defining status and thus in delimiting the behavior patterns to which many interpersonal situations have to conform. Class- or caste-typing, however, would seem to have considerably less significance in defining those interpersonal situations that are integrated on the basis of a traumatic experience which goes to form the invariant reactive personality pattern. It is noteworthy, for instance, that with many, if not all, of the personalities whose life histories are so superbly presented by Davis and Dollard,[15] class

[14] John Dewey—see reference footnote 9, in particular, Chapter 2, Culture and Human Nature—makes this point with good effect. I agree with Dewey in his emphasis on the fact that we must study "ways of interaction," as Dewey calls them. But I think that Dewey could perhaps have defined these ways of interaction more carefully than to write of them as interactions "between different components of different human beings and different customs, rules, traditions, institutions—the things called 'social.' "—same reference, p. 33. I assume here that human beings never interact with social customs. They always interact with other human beings, and in this process of interpersonal interaction, stabilize and standardize for a given society a specific set of customs, rules and institutions.

[15] Davis, Allison, and Dollard, John, *Children of Bondage;* Washington, D. C., American Council on Education, 1940 (xxviii and 299 pp.)—in particular, Part I, Personality Development and Status Controls. Discussion of these adolescent negro personalities as given by Davis and Dollard in Chapter 1, The Mystery of Personality, and Chapter 12, Child Training and Class, recognizes the point, made in the text above, that class and caste controls strengthen an ingrained personality pattern but do not form this pattern.

and caste seem to set the stage for the *how* of personality reaction —aggression by the use of knife or gun, for example, but not for the *why* of personality behavior—*why* this girl is aggressive, *why* that girl is timid. For even approximate understanding of the latter we have to go to cross-class, and probably cross-caste, infant and childhood experience related to the traumatic interpersonal relations between child and significant adult that are characteristic, in their generalized impact, of American culture as a whole. One thinks here of infant feelings of helplessness, weakness, dependency, of deprivations and frustrations, of the earliest experiences of enforced socialization with the often abrupt traumatic training in cleanliness and sex, of sibling rivalry, hostility and competition. All of these are pretty generalized in our culture. They are very different, probably, in Arapesh society or in Samoa. In other words, the invariant personality patterns derive from interpersonal situations that are largely independent of class and caste lines. This does not make them necessarily any the easier to study. It simply points up once again the fact that one of the keys to a significant social psychology is likely to lie in a more thorough understanding than we have had heretofore of the total process of socialization.

INTEGRATION

We have suggested in the preceding pages that the task of a social psychology reorientated on the basis of a theory of interpersonal relations is to study interpersonal situations. These interpersonal situations may be observed and analyzed at four different levels of meaning. Complete knowledge of behavior and meaning at all four levels should give us a complete insight into the dynamic integrating tendencies that operate to produce the situation under review. Generalizations based upon study of many different two- or three-group situations may be tested by reference to larger collectivities which are here conceived as being composed by the integration of various, varied and sometimes exceedingly numerous two- or three-group integrations. The ultimate task of the social psychologist is to be able to give an explanation in dynamic terms for questions of the order of generality of: A and B are in a room; C comes in; what happens?

One or two of the problems of the interrelation of a social psychology thus conceived to other fields of social science study may be noted here. The general relations of interpersonal theory to cultural anthropology and sociological study have already been outlined by Sapir in a notable series of scientific papers.[16] There seems to be little to add to Sapir's insights in this connection. It should be evident that in terms of a powerful social science both anthropology and sociology are able to bring to situational analysis that understanding of ideal and actual patterns of behavior that set the stage for the dynamic meaning and symbolism, in the light of which each individual interprets for himself as he elaborates his significant *me-you* configurations, the behavior patterns of the culture in which he is bred and born. The sociological studies give us a guide to the normal and abnormal, to the extremely wide range of potential choices that are actualized in the lives of individuals acting out their situational rôles. They warn us furthermore against such a false dichotomy as that between the individual and the social. Belief in the referential existence of such entities as the "individual" and the "social" is responsible for such criticisms of interpersonal theory, for instance, which suggest that it suffers from too much study of the "individual" at the expense of the study of institutions which "have an individuality of their own which needs to be psychologically analyzed." [17] But surely whatever individuality institutions possess lies in the very nature of these institutions themselves. They are nothing if not the recognized and established usages which control the relations between individuals or groups of individuals, for example, in respect to the acquisition,

[16] See reference footnote 8 and these two further articles: Sapir, Edward, The Contribution of Psychiatry to an Understanding of Behavior in Society. *Amer. J. Sociol.* (1937) 42:862-870; Sapir, Edward, The Emergence of the Concept of Personality in a Study of Cultures. *J. Social Psychol.* (1934) 5: 408-415.

[17] See, as an example of such criticism, the review of Kardiner's book. *The Individual and his Society;* by Eugene N. Anderson, PSYCHIATRY (1940) 3: 443-445—the quotation is from p. 445 of this review.

control and exchange of material or immaterial things—the institution of property.[18] Hence, in studying interpersonal relations one is, at one and the same time, studying the individual within the context of his institutional life—and the antithesis of the individual and the social is banished to a limbo in which it may well be forever securely interred.

One may remark in passing on from this point that in some cases today the best studies being made of interpersonal relations are to be found in the pages of contemporary story-writers seeking some sort of pattern or order in the web of emotional correspondences that serve to tie their characters one to the other. Social psychologists have largely overlooked this material on the theory presumably that they, as scientists, could not use materials that were not "scientific." Anyone, however, with an ear tuned to the intricate intimacies of the overtones of even the commonest interpersonal situation can often turn to the intuition of the gifted writer for enlightenment where the more clumsy probings of the scientist serve but to mute the strings of communication. One thinks here of some of the situations as described by Dos Passos for instance in *U. S. A.;* or Henry Adams' discussion in his *Education* of the case of President Grant who is said to have taken a dislike to his Minister to England, Motley, because the latter parted his hair in the middle; or again of that extremely acute study of what one terms status behavior and parataxic concomitance in Katherine Mansfield's short stories of family life called *Prelude* and *At The Bay*—where the secret accords and antipathies, the surface agreements and underlying passionate escapes in the relations of husband and wife, sisters, children and grandmother are laid bare with a finality that at once rings true to life and establishes a type situation with which other family situations may be compared. The problem for the social psychologist is not to toss overboard the insights of poet and novelist. It is rather to increase his understanding and appreciation of the validity and truth of these insights so that he

[18] See reference footnote 14 and Ginsberg, Morris, *Sociology;* London, Butterworth, 1934 (255 pp.). This book has always seemed to me to be one of the best introductions to basic sociological principles that we possess.

may use them as useful and fruitful collateral materials in his own plodding efforts to develop and firmly base, in a recognizable scientific method, the more universal characteristics of interpersonal integrations.

One sees no reason to assume that a final statement of these universal characteristics will enable us to dispense with such a concept as that of human nature, although one may well hope that this concept will become more defined in its meaning through the operation of interpersonal analysis. Despite the blasts that have been delivered broadside at human nature by John Dewey for instance, or by the field theorists,[19] all of whom insist as rigorously as does interpersonal theory on the values of situational analysis, it surely remains true that this very situational analysis—study of the "ways of interaction," in Dewey's phraseology—reveals universal patterns of motivation or better, universal patterns of situation integration, that are found whenever and wherever interpersonal situations are to be observed. The superficial and surface pattern of integration may show infinite variation from one culture to another. Yet the integrations themselves, stemming as they do from a broad human base on which all societies and all cultures rest, play a variation on a common theme—the need for satisfactions and securities, for heterosexual union, some measure of privacy, self-preservation, the very need for the "other person" who gives full measure of satisfaction in any interpersonal situation.

Some of these widespread integrating tendencies are found more obviously displayed for our observation than others. The point is, however, that even though some of these universal integrations may not receive overt recognition in this culture or that, nonetheless, deeper analysis may show that they exist in symbolic integrations below the surface level of commonly accepted meaning. One has always felt that the Arapesh peoples of New Guinea were a

[19] See reference footnote 14 and Brown, J. F., *Psychology and the World Order;* New York, McGraw-Hill, 1936 (ix and 529 pp.)—in particular, Chapter 14, The Original Nature of Man. Reference may also be made to Dewey's earlier statement of his position in Dewey, John, *Human Nature and Conduct;* New York, Holt, 1922 (vii and 336 pp.)—in particular, Part 2, The Place of Impulse in Conduct.

good illustration in this connection. On the surface, Arapesh interpersonal relations seem integrated on a basis of gentleness, harmony, peace. But beneath the surface there seem to be hints in
Margaret Mead's descriptions that motivations of hate, fear, anxiety, and aggression receive integration recognition in sorcery and
fear of sorcery. The point is that the social psychologist need not
accept surface motivations as being the beginning and end of all
situation integration. In our own society he recognizes symbolic
disguises and apparent transformations of motives which may give
the appearance of black being white. But he does not take this to
mean—to continue the metaphor—that therefore the full color range
of motivational tendencies is necessarily absent. And he may well
feel that fuller and more exact analysis of primitive societies will
show equally well the existence in some form or other of the universal patterns of integration that he may term human nature. The
existence of suicide surely does not mean that under most circumstances the need for self-preservation is not a common integrating
tendency—nor that again, under certain circumstances, situations
may be integrated in terms of tendencies which bring other satisfactions at the expense of the immediate enjoyment of life in this
present world.

Much then as one may feel that many unjustified uses have been
made of the concept of a human nature by *ex parte* or pseudoscientific theorisers in order to bolster some social or economic
philosophy—and to this extent Dewey's denunciation of the *uses*
of the concept, but not the concept itself, is well founded—one can
still feel sure that the lesson of cultural anthropology has not been
read rightly. To give up the concept of human nature, as referring
to a continuous and primary set of biological and psychological
needs inherent in the structure of man the human animal, is to
give social psychology over to the changing winds of a cultural
relativism, to be blown here and there, anchorless, and ultimately
boatless as well. Nonetheless, this is no reason for social psychology
not to insist on an operational definition of human nature—one that
stems from observed uniformities of integrations in observed situations. Terminology is, in a sense, irrelevant. These universal inte-

grations may be called motives, satisfactions, securities, or needs, only provided one means, by any or all of these, uniformities of situation integration and not attributes, forces, powers, or reified entities. And further, provided one is clear that the discovery and statement of such integrations are neither the beginning nor the end of social psychological study. Interpersonal situations have both generalized and private integrations. Besides establishing universal integrations the aim of the social scientist must be that of showing how differences in kind, emphasis, duration and strength of specific integrations interoperate with more generalized patterns to describe the varied picture that we know of as man's social life.

Plasticity of human nature can mean little if it means only a chaos of nothing molded into something by cultural norms. On the other hand, the concept of human nature does not have the meaning of a granite rock of the biologically given against which the waves of culture break themselves in vain. The key to a valid use of the concept of human nature lies in the development of an adequate theory of the process of socialization, of the manner and means whereby society takes the raw stuff of human nature and molds it, within certain limits, to fit the established patterns of any culture. The growing infant and the child with his serially maturing biological and psychological needs must learn the overt *me-you* configurations of his culture with whatever skill and efficiency he is capable of in terms of the interpersonal integrations that are his lot during his early years. The specific, peculiar and general integrations that link the child to the significant adults about him provide the basis for an understanding of socialization and the development of the individual's own self-dynamisms. When we have a relatively more complete knowledge of the way rewards and punishments, approvals and disapprovals, affection and coldness, bring about the learning of patterns of behavior that are incorporated in the *me* conception of the child and thereafter determine the patterns for reacting to the significant "other" in each interpersonal situation, we will have the means whereby we can evaluate, in this process, the rôle of the biologically given and of the

socially taken. But there seems no reason to assume at the present
stage of investigation that the biological and psychological needs
of man, the human animal, do not have something to say about the
manner in which socialization may proceed and the pleasantness or
unpleasantness of the process itself.

Conclusion

In a sense, and paradoxical as it may sound, the strenuous
attempt to follow through the study of social groups with the aid
of some such concept as that of interpersonal relations in the field
of social psychology leaves the investigator in the position where
social psychology as commonly understood today disappears and
in its place there is established some type of personality study in
which the integrations of individuals in a variety of interpersonal
situations are frankly recognized as the unit of study. Whether this
reorientated discipline is termed social psychology, psychiatry or
socio-psychiatry seems almost a matter of indifference—although
psychiatry, because of popular and semantic associations with the
abnormal and the mentally disordered might not, on a balance, be
as good a terminological expression as the more neutrally toned
term, social psychology. The point, however, is not to argue about
a name or a definition. It is rather to suggest that the concept of
interpersonal relations enables us to take the individual out of the
private preserve of statistician or laboratory expert and by putting
him back in a social situation to enlist the services of psychiatrist,
anthropologist, sociologist and social psychologist for a better
rounded and all embracing study of man-in-situation.

The task then of this newer social psychology or of a reformulated social science is this: its investigators must become aware of
their own biases and realize that a demand for objectivity in any
ultimate sense is like crying for a moon that does not exist. Thereafter, the investigator will bend his best energies to the study of all
the aspects and facets of interpersonal situations. His aim is the
formulation of the basic characteristics of all interpersonal situations.
The result will surely be a social psychology which, as Sapir once ex-

pressed it, will be "not a whit more social than it is individual," in sum, "the mother science" [20] embracing and at the same time comprehending the impersonal problems of the anthropologist and the sociologist in a conceptual field that can focus the results of these impersonal studies on the more personal explorations of how and why individuals react the way they do in interpersonal situations.

In 1932 this insight of Sapir's seemed to many to have a certain dream-like quality about it, a vision, perhaps, not really of this world. Today, however, one begins to see the main contours of this dream as it is being slowly transformed into the reality of everyday study. And the dream becomes no longer a dream but is now seen to be leading the way to that adequate definition of the problems of social psychology without which the sum of human knowledge about human relations cannot materially be increased.[21]

[20] The quotations are from Sapir, Edward, Cultural Anthropology and Psychiatry. *J. Abnormal and Social Psychol.* (1932) 27:229-242—in particular, p. 233.

[21] This paper was first drafted in mid-summer of 1940. Thereafter I was able to consult the recent paper by Cottrell, Leonard S. Jr., and Gallagher, Ruth, *Important Developments in American Social Psychology During the Past Decade* [Mimeographed]; Cornell University, 1940 (55 pp). In their brief comments on interpersonal theory—pp. 28-30—these two authors recognize the significance of this theory for a realistic social psychology—thus providing welcome support for the theoretical position I have outlined in this present paper.

THE TRANSFERENCE
PHENOMENON IN
PSYCHOANALYTIC THERAPY

Janet MacKenzie Rioch

THE significance of the transference phenomenon impressed Freud so profoundly that he continued through the years to develop his ideas about it. His classical observations on the patient Dora formed the basis for his first formulations of this concept. He says, "What are transferences? They are the new editions or facsimiles of the tendencies and phantasies which are aroused and made conscious during the progress of the analysis; but they have this peculiarity, which is characteristic for their species, that they replace some earlier person by the person of the physician. To put it another way: a whole series of psychological experiences are revived, not as belonging to the past, but as applying to the person of the physician at the present moment." [1]

According to Freud's view, the process of psychoanalytic cure depends mainly upon the patient's ability to remember that which is forgotten and repressed, and thus to gain conviction that the analytical conclusions arrived at are correct. However, "the unconscious feelings strive to avoid the recognition which the cure demands"; [2] they seek, instead, emotional discharge, regardless of the reality of the situation.

Freud believed that these unconscious feelings which the patient strives to hide are made up of that part of the libidinal impulse which has turned away from consciousness and reality, due to the frustration of a desired gratification. Because the attraction of reality

[1] Freud, Sigmund, *Collected Papers;* London, Hogarth (1933) 3:139.
[2] Reference footnote 1; 2:321.

has weakened, the libidinal energy is still maintained in a state of regression attached to the original infantile sexual objects, although the reasons for the recoil from reality have disappeared.[3]

Freud states that in the analytic treatment, the analyst pursues this part of the libido to its hiding place, "aiming always at unearthing it, making it accessible to consciousness and at last serviceable to reality." [3] The patient tries to achieve an emotional discharge of this libidinal energy under the pressure of the compulsion to repeat experiences over and over again rather than to become conscious of their origin. He uses the method of transferring to the person of the physician past psychological experiences and reacting to this, at times, with all the power of hallucination.[2] The patient vehemently insists that his impression of the analyst is true for the immediate present, in this way avoiding the recognition of his own unconscious impulses.

Thus, Freud regarded the transference-manifestations as a major problem of the resistance. However, Freud says, "It must not be forgotten that they (the transference-manifestations) and they only, render the invaluable service of making the patient's buried and forgotten love-emotions actual and manifest." [4]

Freud regards the transference-manifestations as having two general aspects—positive and negative. The negative, he at first regarded as having no value in psychoanalytic cure and only something to be "raised" [5] into consciousness to avoid interference with the progress of the analysis. He later [6] accorded it a place of importance in the therapeutic experience. The positive transference he considered to be ultimately sexual in origin, since Freud says, "To begin with, we knew none but sexual objects." [5] However, he divides the positive transference into two components—one, the repressed erotic component, which is used in the service of resistance; the other, the friendly and affectionate component, which, although originally sexual, is the "unobjectionable" aspect of the positive transference, and is that which "brings about the successful result in psycho-

---

[3] Reference footnote 1; 2:316.
[4] Reference footnote 1; p. 322.
[5] Reference footnote 1; p. 319.
[6] Freud, Sigmund, *Gesammelte Werke;* London, Imago (1940) 12:223.

analysis, as in all other remedial methods." [5] Freud refers here to the element of suggestion in psychoanalytic therapy, about which I wish to speak in detail a little later on.

At the moment, I should like to state that, although not agreeing with the view of Freud that human behavior depends ultimately on the biological sexual drives, I believe that it would be a mistake to deny the value and importance of his formulations regarding transference phenomena. As I shall indicate shortly, I differ on certain points with Freud, but I do not differ with the formulation that early impressions acquired during childhood are revived in the analytical situation, and are felt as immediate and real—that they form potentially the greatest obstacles to analysis, if unnoticed and, as Freud puts it, the greatest ally of the analysis when understood. I agree that the main work of the analysis consists in analyzing the transference phenomena, although I differ somewhat as to how this results in cure. It is my conviction that the transference is a strictly interpersonal experience. Freud gives the impression that under the stress of the repetition-compulsion the patient is bound to repeat the identical pattern, regardless of the other person. I believe that the personality of the analyst tends to determine the character of the transference illusions, and especially to determine whether the attempt at analysis will result in cure. Horney [7] has shown that there is no valid reason for assuming that the tendency to repeat past experiences again and again has an instinctual basis. The particular character structure of the person requires that he integrate with any given situation according to the necessities of his character structure.

In discussing my own views regarding the transference and its use in therapy, it is necessary to begin at the beginning, and to point out in a very schematic way how a person acquires his particular orientation to himself and the world—which one might call his character structure, and the implications of this in psychoanalytic therapy.

The infant is born without a frame of reference, as far as inter-

[7] Horney, Karen, *New Ways in Psychoanalysis;* New York, Norton, 1939 (313 pp.).

personal experience goes. He is already acquainted with the feeling of bodily movement—with sucking and swallowing—but, among other things, he has had no knowledge of the existence of another *person* in relationship to himself. Although I do not wish to draw any particular conclusions from this analogy, I want to mention a simple phenomenon, described by Sherif,[8] connected with the problem of the frame of reference. If you have a completely dark room, with no possibility of any light being seen, and you then turn on a small pin-point of light, which is kept stationary, this light will soon appear to be moving about. I am sure a good many of you have noticed this phenomenon when gazing at a single star. The light seems to move, and it does so, apparently, because there is no reference point in relation to which one can establish it at a fixed place in space. It just wanders around. If, however, one can at the same time see some other fixed object in the room, the light immediately becomes stationary. A reference point has been established, and there is no longer any uncertainty, any vague wandering of the spot of light. It is fixed. The pin-point of light wandering in the dark room is symbolic of the original attitude of the person to himself, undetermined, unstructured, with no reference points.

The new-born infant probably perceives everything in a vague and uncertain way, including himself. Gradually, reference points are established; a connection begins to occur between hunger and breast, between a relief of bladder tension and a wet diaper, between playing with his genitals and a smack on the hand. The physical boundaries and potentialities of the self are explored. One can observe the baby investigating the extent, shape and potentialities of his own body. He finds that he can scream and mother will come, or will not come, that he can hold his breath and everyone will get excited, that he can smile and coo and people will be enchanted, or just the opposite. The nature of the emotional reference points that he determines depends upon the environment. By that still unknown quality called "empathy," he discovers the reference points which help to determine his emotional attitude to-

[8] Sherif, Muzafer A. F., *The Psychology of Social Norms;* New York, Harper, 1936 (xii and 210 pp.).

ward himself. If his mother did not want him, is disgusted with him, treats him with utter disregard, he comes to look upon himself as a thing-to-be-disregarded. With the profound human drive to make this rational, he gradually builds up a system of "reasons why." Underneath all these "reasons," is a basic sense of worthlessness, undetermined and undefined, related directly to the original reference frame. Another child discovers that the state of being regarded is dependent upon specific factors—all is well as long as one does not act spontaneously, as long as one is not a separate person, as long as one is good, as the state of being good is continuously defined by the parents. Under these conditions, and these only, this child can feel a sense of self-regard.

Other people are encountered with the original reference frame in mind. The child tends to carry over into later situations the patterns he first learned to know. The rigidity with which these original patterns are retained depends upon the nature of the child's experience. If this has been of a traumatic character so that spontaneity has been blocked and further emotional development has been inhibited, the original orientation will tend to persist. Discrepancies may be rationalized or repressed. Thus, the original impression of the hostile mother may be retained, while the contact with the new person is rationalized to fit the original reference frame. The new person encountered acts differently, but probably that is just a pose. She is just being nice because she does not know me. If she really knew me, she would act differently. Or, the original impressions are so out of line with the present actuality, that they remain unconscious, but make themselves apparent in inappropriate behavior or attitudes, which remain outside the awareness of the person concerned.

The incongruity of the behavior pattern, or of the attitude, may be a source of astonishment to the other person involved. Sullivan [9] provides insight into the process by the elucidation of what he calls the "parataxic distortions." He points out that in the development of the personality, certain integrative patterns are organized in re-

[9] Sullivan, Harry Stack, Conceptions of Modern Psychiatry. PSYCHIATRY (1940) 3:1-117.

sponse to the important persons in the child's past. There is a "self-in-relation-to-A" pattern, or "self-in-relation-to-B" pattern. These patterns of response become familiar and useful. The person learns to get along as a "self-in-relation-to-A" or B, C and D, depending on the number of important people to whom he had to adjust in the course of his early development. For example, a young girl, who had a severely dominating mother and a weak, kindly father, learned a pattern of adjustment to her mother which could be briefly described as submissive, mildly rebellious in a secret way, but mostly lacking in spontaneity. Toward the father she developed a loving, but contemptuous attitude. When she encountered other people, regardless of sex, she oriented herself to them partly as the real people they were, and partly as she had learned to respond to her mother and father in her past. She thus was feeling toward the real person involved as if she were dealing with two people at once. However, since it is very necessary for people to behave as rational persons she suppressed the knowledge that some of her reactions were inappropriate to the immediate situation, and wove an intricate mesh of rationalizations, which permitted her to believe that the person with whom she was dealing really was someone either to be feared and submitted to, as her mother, or to be contemptuous of, as her father. The more nearly the real person fitted the original picture of the mother and father, the easier it was for her to maintain that the original "self-in-relation-to-A" or B was the real and valid expression of herself.

It happened, however, that this girl had had a kindly nurse who was not a weak person, although occupying an inferior position in the household. During the many hours when she was with this nurse, she was able to experience a great deal of unreserved warmth, and of freedom for self-realization. No demands for emotional conformity were made on her in this relationship. Her own capacities for love and spontaneous activity were able to flourish. Unfortunately, the contact with this nurse was all too brief. But there remained, despite the necessity for the rigid development of the patterns towards the mother and father, a deeply repressed, but still vital experience of self, which most closely approximated the fullest realization of her potentialities. This, which one might call her *real self*, although "snowed under" and handicapped by all the distortions incurred by her relationship to the parents, was finally able to emerge and become again active in analysis. In the course of this treatment, she learned how much her reactions to people were "transference" reactions, or as Sullivan would say, "parataxic distortions."

I have deliberately tried to schematize this illustration. For instance, when I speak of the early frame of reference and then just mention the parents, I do not overlook all the other possible reference frames. Also, one has to realize that one pattern connects with another—the whole making a tangled mass that only years of analysis can unscramble. I also have not taken the time to outline the compensatory drives that the neurotic person has to develop in order to handle his life situation. Each compensatory manœuver causes some change in his frame of reference, since the development of a defensive trait in his personality sets off a new set of relationships to those around him. The little child who grows more and more negativistic, because of injuries and frustrations, evokes more and more hostility in his environment. However, and this is important, the basic reactions of hostility on the part of the parents, which originally induced his negativism, are still there. Thus, the pattern does not change much in character—it just gets worse in the same direction. Those persons whose later life experience perpetuates the original frames of reference are more severely injured. A young child, who has a hostile mother, may then have a hostile teacher. If, by good luck, he got a kind teacher and if his own attitude was not already badly warped, so that he did not induce hostility in this kind teacher, he would be introduced into a startlingly new and pleasant frame of reference, and his personality might not suffer too greatly, especially if a kindly aunt or uncle happened to be around. I am sure that if the details of the life histories of healthy people were studied, it would be found that they had had some very satisfactory experiences early enough to establish in them a feeling of validity as persons. The profoundly sick people have been so early injured, in such a rigid and limited frame of reference, that they are not able to make use of kindliness, decency or regard when it does come their way. They meet the world as if it were potentially menacing. They have already developed defensive traits entirely appropriate to their original experience, and then carry them out in completely inappropriate situations, rationalizing the discrepancies, but never daring to believe that people are different to the ones they early learned to distrust and hate. By reason of bitter early experience, they learn never to let their guards down, never to permit intimacy, lest at that moment the death blow would be dealt to their already partly destroyed sense of self-regard. Despairing of real joy in living, they develop secondary neurotic goals which give a pseudo-satisfaction. The secondary gains at first glance might seem to be what the person was really striving for—revenge, power and exclusive possession. Actually, these are but the expressions of the deep injuries sustained by the person. They can not be fundamentally cured until those interpersonal relationships which caused the original injury are brought back to consciousness in the analytical situation. Step by step, each phase of the long period of emotional development is exposed, by no means chronologically; the interconnecting, overlapping reference frames are made conscious; those points at which a distortion of reality, or a repression of part of the self *had* to occur, are uncovered. The reality gradually becomes "undistorted," the self, re-found, in the personal relationship between the analyst and the patient. This personal relationship with the analyst is the situation in which the transference distortions can be analyzed.

In Freud's view, the transference was either positive or negative, and was related in a rather isolated way to a particular person in the past. In my view, the transference is the experiencing in the analytic situation the entire pattern of the original reference frames, which included at every moment the relationship of the patient to himself, to the important persons, and to others, as he experienced them at that time, in the light of his interrelationships with the important people.

The therapeutic aim in this process is not to uncover childhood memories which will then lend themselves to analytic interpretation. Here, I think, is an important difference to Freud's view, which Fromm [10] has also pointed out. Psychoanalytic cure is not the amassing of data, either from childhood, or from the study of the present situation. Nor does cure result from a repetition of the original injurious experience in the analytical relationship. What is curative in the process is that in tending to reconstruct with the analyst that atmosphere which obtained in childhood, the patient actually achieves something new. He discovers that part of himself which had to be repressed at the time of the original experience. He can only do this in an interpersonal relationship with the analyst, which is suitable to such a re-discovery. To illustrate this point: if a patient had a hostile parent towards whom he was required to show deference, he would have to repress certain of his own spontaneous feelings. In the analytical situation, he tends to carry over his original frame of reference and again tends to feel himself to be in a similar situation. If the analyst's personality also contains elements of a need for deference, that need will unconsciously be imparted to the patient, who will, therefore, still repress his spontaneity as he did before. True enough, he may act or try to act as if analyzed, since by definition, that is what the analyst is attempting to accomplish. But he will *never* have found his repressed self, because the analytical relationship contains for him elements actually identical with his original situation. Only if the analyst provides a genuinely *new* frame of reference—that is, if he is truly non-hostile, and truly not in need of deference—can this patient discover, and it is a real *discovery,* the repressed elements of his own personality. Thus, the transference phenomenon is used so that the patient will completely reëxperience the original frames of reference, and himself within those frames, in a truly different relationship with the analyst, to the end that he can discover the invalidity of his conclusions about himself and others.

I do not mean by this to deny the correctness of Freud's view of transference also acting as a resistance. As a matter of fact, the tendency of the patient to reëstablish the original reference frame

[10] Fromm, Erich, Lectures on *Ideas and Ideologies* presented at the New School for Social Research, N. Y. C., 1943.

is precisely because he is afraid to experience the other person in a direct and unreserved way. He has organized his whole system of getting along in the world, bad as that system might be, on the basis of the original distortions of his personality and his subsequent vicissitudes. His capacity for spontaneous feeling and acting has gone into hiding. Now it has to be sought. If some such phrase as the "capacity for self-realization" be substituted in place of Freud's concept of the repressed libidinal impulse, much the same conclusions can be reached about the way in which the transference-manifestations appear in the analysis as resistance. It is just in the safest situation, where the spontaneous feeling might come out of hiding, that the patient develops intense feelings, sometimes of a hallucinatory character, that relate to the most dreaded experiences of the past. It is at this point that the nature and the use by the patient of the transference distortions have to be understood and correctly interpreted by the analyst. It is also here that the personality of the analyst modifies the transference reaction. A patient cannot feel close to a detached or hostile analyst and will therefore never display the full intensity of his transference illusions. The complexity of this process, whereby the transference can be used as the therapeutic instrument and, at the same time, as a resistance may be illustrated by the following example: a patient had developed intense feelings of attachment to a father surrogate in his every day life. The transference feelings towards this man were of great value in elucidating his original problems with his real father. As the patient became more and more aware of his own personal validity, he found this masochistic attachment to be weakening. This occasioned acute feelings of anxiety, since his sense of independence was not yet fully established. At that point, he developed very disturbing feelings regarding the analyst, believing that she was untrustworthy and hostile, although prior to this, he had succeeded in establishing a realistically positive relationship to her. The feelings of untrustworthiness precisely reproduced an ancient pattern with his mother. He experienced them at this particular point in the analysis in order to retain and to justify his attachment to the father figure, the weakening of which attachment had threatened him so profoundly. The entire pattern was elucidated when it was seen that he was reëxperiencing an ancient triangle, in which he was continuously driven to a submissive attachment to a dominating father, due to the utter untrustworthiness of his weak mother. If the transference character of this sudden feeling of untrustworthiness of the analyst had not been clarified, he would have turned again submissively to his father surrogate, which would have further postponed his development of independence. Nevertheless, the development of this transference to the analyst brought to light a new insight.

I wish to make one remark about Freud's view of the so-called narcissistic neuroses. Freud felt that personality disorders called schizophrenia or paranoia cannot be analyzed because the patient is unable to develop a transference to the analyst. It is my view that the real difficulty in treating such disorders is that the relationship is essentially nothing but transference illusions. Such persons hallucinate the original frame of reference to the exclusion of reality. Nowhere in the realm of psychoanalysis can one find more complete proof of the effect of early experience on the person than in attempting to treat these patients. Frieda Fromm-Reichmann [11] has shown in her work with schizophrenics the necessity to realize the intensity of the transference reactions, which have become almost completely real to the patient. And yet, if one knows the correct interpretations, by actually feeling the patient's needs, one can over years of time do the identical thing which is accomplished more quickly and less dramatically with patients suffering a less severe disturbance of their interpersonal relationships.

Another point which I wish to discuss for a moment is the following:

Freud takes the position that all subsequent experience in normal life is merely a repetition of the original one.[12] Thus love is experienced for someone today *in terms of* the love felt for someone in

[11] Fromm-Reichmann, Frieda, Transference Problems in Schizophrenics. *Psychoanalytic Quart.* (1939) 8:412-426

[12] Reference footnote 1; p. 387.

the past. I do not believe this to be exactly true. The child who has not had to repress certain aspects of his personality enters into a new situation dynamically, not just as a repetition of what he felt, say, with his mother, but as an active continuation of it. I believe that there are constitutional differences with respect to the total capacity for emotional experience, just as there are with respect to the total capacity for intellectual experiences. Given this constitutional substrate, the child engages in personal relationships not passively as a lump of clay waiting to be molded, but most dynamically, bringing into play all his emotional potentialities. He may possibly find someone later whose capacity for response is deeper than his mother's. If *he* is capable of that greater depth, he experiences an expansion of himself. Many later in life have met a "great person" and have felt a sense of newness in the relationship which is described to others as "wonderful" and which is regarded with a certain amount of awe. This is not a "transference" experience, but represents a dynamic extension of the self to a new horizon.

In considering the process of psychoanalytic cure, Freud very seriously discussed the relationship of analysis to suggestion therapy and hypnosis. He believed as I previously mentioned that part of the positive transference could be made use of in the analysis to bring about the successful result. He says, "In so far we readily admit that the results of psychoanalysis rest upon a basis of suggestion; only by suggestion we must be understood to mean that which we, with Ferenczi, find that it consists of—influence on a person through and by means of the transference-manifestations of which he is capable. The eventual independence of the patient is our ultimate object when we use suggestion to bring him to carry out a mental operation that will necessarily result in a lasting improvement in his mental condition." [5] Freud elsewhere indicates very clearly that in hypnosis the relationship of the patient to the hypnotist is not worked through, whereas in analysis the transference to the analyst is resolved by bringing it entirely into consciousness. He also says that the patient is protected from the unwitting suggestive influence of the analyst by the awakening of his own unconscious resistances.[13]

I should like to discuss hypnosis a little more in detail and to make a few remarks about its correlation with the transference phenomenon in psychoanalytic therapy.

According to White,[14] the subject under hypnosis is a person striving to act like a hypnotized person as that state is continuously defined by the hypnotist. He also says that the state of being hypnotized is an "altered state of consciousness." However, as Maslow [15] points out, it is not an abnormal state. In everyday life transient manifestations of all the phenomena that occur in hypnosis can be seen. Such examples are cited as the trance-like state a person experiences when completely occupied with an absorbing book. Among the phenomena of the hypnotic state are the amnesia for the trance; the development of certain anæsthesias, such as insensitivity to pain; deafness to sounds other than the hypnotist's voice; greater ability to recall forgotten events; loss of capacity to spontaneously initiate activities; and a much greater suggestibility. This heightened suggestibility in the trance state is the most important phenomenon of hypnosis. Changes in behavior and feeling can be induced, such as painful or pleasant experiences, headaches, nausea, or feelings of well-being. Post-hypnotic behavior can be influenced by suggestion, this being one of the most important aspects of experimental hypnosis for the clarifying of psychopathological problems.

The hypnotic state is induced by a combination of methods which may include relaxation, visual concentration and verbal suggestion. The methods vary with the personality of the experimenter and the subject.

Maslow has pointed out the interpersonal character of hypnosis,

[13] Reference footnote 6; p. 226.
[14] White, Robert W., A Preface to the Theory of Hypnotism. *J. Abnormal and Social Psychol.* (1941) 36:477-505.
[15] Maslow, A. H., and Mittelmann, Bela, *Principles of Abnormal Psychology;* New York, Harper, 1941 (x and 638 pp.).

which accounts for some of the different conclusions by different experimenters. Roughly, the types of experimenters may be divided into three groups—the dominant type, the friendly or brotherly type, and the cold, detached, scientific type. According to the inner needs of the subject, he will be able to be hypnotized more readily by one type or the other. The brotherly hypnotizer cannot, for instance, hypnotize a subject whose inner need is to be dominated.

Freud [16] believed that the relationship of the subject to the hypnotist was that of an emotional, erotic attachment. He comments on the "uncanny" character of hypnosis and says that "the hypnotist awakens in the subject a portion of his archaic inheritance which had also made him compliant to his parents." What is thus awakened is the concept of "the dreaded primal father," "towards whom only a passive-masochistic attitude is possible, towards whom one's will has to be surrendered."

Ferenczi [17] considered the hypnotic state to be one in which the patient transferred onto the hypnotist his early infantile erotic attachment to the parents with the same tendency to blind belief and to uncritical obedience as obtained then. He calls attention to the paternal or frightening type of hypnosis and the maternal or gentle, stroking type. In both instances the situation tends to favor the "conscious and unconscious imaginary return to childhood."

The only point of disagreement with these views that I have is that one does not need to postulate an *erotic* attachment to the hypnotist or a "transference" of infantile sexual wishes. The sole necessity is a willingness to surrender oneself. The child whose parent wished to control it, by one way or another, is forced to do this, in order to be loved, or at least to be taken care of. The patient transfers this willingness to surrender to the hypnotist.[18] He will also transfer it to the analyst or to the leader of a group. In

[16] Freud, Sigmund, *Group Psychology and the Analysis of the Ego;* London, The International Psycho-Analytical Press, 1922 (134 pp.).

[17] Ferenczi, Sandor, *Sex in Psycho-Analysis;* Boston, Badger, 1916 (338 pp.) —in particular, Introjection and Transference.

[18] I am indebted to Erich Fromm for suggestions in the following discussion.

any one of these situations the authoritative person, be he hypnotist, analyst or leader, promises by reason of great power or knowledge the assurance of safety, cure or happiness, as the case may be.
The patient, or the isolated person, regresses emotionally to a state
of helplessness and lack of initiative similar to the child who has
been dominated.

If it be asked how in the first place the child is brought into a
state of submissiveness, it may be discovered that the original situation of the child had certain aspects which already resemble a
hypnotic situation. This depends upon the parents. If they are destructive or authoritarian they can achieve long lasting results. The
child is continuously subjected to being told *how* and *what* he is.
Day in and day out, in the limited frame of reference of his home,
he is subjected to the repetition, over and over again: "You are a
naughty boy." "You are a bad girl." "You are just a nuisance." "You
are always giving me trouble." "You are dumb," "you are stupid,"
"you are a little fool." "You always make mistakes." "You can never
do anything right"; or, "That's right; I love you when you are a
good boy." "That's the kind of boy I like." "Now you are a nice
boy." "Smile sweetly." "Pay attention to mother." "Mother loves a
good boy who does what she tells him." "Mother knows best,
mother always knows best." "If you would listen to mother, you
would get along all right. Just listen to her." "Don't pay attention
to those naughty children. Just listen to your mother."

Over and over again, with exhortations to pay attention, to listen, to be good, the child is brought under the spell. "When you
get older, never forget what I told you. Always remember what
mother says, then you will never get into trouble." These are like
post-hypnotic suggestions. "You will never come to a good end. You
will always be in trouble." "If you are not good, you will always be
unhappy." "If you don't do what I say, you will regret it." "If you
do not live up to the right things—again, 'right' as continuously defined by the mother—you will be sorry."

It was called to my attention that the Papago Indians deliberately
make use of a certain method of suggestion to influence the child
favorably. When the child is falling asleep at night the grandfather

sits by him and repeats over and over—"You will be a fast runner. You will be a good hunter." [19]

Hypnotic experiments, according to Hull,[20] indicate that children, on the whole, are more susceptible than adults. Certainly, for many reasons, including that of learning the uses and misuses of language, there is a marked rise of verbal suggestibility up to five years, with a sharp dropping off at around the eighth year. Ferenczi refers to the subsequent effects of threats or orders given in childhood as "having much in common with the post-hypnotic command-automatisms." He points out how the neurotic patient follows out, without being able to explain the motive, a command repressed long ago, just as in hypnosis a post-hypnotic suggestion is carried out for which amnesia has been produced.

It is not my intention in this paper to try to explain the altered state of consciousness which is seen in the hypnotized subject. I have had no personal experience with hypnosis. The reason I refer to hypnosis in discussing the transference is in order to further an understanding of the analytic relationship. The child may be regarded as being in a state of "chronic hypnosis," as I have described, with all sorts of post-hypnotic suggestions thrown in during this period. This entire pattern—this entire early frame of reference —may be "transferred" to the analyst. When this has happened the patient is in a highly suggestible state. Due to a number of intrinsic and extrinsic factors, the analyst is now in the position of a sort of "chronic hypnotist." First, by reason of his position of a doctor he has a certain prestige. Second, the patient *comes* to him, even if expressedly unwillingly; still if there were not something in the patient which was coöperative he would not come at all, or at least he would not stay. The office is relatively quiet, external stimuli relatively reduced. The frame of reference is limited. Many analysts maintain an anonymity about themselves. The attention is

[19] Underhill, Ruth, *Social Organization of the Papago Indians* [Columbia University Contributions to Anthropology: Vol. 30]; New York, Columbia University Press, 1939 (ix and 280 pp.).

[20] Hull, Clark L., *Hypnosis and Suggestibility;* New York, Appleton-Century, 1933 (xii and 416 pp.).

focussed on the interpersonal relationship. In this relatively undefined and unstructured field the patient is able to discover his
"transference" feelings, since he has few reference points in the
analytical situation to go by. This is greatly enhanced by having
the patient assume a physical position in the room whereby he does
not see the analyst. Thus the ordinary reference points of facial expression and gesture are lacking. True enough, he can look around
or get up and walk about. But for considerable periods of time he
lies down—itself a symbolically submissive position. He does what
is called "free association." This is again giving up—willingly, to be
sure—the conscious control of his thoughts. I want to stress the
willingness and coöperativeness of all these acts. That is precisely
the necessary condition for hypnosis. The lack of immediate reference points permits the eruption into consciousness of the old patterns of feeling. The original frame of reference becomes more and
more clearly outlined and felt. The power which the parent originally had to cast the spell is tranferred to the analytical situation.
Now it is the analyst who is in the position to do the same thing—
placed there partly by the nature of the external situation, partly
by the patient who comes to be freed from his suffering.

There is no such thing as an impersonal analyst, nor is the idea
of the analyst's acting as a mirror anything more than the "neatest
trick of the week." Whether intentionally or not, whether conscious
of it or not, the analyst does express, day in and day out, subtle or
overt evidences of his own personality in relationship to the patient.

The analyst may express explicitly his wish not to be coercive,
but if he has an unconscious wish to control the patient, it is impossible for him correctly to analyze and to resolve the tranference
distortions. The patient is thus not able to become free from his
original difficulties and for lack of something better, adopts the
analyst as a new and less dangerous authority. Then the situation
occurs in which it is not "my mother says" or "my father says," but
now "my analyst says." The so-called chronic patients who need lifelong support may benefit by such a relationship. I am of the opinion,
however, that frequently the long-continued unconscious attachment—by which I do *not* mean genuine affection or regard—is

maintained because of a failure on the analyst's part to recognize and resolve the [patients] sense of being under a sort of hypnotic spell which originated in childhood.

To develop an adequate therapeutic interpersonal relationship, the analyst must be devoid of those personal traits which tend to unconsciously perpetuate the originally destructive or authoritative situation. In addition to this, he must be able, by reason of his training, to be aware of every evidence of the transference phenomena; and lastly, he must understand the significance of the hypnotic-like situation which analysis helps to reproduce. If, with the best of intentions, he unwittingly makes use of the enormous power with which he is endowed by the patient, he may certainly achieve something that looks like change. His suggestions, exhortations and pronouncements, based on the patient's revelation of himself, may certainly make an impression. The analyst may say, "You must not do this just because I say so." That is in itself a sort of post-hypnotic command. The patient then strives to be "an analyzed person acting on his own account"—because he was told to do so. He is still not really acting on his own.

It is my firm conviction that analysis is terminable. A person can continue to grow and expand all his life. The process of analysis, however, as an interpersonal experience, has a definite end. That end is achieved when the patient has rediscovered his own self as an actively and independently functioning entity.

PSYCHIATRY: INTRODUCTION TO THE STUDY OF INTERPERSONAL RELATIONS

Harry Stack Sullivan

THE DATA OF PSYCHIATRY

PSYCHIATRY as a science is concerned with the thinking and doings of persons, real and illusory. Everything personal is data for psychiatry, and relevant exactly to the extent that it is personal. Many of the phenomena of life that at first glance seem subpersonal or impersonal are found to have personal connections which make them of psychiatric interest. The whole subject of human biology is directly or indirectly psychiatric. All contemplations of human thinking and all study of social or group life are tributary to psychiatry. All that is man-made and used by man, all that the anthropologist calls culture, has personal and therefore psychiatric aspects and implications. The range of psychiatric relevance is vast indeed. The primary concern of psychiatry as a science, however, is relatively narrow. Psychiatry seeks to discover and formulate the laws of human personality. It is only indirectly concerned with the study of abstractions less or more inclusive than the person. Its peculiar field is the study of *interpersonal phenomena*. Personality is made manifest in interpersonal situations, and not otherwise. It is to the elucidation of interpersonal relations, therefore, that psychiatry applies itself.

1. The personality that can be studied by scientific method is neither something that can be observed directly nor something the unique individuality of any instance of which would be any concern of the psychiatrist. The individuality of a particular electron is of no concern to the physicist; the individuality of the biologist's dog is not apt to confuse his biology of the dog. It is quite otherwise, however,

with the traditionally emphasized individuality of each of us, "myself." Here we have the very mother of illusions, the ever pregnant source of preconceptions that invalidate almost all our efforts to understand other people. The psychiatrist may, in his more objective moments, hold the correct view of personality, that it is the hypothetical entity that one postulates to account for the doings of people, one with another, and with more or less personified objects. In his less specialized operations this same psychiatrist joins the throng in exploiting his delusions of unique individuality. He conceives himself to be a self-limited unit that alternates between a state of insular detachment and varying degrees of contact with other people and with cultural entities. He arrogates to himself the principal rôle in such of his actions as he "happens" to notice.

2. Psychiatry is the study of the phenomena that occur in interpersonal situations, in configurations made up of two or more people, all but one of whom may be more or less completely illusory. This study has obvious relevance for the doings of everyone under most of the circumstances that characterize human life. Habitual operations on inanimate objects are an exception, in so far as they have come to include nothing personal. They are not the only exceptions, and some people manifest a somewhat less striking preponderance of interpersonal actions than do others. In general, however, anything that one *notices* is apt to be interpersonal and thus within the field of valid psychiatric data. Few interpersonal phenomena may appear in a mechanic's "listening" to a strange noise that has appeared in one's automobile. When he formulates his opinion, however, and particularly when he discovers that he is mistaken, this is no longer the case. Interpersonal factors in the latter situation may overshadow his technical competence to the serious detriment of one's car, may ensue in alterations in one's personal organization such that interpersonal factors seriously complicate all of one's subsequent dealings with auto mechanics, with any mechanics, or even with engineers and experts in all fields pertaining to machinery.

3. Human behavior, including the verbal report of subjective appearances (phenomena), is the actual matter of observation of the psychiatrist; it is important, however, to note that the act of observ-

ing is in itself human behavior and involves the observer's experience. That which one cannot experience cannot be observed, but people seem all much more simply human than otherwise, and the data of psychiatry are for the most part events of frequent occurence. At the same time these data are often matters the *personal significance* of which is veiled from the person chiefly concerned, and more or less obscured in the process of being observed by another. This is always the case with processes that go on in sleep; it is often the case in the mental disorders called *parergasia* [1]; and it is not infrequently the case in the doings of everyday life. Thus, the experience of weariness is often a veiled expression of resentment; and unreasonable worry about someone, the disguised expression of a hostile wish.[2] Neither resentment nor hostility would appear in the person's verbal report of his mental state, because they exist outside of his awareness: it is from observation of his continued behavior towards

[1] "Mental disorder" as a term refers to interpersonal processes either inadequate to the situation in which the persons are integrated, or excessively complex because of illusory persons also integrated in the situation. It implies some—sometimes a great—ineffectiveness of the behavior by which the person is conceived to be pursuing the satisfactions that he requires. It is not, however, to be envisaged as an equivalent of *psychosis*, "insanity," or the like. The failure to remember the name of an acquaintance at the opportune moment is just as truly an instance of mental disorder as is a fixed delusion that one is Napoleon I.

The term, *parergasia*, is used throughout this text to refer to a group of serious mental disorders that make up the particular patterns of interpersonal maladjustment seen in more fully developed form in many patients diagnosed as suffering the *Dementia Praecox* of Kraepelin or the *Schizophrenia* of Bleuler.

The term, *parergasia*, is a part of the psychiatric formulations of Professor Adolf Meyer, to whom the writer, like many another psychiatrist, is greatly indebted.

[2] So great are the difficulties in communicating the viewpoints of psychiatry —and so limited in particular are the capacities of the writer—that one may well distrust as a matter of principle the impressions gained on first reading of any part of this text. If the reader should seem to find something new and important, I must bespeak of him a rereading of each Chapter and finally a rereading of the whole. One of the sociologists who read the fourth version— this is the seventh—remarked that my ideas were contagious, but, like some other contagious things, they had a considerable incubation period.

[Editor's Note: The present paper was meant to be Chapter One of a book which unfortunately was never completed.]

the other person that one may demonstrate their presence "in him." We say that he is motivated to punish or to harm, but judge that these motives are denied his recognition, and are absent from his intentions. When he uses the pronoun "I," he includes in its reference only those motives of which he is aware, and refers to his *self*, a much less inclusive entity than the hypothetical personality with which the psychiatrist invests him. This self is an entity that is of little service as a general explanatory principle in the study of interpersonal relations. The weariness and the worry are fully real to the self, and provoke no feeling of incompleteness or obscurity. If the weariness should suddenly disappear when some new activity is suggested by a third person, or the worry be entirely assuaged by a game of bowling, no suggestion of inconsistency arises to disturb one's feeling of completeness, no awareness of the missing motive ensues. Even if an observer should suggest the probable motivation, no extension of awareness is to be expected, but instead a series of *rationalizations;* that is, plausible statements, in general appealing to prejudices (unwarranted beliefs), held by many persons known to the speaker, without particular regard to probability but only to interpersonal expediency, to the end that the observer shall defer to the "explanations" and thus withdraw the challenge to the other's self-esteem.

4. Psychiatry concerns itself with the way in which each of us comes to be possessed of a self which he esteems and cherishes, shelters from questioning and criticism, and expands by commendation, all without much regard to his objectively observable performances, which include contradictions and gross inconsistencies. We know that these self-dynamisms,[3] clearly the referent [4] of a great

[3] The term, *dynamism,* is used throughout this text to connote a *relatively enduring configuration of energy which manifests itself in characterizable processes in interpersonal relations.* It is to be preferred to "mental mechanism," "psychic system," "conative tendency," and the like, because it implies only *relatively enduring capacity to bring about change,* and not some fanciful substantial engines, regional organizations, or peculiar more or less physiological apparatus about which our present knowledge is nil.

[4] A *referent* is that to which something refers. As should presently appear, all our information is closely related to the formulation of experience in terms that *might be* used in an attempt to communicate with some other person. The

part of our conversation and other social behavior, are by no means inborn, relatively immutable, aspects of the person. Not only do they show significant differences between people from various parts of the world, and between the siblings of one family, but they change their characteristics in a more or less orderly fashion as one progresses from childhood to maturity. Sometimes they undergo rather abrupt and extensive modification in the course of a personal crisis; e.g., a grave mental disorder. These latter in particular, the vicissitudes of the self among the events that make up a severe psychosis, indicate that the content—the expressible convictions and uncertainties—of the self has been acquired in the life of the person chiefly by communication with others. Much of the praise and some of the blame that has come from parents, teachers, friends, and others with whom one has been significantly related, have been organized into the content of the self. A selecting and organizing factor determines what part of these observed judgments of one's personal value, what of the information that one secures through secondary channels (e.g., reading), and which of the deductions and inferences that occur in one's own thinking, shall be incorporated into the self. The growth of the self is regulated in much the same way as is the growth of an organic system of the body; it is kept in vital balance with the rest of the personality, in the functional activities of which it is peculiarly significant.

5. An outstanding activity involving the self is the having, organizing, and utilizing of *information.* Information is that part of our experience of which we are, or may easily become, aware. To be aware of something is to have information about it, and information varies from the merest hint within awareness to the most inclusive of abstract formulations. It is to be noted that information is never identical with any other aspect of reality and that, as in the case of the man's weariness in lieu of resentment, it is sometimes related in a most complicated fashion to the aspects of interpersonal reality

conception of referring pertains to the use in human mentation of abstractions from the events of life, the abstraction usually being closely related to verbal processes—secondary streams of events in which the characteristics of one's particular language are conspicuous factors.

of which it is a function within awareness. The man in question may be defined as "one motivated by resentment." This implies that he will behave in such a fashion as to punish the other person, at the same time ideally being more or less clearly aware of (a) an event that called out the motivation, (b) the state of being resentful, (c) the punitive activity, (d) the activity of the other person, and (e) the satisfactory resolution of the situation integrated by the resentment when the second person shall have been discomfited. Our particular man's resentment, however, is represented in awareness as weariness. He does not formulate the resentment in any such form as "you make me tired"; he has no information about his resentment, and little or no information about the other person's relation to his weariness. If now his behavior *unwittingly* thwarts or humiliates the other, the dynamic system which we call his "motivation by resentment" may be discharged. His weariness disappears. He would still have no information as to the punitive character of his behavior and would regard as unjust and unreasonable any imputation that he had been unkind. Under pressure, he might be led to regret the discomfiture of the other, whereupon weariness would probably return. That night, he might dream of some disaster befalling a more or less disguised representation of the object of his unrecognized resentment. He would thus be seen to have undergone (experienced)—quite dissociated from his personal awareness—resentment, its satisfaction in reality, and its reactivation and secondary satisfaction in fantasy, in the dream. Also, he "himself" has experienced two episodes of weariness, about which he may have an indefinite number of (erroneous) convictions, astonishment, or even uncomfortable uncertainty; these representations within personal awareness amounting to definite misinformation about the interpersonal situation.

6. Suppose now that we review the events leading our hypothetical man to his "psychogenetic" weariness, and find that his wife made a derogatory remark to him a short time before he showed signs of his weariness. If it also appears that this weariness is interfering with some activity planned by his wife, we may be justified in surmising that the underlying resentment was aroused by her expressed disrespect for her husband. Let us now offer this interpretation of the

situation to him. We find him anything but open-minded, he shows
a definite resistance to our attempt to correct his faults of awareness.
He seems determined to remain misinformed. Perhaps he says,
"I *never* mind anything like that; my wife means *nothing* by it," or
turns the situation against us by expressing chagrin at our imputing
such motives to him and his wife. If he is integrated with us by strong
motives of affection or respect, he may be led to entertain our interpretation—usually after a series of unsuccessful rationalizations of
his weariness. Even though he thus becomes somewhat aware of,
"admits," the fact that he is hurt by his wife's apparent lack of respect
for him, he may still maintain that "It is her way; she doesn't know
any better; that's the way they treated each other in her home," and
so forth. In other words, he is claiming that he was made unpleas-
antly emotional by a fixed type of reaction of his wife's, which is
alleged to have no reference to him personally and which, moreover,
is habitual—a sad state of affairs, if true. Let us assume that it is *not*
true, that his wife demonstrates a nice discrimination in her more or
less contemptuous remarks, reserving them exclusively for her husband. It then appears that, though we have been able to improve the
accuracy of his awareness of the character of his motivation, we have
failed to correct his information as to the motivation of the other
person in provoking his previously misrepresented resentment. He
has been punishing the offending person, not for merely existing,
but for the specific contumely, though he has been doing so unwittingly. It is really difficult for him to become clearly aware of his prehension [5] of his wife's hostile action; there is a specific limitation of
his personal awareness of the manifestations of her negative attitude.

[5] The term, *to prehend*, is used throughout this text to mean an intelligible
alteration of the personality by an impinging event. Barring familiarity (similarity) of the event, that which is prehended *tends* to be apprehended or
clearly noticed within awareness. Under various circumstances to be discussed
later, the effect of a particular prehension on selfconsciousness may vary from
focal awareness of the event and its personal meaning to a suppression of the
selfconsciousness, "complete abstraction" or "unconsciousness," or a massive
falsification of the event and its personal implications.

To prehend is to have potential information (or misinformation) about an
event; to perceive is to have information or misinformation in, or readily accessible to, awareness.

Some supplementary process has been called out in the experiencing of her offense to his self-esteem which has interfered with his having information about it. The substitution of weariness for resentment is a part of this self-deceptive pattern, a way of eliminating awareness of the motive called out by the event, and thus of diminishing the tendency to become informed as to "what is going on" in the situation. His wife, as she is represented in his personal awareness— as an objectification of certain of the relatively persistent processes that make up his self-dynamism—does not manifest hostility towards him. Yet destructive interpersonal processes are to be observed, and the observer may well wonder as to the future course of the marriage.

7. One may perhaps question the propriety of referring to hostility and to destructive processes in the matter of our hypothetical man and wife,—whom we shall henceforth identify as Mr. and Mrs. A. A genial neighbor who was present at the scene we observed—Mr. A's weariness after a slight by Mrs. A—would perhaps brush the whole incident aside as trivial, would task us with making mountains out of mole-hills, might even, if he is superficially acquainted with "psychoanalysis," surmise that we wished the couple ill and therefore grossly misinterpreted their attitudes toward each other. He might ask, for instance, if it is not more constructive for one to substitute weariness for resentment, if Mr. A was not in fact doing the very best he could to keep the peace between himself and his wife, and to avoid exposing his friends to a disagreeable scene. The general statement that bears on all these considerations runs somewhat as follows: Whenever two people are collaborating towards the achievement of a common goal, they and their interpersonal relations make up, compose, and are integrated into a *personal situation*. Factors in this two-group which improve the collaboration, which increase the probability of achieving the goal, are constructive; factors that hinder the collaboration, diminish the probability, are destructive —with reference to the personal situation. If Mrs. A makes remarks which, were they directed to the observer, would be offensive, but which have no unpleasant effect whatever on A, we may be permitted some curiosity as to the phenomenon, but we would be in error in inferring the presence of destructive processes in the personal

situation Mr.-and-Mrs. A. If Mrs. A's remarks offend A and he is fully aware of his emotion (and retaliatory motivation towards her), the disintegrative effect on the personal situation might still be unimportant. He might resolve the subordinate and contradictory situation integrated by the hostility without particular damage to the major collaboration. In the given case, however, A is not aware of being offended; he is aware of being weary, without reference to Mrs. A or her provocative action. The situation of collaboration is attenuated or suspended by the weariness. He is more or less withdrawn from the A-and-Mrs. A situation, which becomes subordinate to his preoccupation with himself and his weariness. Under cover, so to speak, of this preoccupation, the action of retaliation goes on in a dominantly hostile, non-collaborative, A-and-Mrs. A situation. A and Mrs. A are not collaborating in an exchange of hostility. She has acted against him, perhaps with full awareness of her motivation; but he "suffers weariness" while unwittingly acting against her, in his weariness ceasing to be aware of her relevance in his motivation, to this extent passing from a personal to a *parataxic* situation, a much more complicated entity in that two of the *four* or more persons now concerned, while illusory, are real antagonists to any collaboration of A and Mrs. A. Our Mr. A has become multiplex. There is the perduring A who is much the same day after day. There is a transient A who has no awareness of Mrs. A's expressed hostility and of resenting it, much less of hostile motives towards her; the transient A is dimly aware of an illusory Mrs. A, who has an unwaveringly friendly attitude, and focally aware of his own weariness. Perduring A has to be recognized in any adequate explanation of the total behavior that is to be observed; transient A, however, has no awareness of incompleteness or inadequacy. This, however, does not imply that transient A is comfortable; on the contrary, he is suffering weariness. And, in final answer to our genial friend of the family, perduring A did not consciously make, show, or choose to manifest, transient A and his weariness, in preference to being angered by his wife; the shift from a more or less adequate pattern of interpersonal relations to the parataxically intricate one happened—and happened so swiftly and by steps so subtle that no trace of what is meant by volition can be discovered in the process.[6]

8. We have been content thus far in our discussion of hypothetical A and Mrs. A to refer to her showing some contempt for her husband, as a result of which he was in some obscure way hurt, slighted, humiliated, offended, angered, and moved to retaliation —although he was not aware of this, but instead felt weary. He *experienced*, lived, underwent, the hostile action; he manifested activity called out by it; but he was not clearly aware of either phase of this, rather avoided our efforts to correct his misinformation about it—and suffered an at first glance wholly irrelevant state, weariness. We have asserted that this course of events was not voluntary but parataxic, an automatic sequence resulting in a complex personal situation including an illusory Mr. A adjusted to an illusory Mrs. A. Let us again review our fancied observations of the sequence, with some extraordinary aids to our senses.

Let us observe Mr. A in the focus of a "slow-motion" camera. When we study our record, we discover that there is ample evidence that Mr. A experienced something connected with Mrs. A's remarks. He glanced sharply at her and looked away very swiftly. The postural tensions in some parts of his face—if not, indeed, in other of his skeletal muscles—changed suddenly, and then changed again, more slowly. The first change may be hard to interpret; the second is apt to reflect the reductions in tone that are habitual in Mr. A when he is tired. Yet farther, let us suppose that, some time prior to the event, we have caused him to drink some "barium milk" and that we are observing the tone of the muscles in his alimentary canal by aid of the fluoroscope at the time that Mrs. A disturbs him. We have noticed that the shadows cast by the barium

[6] The term, *parataxis*, to the writer's knowledge, was first used in a psychiatric sense by Dom Thomas V. Moore, M. D., in a paper entitled "The Parataxes" (*Psychoanalytic Review*, 8[1921]:252-83). It is adopted for use in this text as a generic term with which to indicate sundry maladjustive or nonadjustive situations, some of which might be called in more conventional language "neurotic"—a misleading and much abused word which, with its substantive, "neurosis," might well be relegated to medical history along with "humors" and other monuments of discarded theories.

in the fluid that fills his stomach and small intestines is of a certain character. The insult comes. We observe, from change in the shape and position of the shadow, that the tone of his stomach walls is changing. His pylorus is becoming much more tense, may actually develop a spasm. The lumen or internal diameter of the small intestines is diminishing; their muscular walls are now more tense. Unlike the first changes in the skeletal muscles, these changes in the visceral muscles develop rather slowly but are persistent. We believe that they begin after the first fleeting shift of postural tension in the skeletal muscles, and that their persistence is connected with the continued feeling of weariness. One might surmise, from all these data, that the impulses which appeared in Mr. A as he prehended the hostile action of Mrs. A, tended first to the ordinary expression of anger by changes of facial expression, and tensing of some of the other skeletal muscles—perhaps clenching a fist. It would seem that the impulses had very quickly been deflected from these objectively detectable expressive postures and movements, and that they had then discharged themselves by increasing the tension in the musculature of the alimentary tract.

Now if also in our apparatus for augmenting our observational abilities, we had included a device for phonographically recording the speech and adventitious vocal phenomena produced by Mr. A, we would have found interesting data in the field of this peculiarly expressive behavior. Here, too, there would appear a series of phenomena, beginning, perhaps, with an abrupt subvocal change in the flow of the breath. There might appear a rudimentary sort of a gasp. A rapid inhalation may be coincident with the shift in postural tension that we observed in the skeletal muscles. There may then have been a respiratory pause. When Mr. A speaks, we find that his voice has changed its characteristics considerably, and we may secure, in the record of his first sentence, phonographic evidence of a continuing shift of the vocal apparatus, first towards an "angry voice" and then to one somewhat expressive of a state of weary resignation. In brief, with refinements of observational technique applied to the performances of Mr. A as an organism, we find that we can no longer doubt that he experienced, even if he did not perceive, the personal significance of Mrs. A's hostile remark. We see rather impressive evidence of an *inhibition* of a direct, relatively simple, and presumably effective action on his part, and a series of phenomena that may represent the indirect, complicated, and only obscurely effective discharge of the situation. Along with this, we have already observed an inhibition of awareness of his wife's hostility, and the presence in his awareness of the parataxic, illusory, uniformly affectionate Mrs. A.

9. Some of the circumstances surrounding this illusory Mrs. A are peculiarly significant. She is not *all* that Mr. A perceives about his wife. He does not always deceive himself as to her amiability. He has learned, for example, that he cannot alter her dislike for one of his friends, Mr. B, nor can he persuade her to treat Mr. B civilly. Moreover, he has never inhibited his awareness of anger at his wife on occasions when she has been unpleasant to Mr. B. He has quarreled with her repeatedly about it; has condemned her insolence, her attitude of superiority, and her lack of consideration for his feelings for his friend; has finally informed her, with persisting unfriendly feeling, that he is continuing to see Mr. B at his club. In brief, we need assume that Mr. A has but the one illusion about his wife's disposition; namely, that she is uniformly amiable to him. "Of course, we have a spat now and then; but all married people do. We don't agree on everything, but we do agree on each other. We've been married ten years and she's never found a fault with me. And I—why, I'd do it over in a minute. She has made an ideal wife for me. In fact, I think she has been far too considerate of me, she never thinks of herself." As we hear these sentiments, we cannot doubt Mr. A's happiness, nor can we suspect his good faith. He believes; these are convictions that are a part of his self.

Let us explore farther into his views, and ask him, as tactfully as may be, to account for his wife's devotion to him. We learn that he married her because she was so keenly interested in his career. Even from the first, he had to remind himself that she came first, so self-effacing was she. She understands perfectly how exhausting his work can be; is perfectly content to stay at home when he is tired; of course, he sees to it that she has some good times; he has encouraged her to cultivate her natural gifts of musical appreciation and other artistic expression. He did not know this side of life, before marriage, but he has interested himself in it, for her sake, and is now able to enjoy the company of the artist friends that she has accumulated and, if he says it himself, to keep up his end in their conversations. It certainly has not been all on one side; he has gained quite as much as he has given, and his wife's influence has enriched his life very greatly. He did not know Bizet from Bach before he was married and could not tell a Corot from a Rembrandt. He goes with his wife to all the exhibitions now, is beginning a little collection. We recall, perhaps, at this point that the slighting remark that preceded his weariness showed his wife's contempt for his taste in painting. He almost never misses a symphony concert when he is in town, and has season tickets for the Opera. Here we recall to ourselves a friend's comment that Mr. A sleeps through everything but the Habanera. In a word, while we know that Mr. A does not deceive himself as to his business abilities, does not make many errors of judgment in appraising himself as an executive, and errs rather on the side of underestimating the regard in which he is held by his men friends and acquaintances, it is quite otherwise when he thinks of himself as a husband. His conception of himself as his wife's husband is sadly awry, quite as much in error as is his conception of Mrs. A as his wife. With illusory Mrs. A there goes an illusory Mr. A—the gentleman who is never slighted by this embodiment of amiability and devotion, regardless of the data that our scrutiny of the A-and-Mrs. A situation reveals. I seek by this fanciful tale to illustrate one of the specific *me-and-you conceptions* that we encounter in any exploration of a person's account of his relations with a (to him) significant person.

We shall now suppose that, instead of participating in the scene of domestic harmony, we are invisibly present at one of the family quarrels—perhaps about Mr. B. Mrs. A has just remarked on the number of evenings that she has had to shift for herself recently, owing, she remarks sarcastically, to her husband's devotion to his cronies. Up to this time, Mr. A has maintained equanimity in the face of her slightly veiled hostility. Now abruptly, he takes a deep breath, glares at her, flings down the newspaper, and in a frankly angry voice says that at least he does not have to listen to crackpots discussing art when he is with his friends. This acts as a cue to his wife, who now sheds all pretense of patience with him. "Don't judge my friends by the fools you spend your evenings with, telling each other what big shots you are and how you'd run the government." There follows sundry extravagant abuses about each other's apparently all-encompassing defects, about the imbecility of each other's friends and preoccupations, and, finally, as the heat mounts steadily, Mrs. A shouts, "And if I ever see that swine B around here again, I'll tell him to his face what he is; and what you are to go around with him." Mr. A undergoes an abrupt change. His color changes; his loud-voiced anger gives place to low-voiced rage. He speaks slowly, perhaps "thickly," as if he had difficulty in articulating his words. He is focally aware of a desire to strike, tear, kill, the illusory Mrs. A who is now before him. She is the epitome of malicious persecutions, a human viper whom the law protects while she taunts him with her ability to destroy his every chance of happiness. He says things about her that would shock him if he were to recall them when he is calm again. She laughs at him as he leaves the room. He is trembling as he goes to the hall closet for his coat and hat. He leaves the house, looks unseeingly at a taxi that pulls in towards the curb, and walks on towards the corner—to find a taxicab. A strange woman who passes him is startled by the hateful look he gives her. At the corner he enters the cab he had previously ignored, gives crisp instruction to take him to the club, and becomes lost in revery. Divorce, mayhem, finding his wife in the arms of a lover—whereupon he, in the presence of witnesses, kills both of them; these are some of the courses of action that flow through his mind. He begins to feel better, overtips the chauffeur at his destination, and orders himself a stiff drink. After sipping it in silence, lost in a revery so deep that he would scarcely be able to recall it, he bethinks himself of companionship, and joins in a game of bridge. In the course of his second rubber, Mr. B comes in and waves greeting to him. Mr. A nods somewhat jerkily in return. In retrospect, he would have no information about having seen Mr. B. When the game is interrupted, he asks Mr. C to join him in a drink. As the evening wears on, they become immersed in a discussion of women. The views that A now expresses leave no place for the vaguely amiable, self-effacing woman that we encountered in the first of the illusory Mrs. A's. One gathers that women are the factual source of the belief in personal devils. As the refinements of his self-restraint become progressively beclouded, A proceeds to unfold his personal experiences with marriage. He has been deceived, exploited, cheated, humiliated, ignored, ridiculed. The self-confidence that is so necessary in his business has been undermined systematically. He has listened to so much "wishful thinking" that he is getting unrealistic himself. In short, Mr. A, as he now expresses himself, is quite as different from the happy Benedict of his previous self-revelation, as is the second illusory Mrs. A from the first. A different "me" corresponds to the different illusory Mrs. A.

10. Each "me" and its appropriate "you" are part-aspects of different configurations that recur in the A-and-Mrs. A situation as it is extended in time, as the two go on living together. We might speak of an A'-and-Mrs. A' pattern which is characterized in his consciousness by mutual respect and affection, and an A"-and-Mrs. A" pattern which is characterized by mutual contempt and hostility. Scrutiny might reveal a third, a fourth, a fifth of these me-you patterns in the interaction of A and his wife. Had we chosen to attend to the wife instead of the husband, we would have found a series of recurrent me-you patterns in her consciousness of herself and her husband. Her several me-conceptions would have been rather simply related to her several conceptions of A as "you." Each, too, would be a part-aspect of a configuration that recurs in their relations.

Let us now consider the circumstances that call out these various me-you patterns in the interactions of A and Mrs. A. We have seen A'-and-Mrs. A' and A"-and-Mrs. A". Let us assume a Mrs. A'-and-A' that is an illusion-pair of the tolerant wife-mother to a rather incompetent, absurdly conceited, but devoted husband; and a Mrs.

A"-and-A", the disillusioned victim of an utterly selfish man who regards women as inferior creatures for whose services almost anything is extravagant over-payment. It will be apparent that these two sets of patterns can be fairly congruous aspects of two configurations in the A-and-Mrs. A situation. Mrs. A has a me-you pattern that permits an approximate agreement of mutual illusion when A's motivation is friendly. She has a pattern that "suits" their integration in a frankly hostile relationship. This is usually the case, and the reader, considering his own relations with some intimate, may wonder why I have depicted the pairs of illusions as only imperfectly congruous. The series of me-you patterns and their more or less congruous me-you patterns in the awareness of one's intimate are seldom, severally or collectively, of much value as objectively verifiable descriptions of the two personalities concerned. All that A conceives of Mrs. A, or Mrs. A of A, may be beside the point, excepting in rationalizing their actions with each other. Moreover, the approach towards congruence that we have depicted need not be present; A'-and-Mrs. A' may coincide with Mrs. A"-and-A". A will then feel that he is misunderstood, for this or that reason not to his wife's discredit; and Mrs. A, that she is penetrating one of his crafty attempts to mislead her. If situations of this kind recur fairly frequently, new sets of me-you patterns are apt to develop which are less incongruous aspects of the unitary interpersonal situation with which they are associated. This, however, need not be the case. The incongruity in the coincident me-you patterns may grow to such a point that A comes to think "something is wrong" with Mrs. A, and consults a psychiatrist about her. He reports that "she seems to have undergone a complete change. She misunderstands everything I do, thinks I deceive her about everything. The more I try to reassure her, the more suspicious she gets, the more firmly she believes I am doing underhanded things to her. It doesn't make any sense at all, and you can't reason with her." He speaks of a change having occurred in his relation with his wife. While she has always shown some suspiciousness about people, has attributed bad motives to them more frequently than he himself felt was justifiable, this tendency at first did not involve him. As he looks back, he sees that the tendency to think ill of others had been growing on Mrs. A for some considerable time before she centered her hostility on him.

11. The psychiatrist knows that the present state of the A-and-Mrs. A situation cannot possibly be formulated in meaningful terms until there are extensive data as to its history. He will wish to secure an outline of the whole history of the situation, will take pains to elucidate the events which culminated in the marriage, will inquire as to the circumstances in which the two became acquainted, the events leading up to their engagement, and the course of their relationship up to the marriage. He will ask as to the history of Mr. A's interest in women; was this his first love; if not, what of the earlier attachments. He will ask as to A's impressions regarding the wife's earlier attachments. He will want to know about the course of the courtship; did either of them have periods of uncertainty. He will ask particularly about their setting the date for marriage; was it precipitate, were there difficulties in deciding on it, did either of them have a change of mind once the date had been set—was the marriage perhaps actually postponed. He will inquire about instances of bad feeling between them that had preceded marriage. He will encourage Mr. A to talk about how these incidents affected him, as to how he disposed of his doubts as to her ideal suitability. He will be interested in almost anything that can be recalled from the very beginning of their relationship and will gradually clarify to himself the chronology (the order in time) of A's me-you patterns. Knowing that in most instances of durable relations there is a rather high degree of congruence in the me-you patterns that develop in the two or three people concerned, he will attend to any indications as to Mrs. A's series of me-you patterns about her husband. It will be evident that from early in their acquaintance, there have been me-you patterns that included some measure of hostility or unfriendliness. It will become clear that this type of me-you pattern has tended to increase in significance as they have gone on living together. Disagreeable scenes between them were originally quite infrequent. "Until my friend B began to visit us, we got on quite well together. My wife took a violent dislike to him. I could

never understand it. We got so we never discussed him because it always led to a fight." Careful inquiry will cast some doubt on this peculiar significance given to Mrs. A's dislike of B. The psychiatrist may come to feel that the importance of this particular one of her negative attitudes resides chiefly in its disturbing effect on A. The increasing friction between them could be overlooked by the husband until it involved one of his close personal friends. Had their relations been as harmonious as A thinks, Mrs. A would have offered extensive rationalizations to "account for" her antipathy for Mr. B. Mr. A states that she never explained it, that she was entirely unreasonable about it. The psychiatrist then assumes that A's relationship up to the appearance of Mr. B included complex processes of the general type that we have seen in the substitution of weariness for felt resentment.

The probability that any A has imperfect information about his married life, is in every case very considerable. A high degree of objectivity about someone who is important to one is as rare as the conviction that one is objective is common. The psychiatrist presumes that all the informant's accounts will be markedly one-sided, will show strong personal warp. He knows also that he cannot hope to separate truth and illusion unless his own integration with the informant is studied carefully. In securing this part of the history of the A-and-Mrs. A relationship, the psychiatrist is integrated with Mr. A. Me-you patterns develop in this as in all significant relationships. Somewhere in their conversation, Mr. A may remark "I do not have very much faith in doctors; and I have even less faith in psychiatrists." He then refers to the case of a relative who developed mental disorder which, he was told, was incurable. She had subsequently recovered, thereby demonstrating the unreliability of psychiatric prognosis. The story goes on to reveal that the patient was seen by several psychiatrists; all but the first of whom—an interne in a psychopathic hospital—having expressed opinions to the effect that she would probably recover. The one incorrect unfavorable opinion seems to have been especially significant in crystallizing A's lack of faith in psychiatry as presented in the current interview. As it is unfriendly to the psychiatrist, it must be recognized

to be the presenting feature of a me-you pattern that will have
something to do with the information which Mr. A imparts. This
does not mean that Mr. A will wittingly omit significant data, will
deliberately deceive the psychiatrist as to the facts. It suggests that
certain data will not occur to him during the interview; if they
occur to him afterwards, they will be dismissed as of no interest to a
psychiatrist. A will have no sense of inadequacy to judge what is
important and of interest to a psychiatrist and the particular data,
once recalled and dismissed between interviews, are not apt to
appear subsequently.

Let us suppose now that the psychiatrist seeks to expand his acquaintance with the history of the A-and-Mrs. A situation by consulting other informants. He will desire to confer with some personal
friend of Mrs. A and of the husband. For purposes of exposition,
we shall presume that these friends are unacquainted one with another. We shall have him confer with Mr. C, Mr. D, Mrs. E, and
Miss F. It may become apparent that the impressions of Mrs. A
which C has gained from years of acquaintance with the husband
are strikingly different from the impressions gained by D during
an equally extended acquaintance. Similarly, Mrs. E's impression
of A gained over the years from the wife will be rather strikingly
different from the impression that Miss F has formed. D's information about Mrs. A differs from C's. Mrs. E's information about A
differs from Miss F's. A has never "happened to" tell D about events
that he has related to C; and vice versa. Mrs. A has never "happened to" tell Mrs. E some of the things about A that she has told
to Miss F; and vice versa.

Factors in the A-and-C situation have influenced the communication of information about the third person, Mrs. A. While there
have been some two, three, or four illusory C's in A's objectification
of C; and several more or less congruous illusory A's in C's objectification of A; the underlying configurations of the A-and-C situation
have precluded the reporting of certain of his illusory Mrs. A's in
A's conversation with C. If we were able to call this to A's attention,
he might say that C was not the sort of person to be interested in
such and such attributes of Mrs. A. He might tell us that he had

on certain occasions mentioned to C some matters concerning Mrs. A in these unrepresented aspects. Mr. C had paid no attention to this information, had forgotten it, or left it out of consideration in subsequent discussions of Mrs. A. C's opinion of A did not include the possibility of his feeling toward his wife in these unrepresented ways. C's objectification of the personality of Mrs. A, his illusory Mrs. A, is thus seen to be a fairly simple function of the A-and-C situation, but it is also a function of a C-imaginary-Mrs. A situation; that is, it includes complex processes that are suggested when C says, "Well, if she were my wife . . ." It might well seem that anything which C can offer as his impression of the to him actual unknown Mrs. A will be of little use in formulating an outline of her personality. The psychiatrist could perhaps make little headway if all of his information about A and Mrs. A came through these highly mediate interpersonal channels.

The mental disorder of Mrs. A, the psychiatrist's focal problem, has eventuated in the course of her life with A. While she has been living with A, A has been an important factor in her life. She knows something about his significance, and he knows something about his significance. Her accessible information is bound up in a series of me-you patterns, the variety of which has become restricted to a very hostile Mrs. A'''-and-A''' pattern. While the psychiatrist by appropriate steps could probably recover data on the whole series of A's illusory Mrs. A's, as they are recorded in his memory, a parallel recall could not be obtained in Mrs. A as she now is. In other words, among the changes that she has undergone, there is one that makes it difficult to remind her of the me-you patterns about her husband which are at striking variance with the now dominant pattern. Even though the psychiatrist, in the course of a long conversation, reminds her of an earlier me-you pattern in which Mr. A was represented as anything but a hostile and dangerous person—an achievement that may be quite difficult—he will be no nearer to convincing Mrs. A that she has undergone a striking change in the freedom with which she objectifies her husband. She will probably account for the earlier friendly illusions about her husband as mistakes which she has subsequently corrected. As an alternative, she may hold that Mr. A himself has undergone a marked change. In the first case, when next she sees the psychiatrist Mrs. A will have elaborated some data with which to prove that her former favorable impressions were the result of the fraud and dishonesty in Mr. A which she has finally come to understand. While the psychiatrist may have made her somewhat uncomfortable when first she recalled the earlier personification, this is no longer possible in that connection. She believes entirely the correctness of her present me-you pattern and the belief is not to be shaken.

In the face of so potent a factor, the psychiatrist in pursuit of information as to the history of Mrs. A's me-you patterns must have recourse to her friends. Again, in his conferences with Mrs. E and Miss F, he has to formulate the relation of each with him as best he can, he must make some inquiries purposed to illuminate the characteristics of the illusory psychiatrist to whom each is addressing her remarks. He will seek mediate data on the Mrs. A-and-A situation. He will know that Mrs. E, for example, has developed an illusory A as a particular manifestation of some of the recurrent configurations that have characterized the enduring Mrs. E-and-Mrs. A situation. His inquiry will bear significantly on the history of the latter. Without considerable information on this, Mrs. E's impressions about Mr. A would be practically beyond interpretation. As Mrs. E herself has a husband, the psychiatrist may encourage her to present contrasts between her married life and that of her friend, and between Mr. E and Mr. A as she knows him. Similarly, in his conferences with Miss F, having obtained some clues from time to time as to the illusory psychiatrist with whom she is communicating, he will develop the history of the F-and-Mrs. A relationship. In all these conferences, he will attend to many phenomena besides the actual verbal contexts. He will note, for example, that whenever Miss F is discussing men, her voice, intonation, attitude, and set facial expression indicate something of a rigid attitude. Her replies to not too direct questions confirm his surmise that Miss F has an unfriendly view of men in general. This has value as collateral information concerning the configurations that have characterized the F-and-Mrs. A situation. He comes ultimately to inquire as to Miss F's views of marriage, her preference for the single state, and how Mrs. A may have influenced her in this particular. He may ask finally if Mrs. A in bygone years urged Miss F to marry. She is surprised to recall that such was indeed the case. These contexts shed light on the factors which have resulted in the exclusion of some favorable illusions concerning A from the wife's discussion of him with her unmarried friend. For parallel reasons, Miss F in her account recalls certain facts that may have "escaped" not only Mrs. A herself, but also Mrs. E. In particular, the time-ordering of events—which preceded which—in the recollections respectively of Mrs. E and Miss F, may vary widely. Some of these discrepancies may be especially useful bases for exploration in subsequent conferences with any one of the informants.

12. Everyone with whom one has been in any significant relationship, from birth onward, is a potential informant about one. Informants are able to express a body of illusions that they have developed in the interpersonal situations in which they have been integrated. In the body of illusions that they can communicate, there is data capable of elaboration into more valid information than they themselves have formulated. This is chiefly because everyone prehends much more than he perceives; at the same time, one's behavior is affected by all that one has experienced, whether it was prehended or consciously perceived. The psychiatrist, in developing his skill in interrogating informants, learns to integrate situations the configurations of which provoke the elaboration of information that was previously potential. He thus obtains more data from the informant than the latter has clearly perceived. The informant, so to speak, tells more than he knows. The data are more significant to the psychiatrist because he has more experience and more freedom in formulating interpersonal processes. He is alert to implications; his alertness is oriented to understanding interpersonal processes; and he has many fewer specific inhibitions of alertness in the interpersonal configurations in which he participates. From the relative accessibility of his own past, and from intimate contact with the developmental history of a number of people, he

has a considerable grasp on the actual dynamics of interpersonal relations. He knows more about the processes that can occur in these configurations; in particular, he knows that certain alleged processes are highly improbable. Reports of these alleged events are, therefore, most probably rationalizations, and he is able, from experience or by inquiry, to secure clues to the unwitting motivations that underlie these conventional statements.

Certainty about interpersonal processes is an ideal that should seldom concern one. Information about any situation should be considered as a formulation of probability. Information about a person may vary from very high probability—my companion is in the same room—to extremely low—my companion understands me perfectly. The physical factors in situations are often quite accurately measurable; they can be described in specialized language in a manner that contributes to an approximate *consensus* in the people who are considering the situation. This requires similarity of experience with the specialized language. Two people looking at this page may express different opinions as to the color of the paper.* One may say it is yellow; the other, that it is yellow-green. It is quite possible that a third observer may call it a deep orange; it is equally possible that a fourth may call it a vivid green. In the first pair of observers, the probability is that they had much the same initial prehensions, that the difference is primarily a difference in language. In the third and fourth observers, we must suspect differences in the initial prehensions. The spectral reflection of light by this paper includes green, yellow, orange, and red—the last three in approximately equal degree. The visual efficiency of light of different wave-lengths is rather widely variable in different people, the average maximum being in the yellow-green, falling off rather steeply in the green and orange. The long and the short waves producing relatively little effect when they impinge on the retina, the paper *looks* yellow (or yellow-green). In color-blind persons the experience caused by encountering colored light is markedly different from the average, and, while the meaning of

* [Editor's Note: This refers to the color of the paper on which the journal *Psychiatry* is printed.]

their terms for these experiences are also necessarily different from the average, the more striking difference is in the initial prehension. A person in whom the prehension of green is lacking may none the less state that a green object is green. When we investigate this anomalous situation, we find that he has learned to call a particular gray appearance by the name of green—people have always been talking to him about how beautiful the green fields are, how bright this or that green is, how the traffic light is now green. Despite a fundamental defect in color-perception, he has come to talk about colors much as others do. While he can be led to mention his color-blindness, he has found that it is a difference that does not enhance the regard in which he is held by others. It may make people "nervous" to ride with him when he is driving his car. Some people amuse themselves by testing his color-perception. His language behavior has been developed to shield him from these and many other unpleasant consequences of difference. A discussion with him of the merits of a Monet is obviously a much more complex process than an unsuspecting companion might believe.

When one has regard for the multiple me-you patterns that complicate interpersonal relations, for the possible differences in individual prehension of events, and for the peculiarities of language behavior which characterize each of us—a topic to which we shall return—the practical impossibility of one-to-one correspondence of mental states of the observer and the observed person should be evident. We never know all about another, we are fortunate when we achieve an approximate consensus and can carry on meaningful communication about relatively simple contexts of experience. Most of us spend the greater part of our social life in much less adequate contact with our interlocutors, with whom we manifest considerable skill at avoiding frank misunderstanding, with whom in fact we agree and disagree quite often with very little consensus as to subject of discussion. The psychiatrist of all people knows the relative character of his formulation of the other person, even if he has gained such skill that he is often quite correct.

RECENT ADVANCES IN
PSYCHOANALYTIC THERAPY

Frieda Fromm-Reichmann

IN ORDER to discuss recent advances in psychoanalytic therapy, I wish to review briefly certain basic psychoanalytic concepts which have been accepted by all psychoanalysts. The working-of-the-mind is understood to be a result of dynamic interaction between the unconscious and the conscious parts of the mind, whereby *conscious* and *unconscious* express not only a degree of consciousness but also a difference in the quality and means of expression. Mental health is established by harmonious interaction between the conscious and unconscious mental processes, and by generous adaptation of conscious and unconscious drives and desires to the standards of conscience on the one hand, and to the requirements of the outer world and the relationships with fellow men on the other.

Traumatic interference with harmonious interrelations of the mental systems comes from drives and desires which are incompatible with the personal or environmental standards, either as such or because they are linked with frustrated infantile desires and drives whose memories are retained throughout life in the unconscious. Thus a person develops defenses against these drives and desires which threaten his peace in order to avoid such interference. Because the drives are so powerful these defenses are never quite successful, and the resulting emotional and mental illnesses are compromises between rejected drives and rejecting mental forces.

The aim of psychoanalytic therapy is to bring these rejected drives and wishes, together with the patient's individual and environmental moral standards, which are the instruments for his rejections, into consciousness and in this way place them at his free disposal. In doing this the conscious self becomes strengthened, since it is no longer involved in the continuous job of repressing mental content from his own awareness. The patient can then decide independently which desires he wants to accept and which he wishes to reject, his personality no longer being warped or dominated by uncontrollable drives and moral standards. This process permits growth and maturation.

The methodology of psychoanalytic therapy lies in the patient's learning to understand his problems intellectually and emotionally while reëxperiencing them and working through the dynamics of his conflicts, as they are activated in the interrelationship with the analyst. This relationship itself becomes an object of investigation and interpretation for therapeutic purposes.

Recent advances in psychoanalytic therapy are due first to changing conceptions of the nature of drives elaborated by various modern psychoanalysts. These newer conceptions have not been accepted by a large group who still believe in all of the classical concepts originated by Freud.

Freud thought at first that, except for hunger, all drives were of a sexual nature, and later that there were two types of drives, the erotic and the destructive, whereby he used the term *sex* in his own broad sense.

Freud's concepts were seemingly influenced by the culture of the times in which they were conceived: during the instinctivistic and materialistic trends in natural science and medicine, and the sexual prudishness of the Victorian age.

Modern psychoanalysts do not of course deny that sexual and destructive drives are many times among those which lead up to neurotic and psychotic developments. We believe, however, with Horney, Hill, Sullivan,[1] and others that there are also other power-

[1] Horney, Karen, *The Neurotic Personality of Our Time;* New York, Norton, 1937 (xii and 290 pp.); and, *New Ways in Psychoanalysis;* New York, Norton, 1939 (313 pp.). Hill, Lewis B.,The Use of Hostility as Defense. *Psychoanalytic Quart.* (1938) 7:254-264. Sullivan, Harry Stack, Socio-Psychiatric Research: Its Implications for the Schizophrenia Problem and for Mental Hygiene. *Amer. J. Psychiatry* (1931) 10 [o. s. 87]:977-991; and Conceptions of Modern Psychiatry. PSYCHIATRY (1940) 3:1-117.

ful drives and desires at the foundation of neurotic and psychotic conflicts. These other powerful drives and desires are used by persons, individually, as a defense, in their efforts to adjust to a competitive world, and to gain self-assertion among their fellow men; examples are the need for love and dependence—frequently used as a means of domination—the quest for power, the need for prestige and perfection, and reactive hostility and resentment against those who frustrate the realization of these and other drives.[2]

These drives and desires may or may not have sexual implications—their investigation and interpretation along sex lines is frequently of no therapeutic value to the patient. His need is to see their defensive character, and these and similar drives are frequently just as incompatible with the official standards of our present culture and its repercussions in the individual conscience, and, therefore, just as much subject to rejection as were the forbidden sexual drives at the time of Freud's discoveries.

This leads to the discussion of another advance in psychoanalysis due to the clarification of Freud's concept of *reality*.

Freud speaks of an objective "reality" of the outside world in contradistinction to the private and frequently unreal inner world of the neurotic. While he clearly points out how greatly the person's immediate surroundings are determined by changing environmental influences, he neglects to see that the same holds true for the world at large which is dependent on the changes of culture and is lacking in any universal and eternal psychological character.

The "reality" to which, for instance, a Vienna girl of the upper middle classes had to adjust in the period before the first World War, is a long way from the "reality" to which an American salesgirl has to adapt herself today.

To give another example: such Freudian concepts as the girl's envy of the boy's genitalia or the boy's competitive hatred for his father and his sexual attraction to his mother, hold true and are valuable in therapy with many patients of our particular Western

[2] The latter is in contradistinction to Freud's concept of the primary existence of destructive drives, the so called *death instinct*. There are some of us who definitely do not agree with the concept of the death instinct.

patriarchal culture. Yet, they are not found in matriarchal cultures, and we know that they are social concepts and have no universal and biological significance.

Another result of modern sociologic thinking in analysis is shown in Sullivan's concept of a person's adjustment to reality in terms of adaptation to interpersonal relationships.[3] Such a concept was unacceptable in the early days of psychoanalysis because at that time all human relationships were studied only from their sexual aspect.

Our better understanding of the rôle of human relationships in general goes with more realistic concepts of the special relationship between patient and psychoanalyst.

Freud taught that, ideally, the analyst, as nearly as it is possible, must be a blank to the patient. This is to help the patient express himself more freely about the therapist as his catalytic agent, and to transfer to him and work through with him all the unresolved emotional reactions which he has previously felt towards other people. It also makes it at times possible for the patient to use the psychoanalyst as his new conscience while revising his own moral standards which have interfered.[4]

In many ways this concept of the relationship between patient and analyst has proven to be of great value to the patient, and even more so to the analyst. He has learned to understand how many of the patient's emotional reactions are determined by the therapeutic situation rather than by the person of the therapist. This insight enables him to accept the patient's hatred without counter-hostility, his love and appreciation without personal response or conceit; thus it protects both patient and therapist from inappropriate reactions on the part of the analyst.

To this extent the analyst's reaction would be all right. But, if he went farther, his aloofness would also become a means of pro-

[3] The research work done by the Chicago Psychoanalytic Institute on gastrointestinal syndromes as an expression of the patient's give-and-take relationship to his surroundings should be mentioned in this connection.

[4] Although it is accepted by many psychoanalysts, Freud's doctrine that this conscience with its conscious and unconscious traits is an independent part of the mind seems to some of us more interesting as hypothesis than as proven fact.

tection against his patient's legitimate reactions to him as a person, whether resentment if he blundered, or appreciation when he struck the right chord.

As Ferenczi [5] and his disciples have pointed out at various times we know now that, being unreal, it is a dangerous pretense to think that one of two partners—the analyst—can remain a shapeless non-entity to the other—the patient—in the course of a therapeutic procedure whose very essence is an intimately interpersonal experience and whose aim is the patient's reëstablishment of real contacts in a real world.[6]

Hence, now our attitude is to help our patients, in neutrality, to reëxperience and reëvaluate emotional reactions. However, we do not spend all of our time in an atmosphere of unreal self-protective irresponsibility.

That, of course, does not mean that the analyst will talk about his personal life, personal view-points or emotions to the patient. He will avoid unreasonable emotional counter-reactions, and he will not use the patient to serve his own needs instead of the patient's.

Sexual feelings towards the analyst may come up. The analyst who has gone through analysis himself will meet these feelings as he does his patient's other emotional reactions. According to our recent insight their frequency has been overrated, as have the sexual drives as a traumatic factor in general, and their significance is frequently misinterpreted.

Sex feelings, or expression of such feelings, come up many times as a defense on the one hand, or, on the other, as expression of insecurity in patients who do not know how to express attachment nor how to ask for reassurance other than in terms of sex.

In principle all these interpersonal reactions come up in the course of every psychotherapeutic procedure, if not between all patients and physicians. The difference between the psychoanalytic and other psychotherapeutic methods is that analysis asks that the patient

[5] Ferenczi, Sándor, *Further Contributions to the Theory and Technique of Psycho-Analysis;* London, Hogarth Press, 1926 (450 pp.); pp. 177-238.

[6] Helen McLean offered suggestions along this line in a paper on The Art of Psychoanalysis presented at the meeting of the Washington-Baltimore Psychoanalytic Society, February 8, 1941.

and the therapist be aware of and make use of them for the purposes of treatment. Other methods may neglect to see them or may deny their existence.

Another change in psychoanalytic therapy is due to our changed attitude towards interpretations. When analysis was first used we believed in interpreting every expression of repressed unconscious memories or experience as soon as we could get hold of it in terms of Freud's instinctivistic content and vocabulary. We expected these interpretations to be followed immediately by the neurotic patient's relinquishing the symptoms connected with the material pointed out. We have since learned that these expectations were ill founded. A wide variety of suggestions and warnings as to timing and content of interpretations have been offered; for example, that interpretations are to be made only if the patient's present relationship with the analyst is positive enough to grant their acceptance; or only if the material is connected with the patient's relationship to the analyst, preferably in its negative phases.

At present many analysts feel an increasing inclination to become more thrifty with interpretations from fear of unduly intellectualizing the patient's experience in analysis. Left alone the patient will discover the unconscious meaning of many of his experiences without interpretation. Freud warned us to bear in mind that analysis is a procedure designed to cure the patient, not to show him how clever his analyst's interpretations are. It is to be noted that the content of interpretations has altered in accordance with the changing concepts. The avoidance of scientific terms is recommended.

The most important progress has come from learning to deal not only with the rejected, unconscious material and the unconscious rejecting forces, but also from exposing defenses in the patient's conscious personality. The previously mentioned defensive drives provide an example. Thus, we approach the patient and his problems on a more realistic level, and stress the dynamics of his actual relationships and reactions towards his environment. This, of course, does not mean that we neglect to search for and to study their unconscious background.

All modern analysts accept the classical belief in the paramount importance of confronting the patient with the *non*-conscious sources of his mental life, and of rediscovering and working through unconscious material; most of them in the great therapeutic significance of rediscovering forgotten childhood memories. Others, like Horney, wonder about the need and wisdom of stressing the childhood memories.

In short, our notions of the therapeutic value, timing and contents of interpretations are fluctuating, analysis is moving, and final decisions are to be derived from further experience.

Another advance in analysis comes from a change in the choice of patients. During the last fifteen years attempts have been made to adjust the analytic method to the needs of psychotic patients. Results are still far from satisfactory, but the research under way, while not yet as helpful as we wish, is at least increasing our understanding of psychotic and neurotic processes.

As Freud predicted, the classical conversion hysteria has practically disappeared. Now we understand and treat psychosomatic conditions on a deeper level than previously.

The ever increasing number of neurotic characters has created a new group of patients. Their analyses are long and difficult. A lack of markedly severe symptoms makes it difficult for them to accept treatment. Moreover, the concealed disintegrative forces, and their fondness of themselves concentrate resistance to changes in their personality.

Yet, successful character analyses are most encouraging; and since there is no other psychotherapeutic method which enables real changes in character, this seems to be the field reserved for psychoanalytic therapy for a long time to come.

Many other persons, especially those who do not ask for more than a cure of isolated symptoms, should be submitted to shorter psychotherapeutic methods which are simpler and less expensive than the psychoanalytic procedure in its present state of development.

SUMMARY

Recent advances in psychoanalytic treatment come from reviewing the instinctivistic concepts of human drives and desires; from giving more consideration to the cultural and realistic aspects of the patient's outer world, his personal relationships in general and with the analyst; from putting more stress than previously on the exposure of conscious defenses of the self; and, from including psychoses, psychosomatic syndromes, and neurotic characters in the list of those who may receive psychoanalytic treatment.

CULTURAL PRESSURES
IN THE PSYCHOLOGY
OF WOMEN

Clara Thompson

IN MY study of *The Rôle of Women in This Culture* I
presented a survey of the present status of women in
the United States. I pointed out the basic situation and the changes
which are going on. Although the paper was chiefly concerned with
the positive aspects of woman's evolution, I spoke also of the problems still remaining, and the new problems arising in the new
situations.

It is this problem aspect of woman's present cultural situation
which I shall now discuss. I shall approach this through a consideration of Freud's theories about women, viewing these in the light
of cultural factors.

The importance of cultural influences in personality problems has
become more and more significant in psychoanalytic work. A given
culture tends to produce certain types of character. In *The Neurotic Personality of Our Time* Karen Horney has well described
certain trends found in this culture. Most of these neurotic trends
are found working similarly in both sexes. Thus, for example, the
so-called masochistic character is by no means an exclusively feminine phenomenon. Likewise the neurotic need to be loved is often
found dominating the life of men as well as women. The neurotic
need of power, and insatiable ambition drives are not only found
in men, but also in women.

Nevertheless, in some respects the problems of women are basically different from those of men. These fundamental differences are
due to two things. First, woman has a different biological function

and because of this her position in society necessarily differs in some respects from that of the man. Secondly, the cultural attitude towards women differs significantly from that towards men for reasons quite apart from biological necessity. These two differences present women with certain problems which men do not have to face.

The biological problems of a woman's life cannot be ignored although it would seem that in most cases biology becomes a problem chiefly when it produces a situation which is unsatisfactory in the cultural setup. Menstruation, pregnancy and the menopause can bring to a woman certain hazards of which there is no comparable difficulty in the male biology. Freud was so impressed with the biological difficulties of woman that, as is well known, he believed all inferiority feelings of woman had their root in her biological inadequacies. To say that a woman has to encounter certain hazards that a man does not, does not seem to be the same thing as saying woman is biologically inferior, as Freud implies.

According to his theory woman has a lasting feeling of inferiority because she has no penis. The discovery of this fact at about the age of three is considered sufficiently traumatic not only to lay the foundation for later neurosis but also to have decisive influence on woman's character. She must go through life from that time with the feeling either that she was "born short" or that something terrible had happened to her; possibly as a punishment. This feeling of biological lack, Freud feels, so overshadows all other details in the picture that he is constrained to express a note of complete pessimism about the cure of women. In his paper *Analysis Terminable and Interminable,* published in English in 1937, he says the following: "The feminine wish for a penis . . . is the source of acute attacks of depression . . . because . . . they (women) feel analysis will avail them nothing. We can only agree when we discover that their strongest motive in coming for treatment was the hope that they might somehow still obtain a male organ." Such pessimism would only be warranted if it were assumed that it is the actual physical male organ which women are demanding from analysis, whereas it seems to me that when such a wish is expressed the woman is but demanding in this symbolic way some form of equality with men.

According to Freud, because of the little girl's discovery that she has no penis she enters the Œdipus complex with castration already an accomplished fact, while in the little boy the threat of castration arises as a result of the Œdipus complex and brings about its repression. Out of this situation in the little boy Freud believes much that is important in the superego takes its origin. Since the little girl, feeling herself already castrated, need fear no further threat she has less tendency to repress her Œdipus complex and less tendency to develop a superego.

Furthermore, according to Freud, one fact which reinforces the high evaluation of the penis by the little girl is that she is at the time of its discovery unaware that she has a vagina. She therefore considers her clitoris her sole sexual apparatus and is exclusively interested in it throughout childhood. Since she believes this is all she has in place of a penis this emphasizes her inferiority. In addition, the ignorance of the vagina makes for her a special hazard at puberty because the onset of menstruation brings awareness of her female rôle and requires her to give up her interest in the clitoris and henceforth to seek sexual satisfaction by way of the vagina. With this comes a change in her character. She gives up her boyish aggressiveness and becomes femininely passive.

These are the highlights of the more strictly biological aspects of Freud's theory of the development of women. I shall touch presently on some other details, but now I wish to review the gross outline in the light of my first consideration, the problem aspect of the biology of woman. The question must be asked: is this the true story of the biological sexual development of women? Penis envy dating from an experience in early childhood is sometimes recalled by women patients. In my experience, however, this memory is not recalled by all patients—not even by all of those who present in other respects the clinical picture of penis envy. While a negative finding is not conclusive it suggests that other factors may also contribute to envy of the male. Also, quite frequently, one finds women patients who were not aware of the clitoris as a separate organ and learned it only later in studying biology. This was true even though they had exploited the pleasurable sensations in the region of the clitoris. Although ignorance of the vagina, sometimes until far into adolescence, has been observed especially in hysterics, equally often one finds knowledge of the vagina from an early age and often a history of vaginal masturbation. These facts certainly cast doubt on the idea that the clitoris is always the center of the little girl's interest. It seems that one is in fact entitled to question whether there is, even now, any adequate information concerning the innate sexual interests of women.

However, Freud was usually a keen clinical observer and it may therefore be assumed that his theory was based upon certain facts which he observed. The probable nature of these facts and the principal sources of error in his interpretation of the observations may be considered.

Of the latter, there seem to have been two. In the first place, he saw the problem entirely from a masculine point of view. Horney draws attention to this in her paper *Flight from Womanhood*, published in 1926. In it she marshals data to show that the attitude prevalent in the male about his own genitals was accepted by Freud as the attitude of both sexes on the matter. She indicates that Freud based his theory on the assumption that the penis is the sexual organ most highly valued by both sexes and at no point in his work showed any recognition of the possibility of there being a female biological function in its own right. He saw the woman primarily as the negative of the male. The most extreme example of this appears in his theory that woman accepts her ability to produce a child as a compensation for her lack of a penis. Childbearing is a sufficiently important biological function to have value for its own sake. Surely, only a man could have thought of it in terms of compensation or consolation.

The second source of error in Freud's thinking is the fact that he studied only women in his own or closely related cultures, that because he had no comparative study of other cultures he believed that what he observed was universal woman. Current studies show that this is clearly not the case.

The women observed by psychoanalysts are distinctly women living in a particular culture, the Western culture, a patriarchal culture in a state of transition. It is impossible to separate from the total picture something which one can safely call biological woman. It is assumed that she exists, that she has her reactions to her particular organic makeup, but it is increasingly clear that not all that seems biological is biological. That women behave differently in different types of culture is now beginning to be known, although intensive analyses of women in other cultures have not yet been made. Freud, ignoring these considerations thought the attitudes, interests and ambitions of the middle and upper class women whom he analyzed to be the characteristic attitudes, interests and ambitions of women in general.

Today one realizes that much which even woman herself may attribute to the fact of her sex can be explained as the result of cultural pressures. At the same time, the fact that bearing children must influence women's personality development cannot be denied. Also the type of sexual response characteristic of a woman conceivably has its influence on her character.

For example, it seems probable that the very fact that the male must achieve an erection in order to carry out the sexual act, and that any failure in this attempt cannot be hidden, while the female can much more readily hide her success or nonsuccess in intercourse, may well have an effect in the basic character patterns of both. Even here, however, more complete understanding of the cultural pressures is necessary before it can be stated in what way or to what extent biology plays a part. But one thing seems fairly certain; namely, that to the extent to which a woman is biologically fulfilled—whatever that may mean—to that extent she has no tendency to envy man's biology, or to feel inferior about her biological makeup.

In certain cultures woman can meet with difficulties which would make her biological makeup appear to be a handicap. This would be true when her drives are denied expression or when fulfillment of the rôle of woman puts her at a disadvantage. Both of these situations are true in many respects in the United States today. This is essentially a patriarchal culture and although many values are changing and these changes on the whole are working to the advantage of women, the patriarchal situation still presents limitations to a woman's free development of her interests. Also, the newer situations have their hazards in that they usually throw women into unequal competition with men. By unequal, the reference is not to biological inequality, but an inequality resulting from prejudice and the greater advantages offered the male.

The official attitude of the culture towards women has been and still is to the effect that woman is not the equal of man. This has led to the following things: until very recently woman was not offered education even approximately equal to that given a man; when she did secure reasonably adequate education, she found more limited opportunities for using the training than did a man; woman was considered helpless, partly because she was not given an opportunity to work, and partly because she had no choice but to be economically dependent on some man; and social restrictions were placed on her, especially in connection with her sex life. These restrictions seemed to work to the advantage of the man.

The assumption of woman's inferiority was a part of the prevalent attitude of society and until very recently was accepted by both sexes as a biological fact. Since there is obvious advantage to the male in believing this, he has proved much more resistant to a new point of view on the matter than have women. Women, at the same time, have had difficulty in freeing themselves from an idea which was a part of their life training. Thus it has come about tha even when a woman has become consciously convinced of he value she still has to contend with the unconscious effects of training, discrimination against her and traumatic experiences which keep alive the attitude of inferiority.

The women whom Freud observed were women in this situation and it was easy for him to generalize the effects of the attitude of the culture as a fact of biology.

It seems justifiable therefore not only to consider Freud's theory in the light of his masculine bias but to examine closely the particular cultural pressures which may have produced the picture of woman as he saw her.

He found that the central problem in the neurotic difficulties of most women was penis envy. If this is interpreted symbolically it will be agreed that in this culture where the advantages go to the possessor of the penis women often find themselves in situations which arouse their envy of men, and so, in their relations to men, they show an attitude which can be called "penis envy."

An awareness of the advantage of a penis might be vaguely conscious in a little girl's mind at the age of three—for already at that age evidences that the son is more privileged are apparent in many middle class families. Before one can settle the question of whether this early experience takes place in terms of actual envy of the penis, or whether the boy is envied in a more general way, it must be noticed that until very recently the average girl at puberty was made decidedly aware of the disadvantages of being female. In the Victorian era the transition from the freedom of childhood to the restrictions of adolescence must have been especially conducive of unhappiness. An experience of a patient as recently as fifteen years ago shows vividly the still existing cultural situation. Two children, a boy and a girl, the boy a year and a half older than the girl, grew up in a family where freedom of development was encouraged. They were both very fond of outdoor life, and went on long hikes together, often camping out overnight. At the age of twelve suddenly a great change was introduced into the girl's life. She was told that now since she was about to become a woman she could no longer go away with her brother on overnight trips. This was only one evidence, but one very important to her, of the beginning of the limitation of her activities. She was filled with bitterness and envy of her brother and for several reasons centered her whole resentment on the fact of menstruation. This seemed to her to be the sign of her disgrace, the sign that she had no right to be a person. She became withdrawn and depressed. Her one strong feeling was that she hated to be a woman and did not want to grow up. The condition developed decisively because of the restrictions of adolescence, restrictions which actually changed her whole way of life.

I do not wish to imply that this pathological reaction to the situation at puberty developed in a hitherto healthy girl. Envy of her brother had existed in childhood because of her mother's marked preference for him, but a long period of equality with him had done much to restore her self-esteem. The situation at puberty reëstablished the idea that he was the more favored person.

The changes brought about by cultural restrictions at the girl's puberty are not of a superficial nature. At this time in the Victorian picture a girl passed from a position of relative equality with boys to one of inferiority. This inferiority was shown in several ways. An outstanding point of the picture was the inhibition of natural aggression. A girl might no longer make demands and go about freely. If she was interested in a boy she must not show it directly. She must never expose herself to possible rejection. This would mean she had been unwomanly. She might no longer pursue her own interests with the same freedom as a boy. Obstacles were placed in the way of her education, her play and social life. But especially in her sexual life her freedom of development was curbed. The punishment for spontaneous expression of sexual interests was very great. One impulsive act resulting in pregnancy could ruin a girl's whole life. Her training was in the direction of insincerity about her sexual interests. She was taught to be ashamed of menstruation. It was something to be concealed and any accident leading to its discovery was especially humiliating. In short womanhood began with much unpleasantness. It was characterized by feelings of body shame, loss of freedom, loss of equality with boys and loss of the right to be aggressive. The training in insincerity especially about her sexual being and sexual interests has undoubtedly contributed much to a woman's diminished sense of self. When something so vitally a part of her must be denied it is not a great step further to deny the whole self. The fact that much of this has noticeably changed in the last fifty years seems sufficient proof that this situation was due to a cultural attitude and had nothing to do with innate femininity. Freud, observing this cultural change in the girl's status at puberty, attributed it to the necessity of accepting her feminine passivity, which, as he said, she could not do without a struggle. Is it not more accurate to say that at puberty it became necessary for the girl to accept the restrictions placed on women, and that this was usually unwelcome? In a word, the difficulties of adjustment found in the girl at puberty are the results of social pressures and do not arise from the difficulty of giving up the clitoris in favor of the vagina.

The cultural attitude about the sexual life of women has been one of denial. In former years there was denial almost of its very existence. Today there is still some tendency to deny that it is as important or urgent as the sexual life of men. Passivity and masochism are usually considered essential characteristics of a woman's sexual drive. Passivity was clearly forced upon her by the inhibition of the right to aggression. Her masochism also often proves to be a form of adaptation to an unsatisfactory and circumscribed life.

Not only in her sexual life has the woman had reason to envy the man. The circumscribing of her intellectual development and the discouragement of personal initiative have been frustrating. Partly from lack of training and partly because of man's drive for ownership woman has had to accept a position of economic dependence on man, and this is still the rule.

Out of this situation come several personality traits which are generally considered typically feminine and which have even been described in psychoanalytic literature as the outcome of woman's biological makeup. Women are supposed to be more narcissistic than men, to have a greater need to be loved than men, to be more rigid than men and to have weaker superegos than men—all of these in addition to the already mentioned attitudes of passivity and masochism.

A review of the actual position of economic helplessness of women of the recent past and the relative economic helplessness of many women today leads one to question the innateness of these personality traits. The function of childbearing cannot but have some effect on the personality of woman but when this function is accompanied by the necessity to legalize the process by marriage and economic dependency—with the only alternative social ostracism and added difficulties in the economic sphere, if she does not marry—one cannot help thinking that woman's greater need to be loved and to have one meaningful sexual relation rather than the more casual sexual life of the man comes about chiefly because she lives in a culture which provides no security for her except in a permanent so-called love relationship. It is known that the neurotic need of love is a mechanism for establishing security in a dependency relation. In the same way to the extent that a woman has a greater need of love than a man it is also to be interpreted as a device for establishing security in a cultural situation producing dependency. Being loved not only is part of woman's natural life in the same way as it is part of man's but it also becomes of necessity her profession. Making her body sexually attractive and her personality seductive is imperative for purposes of security. In the past centuries she could feel safe after she had married and could then risk neglecting her charms, but today, with the present ease of divorce the woman who depends on a man for her means of support and social position must continue to devote a great deal of her time to what may be called narcissistic pursuits, that is, body culture and concern about clothes. One sees that woman's alleged narcissism and greater need to be loved may be entirely the result of economic necessity.

The idea that women must have weaker superegos than men, as stated by Freud, derives from the notion that in the little girl the Œdipus complex is usually not repressed. Because she enters the Œdipus phase after accepting the fact of castration she has no fear to drive her to repression and the formation of a superego. Not only Freud but other writers, notably Sachs, have pointed out that women therefore often lack strong convictions, strong consciences, but rather tend to take on the convictions and standards of any men on whom they become dependent in the course of their lives. This is said to be especially noticeable in women who have loved several men. Such a woman is supposed to adopt in succession the attitudes of the various men.

Undoubtedly there are many women who answer this description, but the character trait of having no strong beliefs or convic-

tions is not found universally in women and also occurs frequently
in men in this culture.

It is an attitude typical of people who have found that their
security depends on approval of some powerful person or group.
It is relatively easy to become converted to any ideology which
will bring one advantage, especially if one has never for neurotic
or reality reasons been able to achieve sufficient independence to
be able to know one's own mind. This could scarcely but be the
case with the Victorian girl who was not permitted to free herself
from her father until she was safely entrusted to the protection of
another man. For cultural reasons, the girl had to continue to be
dependent on her father and emancipation from the childhood tie
was not encouraged. Such a situation is not conducive to the development of independent standards. That some women despite
this became independent is remarkable.

One other statement of Freud's requires consideration: the idea
that women are more rigid than men and lose their capacity for
intellectual and emotional growth earlier. He points to the fact that
a woman of thirty often seems already incapable of further development while a man of the same age is at the beginning of his best
period of achievement. Although he does not explain just how this
is the result of a woman's sex, the implication is that it is the outcome of the difficulties of her sexual development. To quote him:
"It is as though the whole process had been gone through and remained inaccessible to influence for the future; as though in fact
the difficult development which leads to femininity had exhausted
all the possibilities of the individual." One might be tempted to
believe that because a woman's period of sexual attractiveness is
shorter than that of a man she grows old mentally and emotionally
earlier. However, here too the cultural factors so dominate the
picture that it is hard to see anything else. As long as a woman's
sole opportunity for success in life was in making a successful marriage her career was made or lost by the age of thirty. A woman of
thirty in the Victorian era and even in some situations today has no
future. It is well known in psychoanalytic therapy that for successful outcome of treatment an actual opportunity for further develop-

ment of the person must exist. This consideration would seem to offer an adequate explanation of the greater rigidity of women, if in fact any such greater rigidity can be demonstrated. I believe that there is no dearth of inflexible personalities among men who have reached the height of their development by the age of thirty, whether because of inferior mental equipment, unfortunate early training or lack of opportunity. Moreover, today there are many examples of women not dependent on their sexual value for security who remain flexible and capable of development. All that may be said with certainty is that woman's lack of opportunity and economic dependence on men can lead to early rigidity and a narrowed outlook on life, as can any situation which curbs spontaneous development in either sex.

What I have said thus far shows that the characteristics of women which Freud has explained as the result of her biological vicissitudes beginning with the discovery that she has no penis can be quite as satisfactorily explained in terms of the cultural pressures to which she is subjected. The latter hypothesis must certainly be entertained —if only for economy's sake—before separating the female of man from the realm of general biological principles and making her something biologically unprecedented.

It is clear that Freud's theories were originally developed about Victorian women. Let me now discuss in contrast the woman of today. The position of women has changed greatly and if the cultural factors are important she is no longer as sexually inhibited and restricted, her opportunities for self-development are greatly increased and marriage is no longer the only means of economic security. These facts have undoubtedly influenced the character of women. So much so that a new type of woman is emerging, a woman capable of independence, whose characteristics differ from those described by Freud. However, the present is still a situation of transition. It takes a long time for a cultural change to come about especially in its psychological implications for nondependent persons. Something of the Victorian attitude still persists in the psychology of most women. One finds several remnants of it, for example, the notion that it is more womanly for a woman to marry and let a man support her. The majority of women still accept this idea, to be sure not as early in their lives as their grand-mothers did. They often have a few years of independence first. For some the alternative of marriage with economic dependence, or independence with or without marriage, presents a serious con-flict. Also under the influence of tradition and prejudice many women are convinced that their adequate sexual fulfillment, in-cluding children, and an adequate self development are not to be reconciled. Men have no such tradition and with them the two interests usually reinforce each other. In this, certainly, women still have real grounds for envying men.

In this specific, limited sense Freud's idea that women have envy because they have no penis is symbolically true in this culture. The woman envies the greater freedom of the man, his greater oppor-tunities and his relative lack of conflict about his fundamental drives. The penis as a symbol of aggression stands for the freedom to be, to force one's way, to get what one wants. These are the characteristics which a woman envies in a man. When this envy is carried to a more pathological degree the woman thinks of the man as hostile to her and the penis becomes symbolically a weapon which he uses against her. In the pathological picture called penis envy by Freud the woman wishes to have the destructive qualities she attributes to the man and she wishes to use this destructiveness against him.

There remain to be dealt with the ways in which women have met the problem of feeling inferior to and hating men, or to use the Freudian language, have dealt with their penis envy. Freud outlined three solutions: a woman may accept her feminine rôle; she may develop neurosis; or her character may develop in the direction of a "masculinity complex." The first of these seemed to him to be the normal solution.

Here again the problem arises as to what is biological woman and what is cultural woman. Certainly biologically woman can only find her fulfillment as a woman and to the extent to which she denies this she must be frustrated. However, there are other implications in the idea of accepting the feminine rôle—it may include the acceptance of the whole group of attitudes considered feminine by the culture at the time. In such a sense acceptance of the feminine rôle may not be an affirmative attitude at all but an expression of submission and resignation. It may mean choosing the path of least resistance with the sacrifice of important parts of the self for security.

The solution of envy of the male by way of neurosis may be considered a solution by evasion, and although many interesting facts could be considered here the influence of the cultural pressures does not differ greatly from that found in the next type of situation.

The solution by way of developing a masculinity complex deserves careful consideration. One significant difference of neurotic character structure from neurosis arises from the fact that the character pattern is in many ways acceptable to the culture. It represents not only a working compromise of the person's conflicting trends, but also takes its pattern directly from the culture. The culture invites masculinity in women. With the passing of the old sheltered life, with the increasing competition with men growing out of the industrial revolution as well as out of women's restlessness, it is not strange that her first steps towards equality would be in the direction of trying to be like men. Having no path of their own to follow, women have tended to copy men. Imitating of a person superior to one is by no means unusual. The working man seeking to move up the social and economic scale not only tries to copy the middle class way of life but may try to adopt the middle class way of thinking. He may try so hard that he becomes a caricature of the thing he wishes to be, with loss of sight of his real goals in the process.

In the same way women, by aping men, may develop a caricature situation and lose sight of their own interests. Thus, one must consider to what extent it is profitable for a woman to adopt the ways of a man. To what extent can she do it without losing sight of her own goals. This leads inevitably to a consideration of what characteristics are biologically male and what have developed secondarily as a result of his way of life. Here, as in the consideration of femininity, the same difficulty in separating biological and cultural factors is found. Not many years ago a woman's decision to follow a profession—medicine, for example—was considered even by some analysts to be evidence of a masculinity complex. This rose from the belief that all work outside the home, especially if it called for the exercise of leadership, was masculine, and anyone attempting it therefore was trying to be a man.

It is true, practically speaking, that in the business and professional world it often paid to act like a man. Women were entering a domain which had been in the possession of men, in which the so-called masculine traits of decisiveness, daring and aggression were usually far more effective than the customarily ascribed traits such as gentleness and submissiveness. In adaptation to this new way of life, women could not but tend to change the personality traits acquired from their former cultural setting. The freedom which economic independence brought to women also had its influence in developing characteristics hitherto found only in men. It seems clear, however, that such changes are not in themselves in any fundamental sense in the direction of masculinity. It is not useful to confuse the picture of the independent woman with that of an essentially pathological character structure, the masculinity complex.

By this, I mean that the culture now favors a woman's developing certain characteristics which have been considered typical of men; but that in addition she may be neurotic and may exploit the cultural situation to protect herself from certain anxieties which have arisen in part from her difficulties of self development because she is a woman and in part from other privations and traumata. Obviously, if a woman develops characteristics which indicate that she unconsciously considers herself a man, she is discontent with being a woman. It would be fruitful to inquire what this "being a woman" means to her. I have suggested the possibility of several unpleasant meanings. Being a woman may mean to her being inferior, being restricted, and being in the power of someone. In short being a woman may mean negation of her feeling of self, a denial of the chance to be an independent person. Refusal to be a woman therefore could mean the opposite, an attempt to assert that one is an independent person. The woman with a masculinity complex shows an exaggerated need for "freedom" and a fear of losing her identity in any intimacy.

It has become clear in the treatment of some related situations that the development of this character pattern is not solely the result of conditioning against being a woman. More basic may be a threat to the personality integrity from an early dependency, a domineering selfish mother, for example, or from the undermining of self esteem by a destructive mother. In short, many of the forces which make for the development of neurotic mechanisms in general can contribute to this one. These women fear dependency because dependency has been a serious threat to them. Such women are often unable to have any intimate relationship with men; and if they marry, show a hostile revengeful attitude towards the husband. The marriage relationship is sometimes, however, quite successful when circumstances leave them free to work and at least partially support themselves after marriage. Pregnancy is apt to be a special difficulty because of its at least temporary threat to this independence. And they are always afraid of getting into someone's clutches and losing control of the situation.

If the masculinity complex is not developed primarily as a defense against a feeling of biological lack, if the feeling of cultural inferiority at being a woman is not the sole cause of its development, but on the other hand any difficulty in any important dependency relation can contribute to its formation, why then does it take the particular form of wishing to be or pretending to be a man with associated hatred of men?

Two things in the situation encourage this type of character defense. First, because of the general cultural trend there is secondary gain in such an attitude. It looks like progress and gives the woman the illusion of going along in the direction of the freedom of her time. Second, it offers a means of avoiding the most important intimacy in life, that with a man. This relationship because of its frequent implication of dependency and subordination of the woman's interests especially reactivates all of the dangers of earlier dependencies. The struggle for some form of superiority to men is then an attempt to keep from being destroyed. Men are punished for all that women have been suffering in all sorts of dependency situations.

So it would seem that solution of envy of the male by the development of the masculinity complex does not have a simple origin and that sources not simply relating to sexual comparisons are important in it.

In conclusion, let me say that psychoanalysis thus far has secured extensive acquaintance with the psychology of women in only one type of culture. Facts observed in a particular part of the Western world have been interpreted by Freud as an adequate basis for an understanding of female psychology in general and as evidence for a particular theory about specific biological factors in the nature of woman. I have pointed out that characteristics and inferiority feelings which Freud considered to be specifically female and biologically determined can be explained as developments arising in and growing out of Western woman's historic situation of underprivilege, restriction of development, insincere attitude toward the sexual nature, and social and economic dependency. The basic nature of woman is still unknown.

THE RÔLE OF WOMEN
IN THIS CULTURE

Clara Thompson

A COMPREHENSIVE presentation of the situation of women in this culture is far beyond the scope of this paper. It is a task for careful research. The aim here is merely to present observations and speculations on the cultural problems seen through the eyes of psychoanalytic patients. This offers a limited but a very significant view of the situation.

These observations are limited in the first place because for economic reasons psychoanalysis is not yet available to any extent to the lower classes. Secondly, for emotional reasons, groups with strong reactionary cultural attitudes are seldom interested in psychoanalysis. Finally, individuals leading fairly contented lives lack the impulse to be analyzed. This means that we are dealing in this paper chiefly with the ideas and points of view of the discontented, and they happen to be for the most part from the upper classes. Although this is a special group within the culture, it is an important group because, on the whole, it is a thinking group, nonconformist, and seeking to bring about changes in the cultural situation. The study of the types of cultural problems presented by women in analysis thus gives important information about the problems of women in the culture.

There will be no attempt in this paper to make an extensive study of early conditioning and traumatic factors in the lives of women but rather to show how women have found means of expressing their strivings, neurotic and otherwise, in the present culture of the United States.

When Freud first wrote his *Studies in Hysteria* in the 1890's, he described a type of woman with ambitions and prospects very different from those found in the average psychoanalytic patient of today. That a radical change has occurred is partly due to Freud's own efforts in clarifying the whole question of the sexual life, but largely due to changes in the economic and social status of women. These changes were already occurring before the time of Freud.

In this country today women occupy a unique position. They are probably freer to live their own lives than in any patriarchal country in the world.[1] This does not mean that they have ceased to be an underprivileged group. They are discriminated against in many situations without regard for their needs or ability. One would expect, therefore, to find the reality situation bringing out inferiority feelings not only because of a reaction to the immediate situation but because of family teachings in childhood based on the same cultural attitude. One would expect to find, also very frequently, resentment towards men because of their privileged position as if the men themselves were to blame for this. These are some of the more important factors that contribute to a woman's feeling of inferiority.

As we know, the culture of Europe and America has been based for centuries on a patriarchal system. In this system, exclusive ownership of the female by a given male is important. One of the results has been the relegating of women to the status of property without a voice in their own fate. To be sure, there have always been women who, by their cleverness or special circumstances, have been able to circumvent this position, but in general, the girl-child has been trained from childhood to fit herself for her inferior rôle; and, as long as compensations were adequate, women have been relatively content. For example, if in return for being a man's property a woman receives economic security, a full emotional life centering around husband and children, and an opportunity to express her capacities in the management of her home, she has little cause for discontent. The question of her inferiority

[1] For a period in the history of Soviet Russia some interesting improvements in the status of women came about.

scarcely troubles her when her life is happily fulfilled, even though she lives in relative slavery. If, therefore, the problem of women today simply referred to their position in a patriarchal culture, the task would be much simpler. However, without considering the fact that the individual husband may be unsatisfactory and so produce discontent, other factors are also at work to create dissatisfaction. As Erich Fromm has said, "When a positive gain of a culture begins to fail, then restlessness comes until a new satisfaction is found." Our problem with women today is not simply that they are caught in a patriarchal culture, but that they are living in a culture in which the positive gains for them are failing.

Industry has been taken out of the home. The making of clothes has been entirely removed, and now it is necessary to know only the most rudimentary types of cooking. Factory-made clothes and canned goods have supplanted the industry in the home. Large families are no longer desired or economically possible. Also, other more emotionally tinged factors contribute to the housewife's dissatisfaction. The home is no longer the center of the husband's life. Once he ran a farm or a small business close to his home. In this his wife shared his problems, probably more than he realized. Today, a man's business is often far from his home and his wife's possible contribution to it may be nothing. If one adds to this the fact that the sexual life is often still dominated by puritanical ideas, the position of the present day wife who tries to live in the traditional manner cannot but be one with a constant narrowing of interests and possibilities for development. Increasingly, the woman finds herself without an occupation and with an unsatisfactory emotional life.

On the other hand, the culture is beginning to offer her something positive in an opportunity to join in a life outside the home where she may compete with other women and even with men in business. In the sexual sphere, too, with the spread of birth control knowledge and a more open attitude in general about sex, there is an increasing tendency in and out of marriage to have a sexual life approximating in its freedom that enjoyed by the male. However, these things do not yet run smoothly. In other words, we are not yet dealing with a stable situation, but one in transition; therefore, one in which the individual is confused and filled with conflict, one in which old attitudes and training struggle with new ideas.

Woman's restlessness began to make itself felt about the middle of the last century. Prior to that and even for some time afterwards, the position of woman was fairly clear-cut and stable. Her training was directed towards marriage and motherhood. If she made a good marriage, she was a success. If she made a bad marriage, she must try to adjust to it because it was almost impossible to escape. If she made no marriage, she was doomed to a life of frustration. Not only was sexual satisfaction denied her but she felt herself branded a failure and must live on sufferance in the home of her parents, or of brother or sister, where she might have a meager emotional life from the love of other people's children. Not only must she suffer actual disappointment but she had the additional burden of inferiority feelings. She had failed to achieve the goal demanded by the culture—and for women there was only one goal.

Even in those days there were a few exceptions. For instance, the Brontës, although leading very frustrated lives, at least were able to develop their gifts and to achieve success. But work and the professions were for the most part closed to women. If one's own family could not provide for an unmarried woman, she might find a home as governess or teacher in some other family. However, there were occasional daring women. As early as 1850 a woman had "crashed" the medical profession. She was considered a freak and accused of immorality. She had to face insults and gibes from her colleagues. Very slowly the number of women physicians increased. Still later, they entered the other professions and business. On the whole, the number of women who in one way or another became independent of their families before 1900 was small. The World War speeded the process and gave the stamp of social approval to economic independence for woman. Since then, she has been able to enter almost every field of work for which she is physically capable, but even yet she is seldom accepted on equal terms with men.

Many interesting factors are revealed in this new situation of women. In the first place they are young in their present rôle. Comparatively few of them have the background of mothers or grandmothers who engaged in any work outside the home. They have to work out a new way of life with no precedent to follow and no adequate training from early childhood to help them take the work-drive seriously or fit it into their lives. It is not strange that the outstanding successes are few and that the great majority of women effect some compromise between the old and the new. For instance, the majority still plan to work only until they marry. This is true not only of the relatively unskilled worker but often of the highly trained. This may mean that the young woman not only does not do her pre-marital job well and in a way to give her satisfaction, but also nothing in her pre-marriage activity is helpful in fitting her for the business of homemaker.

Secondly, even when the individual has the courage in herself to attempt the new road, she has to cope with emotional pressures not only from society as a whole but from the individuals most important to her. One of the most significant of these pressures is the attitude of a prospective husband who has his own traditions and wishes for his future wife and, since he is often confused in his attempt to adjust to the new ways of life, may interpret the woman's struggle to find a place for herself as evidence of lack of love or a slur on his manhood.

Even the attitude of parents is often far from constructive. They do not have as great an emotional stake in a daughter's business success as in that of a son, and they are less likely to make sacrifices for her career. Sometimes they actually oppose it. For example: a young woman announced her wish to study medicine. Both parents disapproved and persuaded her to seek her career in music. She acceded to their wishes and spent several years in study. At the end of that time, she remained dissatisfied and again expressed her wish to study medicine. This time the parents persuaded her to take up nursing. When she had completed this course, she again asked to be allowed to study medicine and finally obtained her wish. She proved to have outstanding ability.

Because so much of the child's ideals is modeled on attitudes of the parents, the girl may be further handicapped by incongruities built into her own ego. For example, a young woman brought up in a southern home, where nothing was expected of women except to be charming, found herself in adult life in a profession where she must compete to hold her own. Both healthy and neurotic factors had driven her from her parents' adjustment. Her superior intelligence had stimulated her to go far in education, and lack of social ease—rising out of physical inferiority feelings—had reënforced this drive. Nevertheless, her ways of adjustment were definitely modeled on her past. Although she was in a position where she should be a leader with definite views and initiative to execute them, she was constantly deferring to men, seeking to flatter them by playing the yielding clinging vine, accepting their advice even when she thought differently. Her conscious desire to be a modern woman led her to pretend to herself that she did not want to marry. To prove it she had several extra-marital sexual affairs but in them she was frigid. She constantly felt humiliated because she had not achieved the traditional goal of marriage.

This example serves to show how the inconsistencies and conflicts —rising when a cultural situation is in a state of rapid transition— become a part of the neurotic conflict of the individual, even as they influence the form of the neurotic behavior.

Finally, social institutions put obstacles in the way of change of a woman's status. In the economic sphere she must usually accept a lower wage than men for the same type of work. She must usually be more capable than the man with whom she competes before she will be considered his equal.

Even with increased economic freedom, there is considerable variation in the social satisfactions available to independent women. In some groups any type of relationship with men or women is open to the woman who is emotionally able to accept it. In other groups a woman's social life may be even more restricted than it was in the days when she was overprotected in the home. In the latter groups, unless she shows great initiative in changing her situation, she may find herself forced to associate entirely with her own sex. While this is in itself a great cause for discontent, many individuals find a more or less satisfactory solution for its limitations, while others find neurotic security in the manless world. Thus it is possible for a woman teaching in a girls' school to reach the age of 40 still living fairly happily on an adolescent "crush" level.

Whatever the problems created in the new life of woman, her status must continue to change for she is being driven out of the home by her restlessness due in part at least to her lack of occupation. The life of the married woman today who has no special work interest is not exciting. She has a small home, or in many cases only a small apartment. She may have no children; she may have at most three. Even if she does her own housework it is so simplified by modern inventions that it can fill only a few hours of her day. As has already been said, because of the nature of modern business life she often has very little share in her husband's interests. What can she do? She may make a cult of her child, or she may play bridge or have some other play life, or she may engage in some volunteer employment—in which she is apt to be no longer welcome since trained workers are increasingly preferred—or she may go to work seriously. The last solution is growing in popularity.[2]

Let us consider three frequently encountered types of reaction to the current situation: women who marry and try to live according to the old pattern but find themselves unemployed and often discontented; women who work and do not marry; and, women who marry and engage in serious work outside the home.

The first group, those who marry and have no other work interest, have already been discussed at some length. This is a very large group. It often happens that intelligent and capable women find themselves in this situation because they had not been aware of the reality before marriage and no preparation for any other type of life had been made. That is, these individuals had married with the phantasy that life after marriage could be lived somewhat in the old-fashioned way according to the pattern of the home life

[2] We must not forget that there still are women in this culture who function successfully according to the old stable pattern of the last century and contentedly manage their homes. These women need not concern us.

of their childhood. Many college women are in this group; especially college women who married immediately after graduation and did not fit themselves for any profession or work. Making a cult of the child is unfortunately a fairly frequent solution. By the term *cult* is here meant an anxious concern about the child's welfare where the mother goes to excessive lengths to apply all modern psychological and hygienic theories to the management of her child's development. This can be very destructive for the child.

Another type of woman finds in the marriage with no responsibility the fulfillment of her neurotic needs. This is the very infantile woman. For her marriage is a kind of sanitarium life. She often shirks childbearing and in her relationship to her husband she has the position of spoiled child. Many of these women could not survive outside the protected atmosphere of their marriages.

Of the second group, those who work and do not marry, there are two main subdivisions. First, there are those to whom work is everything; that is, there is no love life of significance. This woman differs from her predecessor, the *old-maid,* in that she is economically independent. She may, however, be even more miserable because her life is often very isolated, whereas the *old-maid* of the past generation usually lived in a family and had a kind of vicarious life. Many of these individuals do find some kind of sublimated satisfaction; for example, working for some cause even as their predecessors worked for religion. This group might be characterized as having found economic freedom without emotional freedom.

The second group are those who have a love life in addition to work. This love life may be homosexual or heterosexual, and the relationships may vary from the casual with frequent changes of partner to a fairly permanent relationship with one person, a relationship which may differ very little from marriage. In all of them, however, there is one important difference from a married partnership. The individual considers herself free although she actually may be very involved emotionally. She regards her work as the most important and permanent thing in her life.

In the group who marry and engage in work outside the home, several possibilities of relationship exist. Husband and wife may continue to lead independent business lives. They may be interested in each other's work without being competitive in any way. There may be real enjoyment in the success of the other. This is the ideal situation. It is more likely to work when the two are engaged in different types of occupation.

The husband's resentment and competitive attitude may crush the wife's initiative, a situation which was more frequent a few years ago. The man feels that his virility is threatened. He fears that people will think he can not support her or he fears that he will lose his power over her, and so forth. In such situations, if the marriage continues, the wife must give up her work—often without any interest adequate to take its place.

The wife who proves to be the better breadwinner may win out in the competition, especially since the depression. This is culturally a most revolutionary situation; it can make a great many difficulties. The woman needs extraordinary tact in handling it. If under the influence of her own cultural training she feels contempt for the husband or a desire to rub it in, matters can become very bad. In general, the man needs some face-saving explanation. He can not say that he prefers to keep house, even when, occasionally, this is the case. He could not accept it himself and most of his acquaintances would think less of him for it. So, he has to be unable to get work and, therefore, keeps house to help his wife who is working, or he must be ill, or he must be getting an education, in all of which cases he is able to accept his wife's economic support without loss of self-respect. The following is a situation in which a man's neurosis provided a practical solution for this sort of marriage. A young woman who had been a school-teacher was forced because of state law to give up her position when she married. The teaching had been a satisfactory means of expression for her, she found adjustment to the culturally usual feminine rôle in marriage difficult, and became more and more unhappy. After three years of marriage, during which two children were born, the husband developed a *nervous breakdown* and became unable to work. However, he had no serious difficulty in doing the housework and caring for the children. Because of the economic necessity, the woman

again was able to get her teaching position and return to the life
she enjoyed. By the complete reversal of the usual rôles, this marriage was put on a firm basis. The neurosis saved face for the husband, and it is also likely that without it the wife could not have
accepted the situation, although she certainly seemed to gain more
by it than did he.

Thus far we have said almost nothing about childbearing. What
has become of this important biological function in our culture? In
the present economic situation in the United States increase of
population is not desired. The fact that small families are the rule
is one of the factors driving women out of the home. Now that
they are out of the home a kind of vicious circle is formed, for
it is no longer convenient to be occupied in the home by one or
two children. Much conflict centers here, for it is one of the problems of the culture which as yet has no generally satisfactory solution. Individual women have worked out ways of having both children and a career, but most women still do the one or the other;
and in either case there are regrets and often neurotic discontent.
The business or professional woman who had decided against children, consciously or unconsciously, does not want them; her difficulty arises from the fact that she often can not admit this to herself. Perhaps some biological yearning disturbs her, or some desire
to have all of life's experiences, or perhaps there is merely the influence of the traditional cultural pattern which might be expressed
thus: "A woman is expected to want a child." She may thus feel
it her duty to prove her adequacy as a woman by having a child.
She may resist, devote herself to her career, but it bothers her and
makes her feel inferior. On the other hand, the problem is not solved
by going to the other extreme and trying to prove one's adequacy
as a woman by having a child or two. The women of past generations had no choice but to bear children. Since their lives were
organized around this concept of duty, they seldom became aware
of dislike of the situation, but there must have been many unwanted
children then. Nowadays, when women have a choice, the illusion
is to the effect that unwanted children are less common, but women
still from neurotic compulsion bear children they can not love. It

seems likely that the woman who really desires a child will find herself able to give it the necessary love, whether she devotes her life to its care or entrusts it to another while she is working. Since solutions to the practical difficulties are being found by way of day nurseries and nursery schools, it is probable that any woman with a genuine desire for motherhood can find a way in this culture today.

While the change in woman's attitude towards sex has been implied in many of the foregoing remarks, it is a subject sufficiently important to merit separate consideration. Intimate records of the sexual life of women are not to be expected before the psychoanalytic era. They have been accumulating in the last fifty years, a period, however, in which great changes have been taking place.

Let us glance at the picture which Freud first described early in the 1890's. Young women of good family grew up apparently in sexual ignorance; they were allowed no legitimate opportunity to gratify their sexual curiosity in theory or in fact. At puberty they entered a life of severe restrictions by which an artificial form of behavior was fostered. Further general education was discouraged and, while on the one hand they were to show no interest in sex in any form, they at the same time must devote their lives to getting husbands. This situation must have led to profound confusion in the minds of many an adolescent girl. She knew she must marry, bear children, but never admit that she enjoyed sex. Certainly, adjustment was achieved by the women of that generation at great emotional cost. Freud's first insights about the importance of the sexual life and its significance in neurosis arose in such an atmosphere, at the very time women were beginning to be pushed out of the home. The fiction of purity, chastity, and innocence was becoming increasingly difficult to maintain. Reality pressures, in which Freud's discoveries had no small part, were making adequate sexual information more important. A greater frankness and sincerity about the sexual life was coming about. The problem could no longer be handled by overprotection and ignorance. As a result, the pendulum was swinging toward the revolt against all restraint which became manifest in the United States between 1920 and 1930. It then appeared not only that women were realizing their legitimate sexual stake in marriage, but even high school girls felt a necessity for sexual episodes to herald in a rebellious way the coming of the new freedom. One of them, a patient, in comparing the old and the new, said, "Men used to think they had to pay a woman. Now they've discovered that the girls like it too." At any rate, escaping from chaperons, going into industry—in other words, leaving the protected convent-like atmosphere of the Victorian era—women found themselves overwhelmed with new emotional problems for which they had even less preparation than had they for the economic changes. Sexual freedom resulted, but in many cases the freedom was not without expense. The woman in trying to overthrow her early training was unable to get her own consent, as it were, and found herself frigid. The reverse swing of the pendulum appeared in the 1930's. Under Fascism, especially in Germany, an attempt was again made to force women back into the home, at the same time according a fanatical approval of a certain type of sexual freedom. In World War II women were again thrust into "man's" work, even participating in war activities in greater numbers than ever before.

It is difficult to portray the sexual attitude of today's women. There are many different, often half-digested, attitudes. The culture still leans to the conservative side. The tendency is still to expect the woman to confine her sexual life to her marriage partner. Children born out of wedlock are still stigmatized in some groups, though certainly with nothing like the ferocity of fifty years ago. One still may encounter as a patient a woman who feels she can never get over the disgrace of having been pregnant two months before her marriage. While most of one's female patients accept sexual life out of marriage as a matter of course, many of them are unwilling to defy the culture to the extent of bearing children. Absence of virginity at the time of marriage is no longer a universal cause for dismay but it can still be disturbing to some people. In but few groups can the woman openly acknowledge that she has a lover. In general, she must be more secretive than is a man. In brief, in many situations today, a woman may have any kind of sexual life that she wishes if, and only if, she does not make herself conspicuous.

One result of these circumstances seems inevitable: marriage becomes much less important than it was. A woman once needed it as a means of economic support as well as a source of sexual satisfaction. Both factors have shrunk in importance. The companionship of marriage can conceivably be found in other situations; no satisfactory substitute has yet appeared to satisfy the economic and emotional needs of children.

The official attitude of the culture then is conservative but the practical attitude in certain groups is radical. The best examples of the latter are found in the group of women who work and have a sexual life outside of marriage, although the same types of behavior can also be seen in some married women. As suggested above, nominal freedom of behavior does not necessarily indicate inner freedom from conflict. Many women avail themselves of sexual opportunities, but can not rid themselves of a sense of guilt arising from old ideas; or the sense of guilt may be repressed and in its place may come frigidity—a denying that the act is taking place—promiscuity as a kind of defiance of the inner prohibition, or other compromise behavior. Moreover, sexual freedom can be an excellent instrument for the expression of neurotic drives arising outside the strictly sexual sphere, especially drives expressive of hostility to men, or of the desire to be a man. Thus promiscuity may mean the collecting of scalps with the hope of hurting men, frustrating them, or taking away their importance, or in another case it may mean to the woman that she is herself a man. For example, a young woman whose business life threw her into sharp competition with men was proud of the fact that she acted like a man in her sexual life. She had a series of lovers to no one of whom she allowed herself to become attached. If she found herself becoming involved, she was upset until she had succeeded in discarding the man in such a way that he would conclude that she had no interest in him. This to her mind was acting like a man; permitting an emotional attachment to develop would have been acting like a woman.

It is then apparent that, while the sexual emancipation of women may be a step forward in personality development for some, it may only offer a new means for neurotic expression to others.

Overt homosexuality among women is probably more frequent at the present time than formerly. The diminishing emphasis on marriage and children helps to bring it to the fore, and the social isolation from men that now characterizes some types of work must be an encouragement to any homosexual tendencies which exist. It seems that many women who would otherwise never give overt expression to these tendencies are driven together by loneliness, and in their living together all degrees of intimacy are found. The culture seems to be decidedly more tolerant of these relationships between women than of similar ones between men.

The question that is raised in any study of change, whether by evolution or revolution, takes the form: can one say that people are more benefited or harmed? Have our women actually solved any of their problems in the last fifty years? When Freud analyzed his first cases, he described some of the basic conflicts which we still encounter, albeit the emphasis is different. Then, the young girl who might wish to be a boy could only give symbolic expression to this in the form of hysterical phantasies. Today, she may live out the phantasy, at least in part. In her business relations and in her sexual relations she may act in many ways like a man. Many a woman with severe personality difficulties uses the new opportunities provided by the culture for neurotic purposes without much benefit except that in so doing she is able to be a "going concern." On the other hand, many women use the present day situation more constructively. As they acquire more freedom to express their capacities and emotional needs, they find less actual reason to envy the male. The handicap of being a woman is, culturally speaking, not as great now as it was fifty years ago.

Inevitably, poorly adjusted people are in the vanguard of revolutionary movements. This one for the emancipation of women is certainly no exception. Women who studied medicine in the early years were on the whole those who had great personal problems about being women. Many a parallel example readily comes to mind. Some therapists may carry the marks of experience in those days. In any case, there is a temptation to view all change as neurotic. This obviously is an extreme stand. Neurotic drives often find expression in the present day activities of women but this is no reason for dismissing as neurotic the whole social and economic revolution of woman along her particular path among the world-wide changes.

REMARKS ON THE
PHILOSOPHY OF
MENTAL DISORDER

Frieda Fromm-Reichmann

SEVERAL YEARS AGO a South American woman in her early thirties, whom I shall call Margherita, was under treatment with me for a serious mental disorder. She had been suffering for 8 years from schizophrenia, catatonic type, and had part of the time been in a catatonic stupor, that is, mute, practically without motion; there had been no voluntary food intake or elimination; at other periods she was assaultive and given to self-mutilation, and she had made several suicidal attempts.

This young woman had been for 4 years at several mental hospitals in her South American home state, and then another 4 years under intensive psychotherapy with me at the Chestnut Lodge Sanitarium, until she reached, at last, a state of full recovery and personality maturation. In our therapeutic interviews, she had gained insight into the dynamics of her previous mental disorder, and she had become sufficiently aware of her interpersonal relationships to be able to handle them. She returned to her native country and has successfully lived there since then without needing any psychiatric help.

During the last 2 years of her treatment and hospitalization she had started to write some poetry and poetic prose, partly in English, partly in Spanish. Since her productions seemed to show remarkable talent, I sent them to a well-known poet and art critic in order to make sure that this was not just a nice pastime for an otherwise not too articulate schizophrenic person, but an expression of artistic creativeness which deserved encouragement. The critic confirmed my initial impression; and thereafter the woman's productivity was encouraged for therapeutic reasons. It seemed important in the process of this recovery of a schizoid personality to have her find valid means of artistic expression; all the more so since I did not consider it the goal of the treatment for the young woman to learn to lead a conventional life with the standard means of social adjustment used by the average so-called healthy citizen in this culture. Since then Margherita has published a considerable number of poems in various English and Spanish art magazines, has won several poetry contests, and is now assembling her works for publication in book form.

Shortly before this woman's projected dismissal from Chestnut Lodge Sanitarium was put into effect, she went one day to the municipal hospital whose job it is to decide whether a mental patient needs hospitalization or not; there she complained of being kept at the Sanitarium against her will. Upon her return, she reported these events to me, and I asked myself what could have moved the young woman to complain on the eve of her dismissal about being kept at the Sanitarium against her will. At first, I did not find the answer. Suddenly it dawned upon me, and I asked her why she was afraid to really get well, the connotation being the following: The patient went to see a psychiatrist who did not know the history of her illness and treatment, shortly before her psychotherapist considered her ready to leave the hospital—that is, at the time when she would appear well to a physician who did not know her background, but when she was still considered to be in need of treatment as an out-patient by the psychiatrist who had known her for a long time. This could only mean that she was afraid to go through the last psychotherapeutic phase with her own psychotherapist. When I questioned her about this, the patient broke into spontaneous, healthy tears and said, "Are you surprised at my being afraid; how could I help it? Remember, I have been in mental hospitals for 8 years. All my friends and relatives have been living their lives during these years, and I could not participate. How do you expect me to ever catch up with them?"

My serious answer was, "That is true; however, you have gathered during these years a tremendous amount of human experience, having had the opportunity to observe practically all types of emotional experience in your fellow patients and in yourself. And what are these emotional experiences of the mentally disturbed other than human experiences of the kind we all go through, seen as if under a magnifying glass?" This I said not for the sake of reassurance, for which a schizoid personality such as Margherita would not "go" anyhow. I said it because of my belief that it was actually so and in the spirit of putting something into words which Margherita would realize immediately, once this knowledge was recalled to her awareness. Upon hearing me, Margherita stopped crying and said, "You mean to say it is just a matter of the courage to look at life from the other side of the fence?"

I have started with this account from the treatment history of this former mental patient because it contains in brief what I have to say about the philosophy of mental disorder; and I want to elaborate on four points which follow from this account:

1. Serious mental disturbance—psychosis—can potentially be treated successfully by a collaborative effort between the mentally disturbed person and the psychiatrist as participant observer, with modified psychoanalysis—dynamically oriented intensive psychotherapy—even after many years' duration.

2. A person can emerge from a severe mental disorder as an artist of rank. His previous liabilities in terms of his pathogenic history, the expression of his subsequent mental disorder, that is, symptomatology, or his inner responses to either of them can be converted into assets.

3. The emotionally and mentally disturbed reactions which Margherita and her hospitalized fellow patients showed are different in degree only, and not in kind, from the emotional and mental experiences and modes of expression of so-called healthy people.

4. Special sensitiveness, alertness, and consideration for the past and present suffering of the mentally disturbed is required from the psychiatrist who wants to understand what these people have to convey. How does this special sensitiveness, alertness and con-

siderateness, which the psychiatrist has to develop in his dealings with the mentally hurt and disturbed, influence interpersonal contacts with the emotionally healthy?

Let me elaborate first on my third point, that the emotional and mental experiences and modes of expression of mentally disturbed and of not disturbed people differ only in quantity and not in quality. This fact is well known to any psychiatrist who experiences it as a participant observer while doing modern, intensive psychotherapy with his patients. In addition, I would like to prove this point by discussing two sets of facts: first, the common denominator in physical symptoms, mental symptoms, and modes of emotional expression in the healthy; and second, the similarity between the mental productions of the psychotics, while they are awake, and the mental productions of the so-called healthy, while they are asleep, that is, in their dreams.

Every general practitioner knows that many physical symptoms are not only the expression of the patient's disease but also an expression of a tendency or the tendency in the physical organism toward regaining health. Take, for example, a patient who suffers from cardiac disease. He may rush up a flight of stairs and almost faint as he reaches the top, the fainting being an expression of his cardiac disease as well as a warning signal not to enter into the serious danger of repeating this effort. Now think of a patient who wounds himself with an infected article. A wall of white blood cells —pus—will be built up around the wound. There will be local pain and inflammation; yet at the same time this wall of white blood cells, which constitutes the symptomatology of a local inflammation, will serve as a protection against the spreading of the infection, thus preventing a local infection from turning into a generalized one. A third and last example: a patient is suffering from bronchitis; among other signs he will show the symptom of coughing. At the same time, the coughing helps toward discharge of mucous substance, thereby freeing the bronchi from this mucous substance and facilitating the clearing up of the bronchitic process.

The same holds true for processes of mental illness. Its symptoms, too, both express the illness and show the mentally disturbed person's tendency toward mental health, that is, toward adjustive success in his relationships with other people. For example, a patient may suffer from compulsive handwashing; that is, he feels he has to wash his hands each time he touches an object or a person which may contaminate him. Such handwashing may take place any number of times, say from five to twenty or more times a day, and come to interfere seriously with the smooth-running maintenance of the patient's relationships with other people, all the more so since his hands will soon look red and chapped, thus leading him to hide them, if not himself, from other people. Should this person, however, resist his compulsion, then his fear of being contaminated, which he tries to counteract with the compulsive handwashing, would become so severe that that in turn would interfere even more with healthy interpersonal adjustments than does the compulsive handwashing. The compulsion is thus an expression of a mental disturbance but also an attempt to alleviate it.

Again, a patient has withdrawn his interest from the outward world; he is aloof, detached, and uncommunicative; he shows the symptoms of a schizophrenic disturbance. But this symptomatology may be this person's way of avoiding the danger of "another rebuke," as one patient put it.[1] The patient shows withdrawal of interest, aloofness, and detachment, which are signs of his schizophrenic disturbance, as a means of protecting himself from additional fear and potential hostility, which might be aroused against the person who evokes the fear and against the people in his previous life who have done so before.

As another example, consider a patient who shows a negativistic attitude as a sign of mental disturbance; that is, he may not feel like doing anything that is suggested to him just because it has been suggested, or he may be driven to do the opposite. Such behavior constitutes, indeed, a serious disturbance in the patient's contacts with other people. Yet, at the same time, the patient may show this because he has given up hope of ever getting attention from

[1] Fromm-Reichmann, Frieda, A Preliminary Note on the Emotional Significance of Stereotypies in Schizophrenics, *Bull. Forest Sanitarium,* 1:17-21.

his fellow men in any other way. Hence, his negativistic behavior constitutes also an attempt at maintaining or reestablishing interpersonal contacts, an attempt in the direction towards mental health.[2]

Think now of an obsessional patient who shows the symptoms of obscure power actions and all types of magic performances which interfere with the healthy set-up of human interrelationships. I think, for example, of a patient who made it her job to stand for many an hour on many consecutive days at the corner of the street where I was living, in order to secure the secret satisfaction of finding out, in spite of me, what coat I was wearing. Another one hoped to exert magic power over me after having succeeded in finding out what toilet water I used and then using the same kind herself.

What time- and energy-consuming, obscure, and magic attempts at exerting power over another person! What an interference with the establishment of healthy human relationships! Yet again, these signs of severe interpersonal difficulties serve at the same time to hide a lifelong insecurity and constitute an attempt at remedying this insecurity. In other words, they are an attempt at maintaining what is left of the obsessional person's self-esteem or at reestablishing it. This, however, means an attempt at maintaining or reestablishing relationships with other people, because one can respect others only to the extent that one respects oneself. Or to put it differently, one can love others only to the extent that one loves oneself.[3]

The Bible expresses the same idea in "Love thy neighbor as thyself," thus meaning that you cannot love him more than you love yourself. Let us forget about the masochistic interpretation of this Biblical quotation by which this statement is supposed to mean that one should love one's fellow men more than oneself; such interpretation is an outgrowth of the present masochistic and unwise

[2] Sullivan, Harry Stack, Conceptions of Modern Psychiatry, PSYCHIATRY (1940) 3:1-117. See especially p. 39.

[3] Reference footnote 2. See also Fromm, Erich, Selfishness and Self-Love, PSYCHIATRY (1939) 2:507-523.

culture. It has nothing to do with the original concept in which a decent self-love and a reasonable self-respect are considered to be the roots of decent and healthy human relationships.

The symptomatology of the obsessional is, therefore, just as the symptomatology in the three other examples of mental symptom formation, not only an expression of mental disorder but also an expression of an attempt at reestablishing mental equilibrium in terms of maintaining and reestablishing valid interpersonal relationships.

Let us ask now: does this statement about the two-sided motivation of emotional expression in the mentally disturbed sound familiar to many persons, because they are aware of the same two-sided motivation in their own interpersonal adjustive processes?

What happens, for example, when one feels angry? The anger stands first for itself, as an unpleasant interference with one's smooth-running contacts with other people. However, frequently enough it stands at the same time as a self-deceiving mask of anxiety, anger being the only emotional discharge from anxious tension to which a person may dare to give vent. Direct display of anxiety goes in the culture with an alleged loss of prestige in the eyes of other people and with a loss of self-esteem. Thus, it creates a more severe disturbance in interpersonal relationships than the release of anger. Hence, conversion of anxiety into anger represents successful interpersonal adjustment, and anger expresses both an unpleasant interpersonal experience and an attempt to avoid the more unpleasant interpersonal experience of anxiety.

Consider now the people, known to all of us, who are given to boasting and bragging, thus showing a picture of pseudo-euphoria, seemingly characterized by a disproportion between their self-appreciation and the appreciation of their accomplishments by their fellow men. Frequently this seeming euphoria is nothing but a deceiving mask for a person's low self-esteem. Where there is low self-esteem there is, as said before, low esteem of others and fear of low appreciation by other people. Both feelings constitute, of course, a serious interference with a healthy interpersonal adjustment, so that a mild megalomania, as described above, is not only the sign of a disturbance in one's relationship with oneself and with others, but also an expression of an adjustive attempt in maintaining a satisfactory relationship with oneself and with one's fellow men.

From these examples, one can see that many emotional experiences and modes of expression in healthy people have in common with the symptoms of the mentally ill and of the mentally handicapped the fact that both may be understood as an expression of disrupted interpersonal contacts as well as the expression of the human mind's tending toward maintenance or reestablishment of mental health in terms of security and satisfaction in one's interpersonal adjustments.

Hence, it follows that my thesis is correct, that the difference between the emotional experiences and modes of expression of the mentally healthy and the mentally disturbed is one of quantity and not of quality. As Sullivan puts it: "In most general terms, we are all much more simply human than otherwise, be we happy and successful, contented and detached, miserable and mentally disordered or whatever." [4]

Another proof that this statement is correct—surprising though it may seem to some people—is the similarity of the mental processes of the so-called healthy while asleep, known as dreams, and the mental processes of the mentally disturbed. There are hallucinations, illusions, and delusions in both. There is disturbance in logical thinking or expression, change in concepts of time and space. There are displacements, condensations, and distortions in feeling regarding the persons towards whom the process is directed. Frequently there is the expression in pictures, images, and allusions instead of in words, both in dream productions and the productions of the mentally disturbed. [5]

Sullivan and the Austrian psychoanalysts Silberer and Tausk

[4] Sullivan, reference footnote 2.

[5] Jung, C. G., *The Psychology of Dementia Præcox*, Nervous and Mental Disease Publ. Co., New York, 1936; see especially pp. 10-11, 21, 82, 83, Freud, Sigmund, *Basic Writings*, Modern Library edition; see section on Dream Interpretations. Sullivan, reference footnote 2; p. 33 ff.

have studied the changes in mental operations which people undergo under utter fatigue and while gradually falling asleep. They show the same similarity to the operations of the mentally disturbed in the making, as the dream processes do ultimately. Silberer describes, among other examples, the following illustrative conversion of thought processes into imagery.[6]

While falling asleep, he was pondering about a complex philosophical problem, the correct solution and formulation of which seemed to offer insurmountable difficulties. Following this he saw himself at one bank of a stream knowing that he should cross that stream but feeling that there were insurmountable difficulties in doing so because he could not see any bridge. This way of expressing thought processes in pictures, as all persons experience it while falling asleep and while dreaming, is exactly of a piece with the dynamics of many mental processes in the mentally ill. This means that every so-called healthy person goes in his dreams through a transitory psychotic state of a piece with the condition the mentally disturbed undergoes persistently while awake until he regains mental health.

If one is given to teleological thinking, one can believe that the transitory psychotic state undergone by everyone while dreaming may serve as a safeguard against mental illness. In this connection the words of the German philosopher Nietzsche should be remembered. "The man who does not lose his mind over certain things has no mind to lose."

To illustrate how serious modern psychotherapists are in their concept of the similarity between the dynamics of dream processes and mental processes in the mentally disturbed, I may mention in passing that the recital of dreams in psychotics, especially schizophrenics, is discouraged for the purposes of psychotherapy. It is felt that the experiences which they communicate from their waking life have so much of a dream-like character that the reproduc-

[6] Sullivan, reference footnote 2; p. 72. Silberer, Herbert, *Der Traum—Einfuehrung In Die Traumpsychologie,* Stuttgart, 1919. Tausk, Victor, Zwei Homosexuelle Traeume, *Internat. Ztschr. f. Psychoanal.* 2:36-39, 1914. No English translation is available.

tion of their mental experiences while asleep will only add to their state of disturbance and not contribute to therapeutically valid insight.

So much about the suggestion that the difference between the mentally healthy and the mentally disturbed is one of degree and not of kind; and about the double proof as seen in the similarity in the dynamics of the symptoms of the mentally disturbed and the types of emotional experience and modes of expression in the mentally stable, and in the similarity between dream processes and psychotic productions. Both show the same two-sided motivation, and they are different only in intensity, not in principle.

Now as to my second statement, that a person can emerge from serious mental disturbance of many years' duration as a creative artist. In elaborating this, I shall not comment on the complex problem of the psychology of artistic creativeness, which is outside my field and beyond the scope of this paper. I want only to discuss the possibility of the conversion of a person's mental liabilities into various types of assets, among them poetic creativeness, as in the case of the girl Margherita. She grew up in utter loneliness in a family group where there was bareness of any understanding of the values which mattered to her, and where she was forced to accept her family's values. This utter loneliness and isolation made first for the development of her mental illness yet ultimately also for her ability to express her lonely strivings in poetic language.

This is one way of converting the liabilities of a traumatic life history with subsequent mental disturbance into a creative asset.

A second possibility is that a person may be able to turn the skills and powers, whose development were forced upon him in counteracting his difficulties in living, and the mental symptomatology derived from it toward a creative end.

Consider, for example, a factory worker, Mary, the unwanted eldest daughter of an alcoholic father who used all his earnings to buy liquor and of a chronically over-worked mother who had to earn the living for the entire family, which included five younger siblings who had come a year apart. It was Mary's job, from her

third year, to take care of the babies, and she learned early to protect them as best she could from what she herself had suffered:
the assaultiveness of an alcoholic father, the irritability of an over-
worked mother against her unwanted children, and the physically
and emotionally unhealthy atmosphere of unsanitary, overcrowded,
and noisy quarters. When she was sixteen, Mary escaped this atmosphere by getting married to an alcoholic husband. Because of
the sensitiveness and skills she had acquired in her own childhood
she was able to protect her own children from that which she and
her siblings had suffered until her little family ran so completely
out of money, as a result of her alcoholic husband's losing his job,
that they had to let her nagging in-laws, whom her husband had
previously maintained, live with them in their small apartment. The
repetition of life in inescapably noisy, overcrowded quarters, where
she could no longer protect her babies from facing the results of
their alcoholic father's and their now overworked mother's ill
moods—that is, the pressure from the repetition of her own thwarting childhood experiences—led to a schizophrenic break. A skillful
psychiatric social worker succeeded in finding out from Mary the
reasons for her break-down. She secured separate living quarters
for Mary's in-laws; temporarily a separate bedroom for Mary; and,
guided by Mary's ability to express her longing for privacy and
quiet, a special job in the factory where Mary had worked before
—precision work, which had to be done in a separate room by a
skilled worker who did not mind being by herself. This work was
disliked by the other workers because of the solitude which went
with it. With Mary's pathological hypersensitivity to crowds, this
was just what she wanted, and she recovered from her schizophrenic
break-down while doing it; that is, she became one of the many
schizoid persons who succeed in turning their symptomatology
into a creative asset. Her work was also a valuable contribution to
the war effort of her country.

Another way in which mentally incapacitated people may be
able to turn their difficulties into assets is by "sublimation." These
people may succeed in unwittingly solving their difficulties in living
by combining their anxiety-provoking, socially inacceptable tend-

encies—such as one finds as reason for, and as outcome of, any mental disorder—with socially acceptable techniques of living which the culture provides.[7] Thus they succeed in turning their mental liabilities into assets.

To illustrate—John, the oldest son of happily married parents who gave him their undivided love, was faced at the age of 3 with the arrival of a brother with whom he had to share the parental love. His parents had neglected to prepare him adequately. Subsequently, he found himself hating a darling little brother, who deprived him of part of the parental attention, and hating kind and understanding parents who made him share their love with the little brother. From this utterly painful childhood experience which repeated itself time and again in subsequent years according to John's interpretation of life events, he learned that is was necessary to stay away from people lest one might find oneself loving them or being loved by them, only to head for subsequent disappointments from which one would come to hate these same people. Having great artistic abilities, he studied sculpturing and used his talent to model people who frightened him with the threat of mutual closeness. Thus the possibility of human intimacy was turned each time into an impersonal artistic experience. In other words, John succeeded in turning his socially inacceptable fear of getting into undesirable love-hatred entanglements with people into creative accomplishments which are appreciated in the culture.

Other creative people, who are hindered by their mental difficulties in getting what they want from life, may be able to make an asset of their unfulfilled longing for the unattainable. They may feel so keenly that they are unable to get what seems desirable to them that they try to counteract grief or sickness over the lack by creative expression of that which they cannot live [or experience in actuality]. These are then the people whose lives are so strikingly in contrast to their teachings or other spiritual performances or creations. If not many of them, at least some of them, are able to give spiritual life to the vision of what their actual lives should be like, not in spite of, but because of their inability to live it. Too handicapped to live what

[7] Sullivan, reference footnote 2; p. 61 ff.

they want, yet sensitized and pushed by their ever so strong, yet unfulfilled longing, they are specifically equipped and called upon to give creative expression and to erect a spiritual monument, as it were, to their ardent desires which have to remain dissatisfied in actuality. In so doing, they may also safeguard against additional difficulties in living by which they are threatened because of the constant pressure of their unfulfilled desires.

This possibility of turning liabilities into assets is another example of the two-sided motivation of human modes of expression.

Cultural history furnishes an immortal example of the functioning of this mechanism in the life and work of the philosopher Arthur Schopenhauer. He led the life of an isolated, haughty, paranoid, megalomanic hater and cynic. He looked down upon his father and he hated his mother, who being the inspiring muse and the spiritual center of a salon for the famous writers and artists of her time, showed no sign of furthering her young son's accomplishments. When he told her that he had won an honorable prize for his first philosophical thesis, "Note on the fourfold root of sufficient reason," his mother's answer was, "I did not know that you were interested in botany." After this experience, it is not surprising that young Schopenhauer developed an intense hatred for women and a distrust of them.

In keeping with his cynical and haughty general personality development, Schopenhauer was opposed to the popular revolutionary movements of his time. Yet what did this lonely hater of people in general, of women, and of the suppressed classes in particular, teach in his writings?

In his *Notes on the Basic Principles of Ethics*, he teaches, "That all human beings are alike and identical in a metaphysical sense," "That all virtues and ethical values arise from the intuitive knowledge of human equality," and that "Sympathy and compassion" are the "basis of justice and of all ethical concepts."

If one reads Schopenhauer's *World as Will and Idea* under the viewpoint of reflections of the author's unresolved difficulties in living and of his unfulfilled longings, one will find many data to corroborate my thesis that this schizoid, paranoid philosopher succeeded in converting his unfulfilled longing for the unattainable into the eternal spiritual monument which is his philosophical writings.[8]

Talking about Schopenhauer takes the investigation of the assets of people with mental difficulties out of the realm of my personal experience into the realm of world famous examples to which every reader could add any number from his own knowledge. Let me recall the great mentally disturbed poets Hoelderlin, Lenau, and Oscar Wilde; the writers Edgar Allan Poe and Charlotte Brontë; and the composers Schumann and Tschaikowsky. Think also of the mental difficulties of the great painter Van Gogh, torn throughout his life between art and religion and driven from the grey monotony of his Dutch homeland by an irresistible longing for the sun, "not its rays, but the sun itself!" As a result of this compulsive longing, he went south—Southern France—in search of the sun. Under the influence of his religious longing and his striving for the sun, he built the sunflower-covered, bright yellow "House of Friendship," where artists were supposed to live and work together in the spirit of original Christian communism. His vision did not materialize, but his unfulfilled and eternally unreconciled longings for life and love, sun, religion, and art were converted into the creativeness as a result of which he gave the world, within 2 years, the incredible collection of colorful paintings which are so widely known.

When, at last, the artist Gauguin came to visit and live with Van Gogh in the "House of Friendship," the visit was a complete and very painful failure. This was taken by Van Gogh as a definite proof that his dreams of unifying art and friendship, love, sun, and religion could not be fulfilled. He broke down and was hospitalized voluntarily. Several paintings of the mental hospitals where he lived, the portrait of one of his attendants, and one later of his psychiatrist friend, Dr. Gachet, are creative monuments of the time

[8] For a short orientation on Schopenhauer's life and work, see Edman, Irwin, *The Philosophy of Schopenhauer,* Modern Library edition. His collected papers have been translated into English by Haldane, Saunders, Bullock, and Thompson.

of his illness. Only his very last paintings show clear marks of mental disorder in the great artist, who was to end his life a prey of his difficulties in living. The lonely, disillusioned, mentally disordered artist shot himself while leaning against the lonely tree which we all know from several of his paintings.[9]

I have mentioned the composer Robert Schumann as another example of a person who converted the liabilities of a serious mental disorder into assets of eternal creative value. This schizophrenic artist was so withdrawn, seclusive, and disinclined to talk that, instead of talking, he started very early to depict his emotional experiences in musical compositions. This statement is not my interpretation of his works, but comes from the composer's statements. It holds, for instance, for his lovely piano compositions "Scenes from Childhood," or even more so for "The Davidites' March" in which he musically depicted the various aspects of his own personality as he experienced them: he is Florestan, the passionate fighter on the one hand; Eusebius, the melancholy dreamer on the other; and Master Raro, the umpire who observes his split in personality.

Another outcome of Schumann's schizoid verbal inarticulateness was his use of the great poetry of some of his contemporaries in courting his wife and expressing his love to her. This is, according to the statements in some of his letters to his mother, how he came to use the famous poetry of others as texts for the composition of

[9] From the vast literature on Van Gogh, the classical biographical study by Julius Meier-Graefe should be mentioned, translated into English by John Holroyd Reece, 2 vols.; published in 1922 and 1926 by the Medici Society, London and Boston; in 1928 by Payson and Clarke, New York; in 1933 by Harcourt Brace, New York; and in 1936 by Michael Joseph, London. An excellent short biography and evaluation of Van Gogh's work with first rate reproductions of his paintings in color and in black and white has been published by the Phædon Press, Vienna and New York: Uhde, Wilhelm, *The Life and Work of Vincent Van Gogh.* There is a novel based on the life of Vincent Van Gogh by Irving Stone, *Lust for Life,* Modern Library edition. Pathographical studies have been done by Jaspers: Strindberg and Van Gogh, *Research in Applied Psychiatry* (1922) 5; and by Riese, Walther, *Vincent Van Gogh in der Krankheit—Grenzfragen des Nerven und Seelenlebens,* Vol. 125, J. F. Bergmann, Munich, 1926

many of his famous songs, "Frauenliebe und Leben," and so on.[10]

Schumann's dislike for speaking may also be held responsible for his being the only composer of his time, except Richard Wagner, to write an opera without recitatives. This opera, "Genoveva," is not one of Schumann's great compositions. Schizophrenic artist that he was, he was too little interested in dramatics, in contrast to lyrics and epics, to write good opera. Nothing but the overture to "Genoveva" is performed today. However, composition of operas without recitatives has been of real importance in the further development of this style of composition.

In reflecting on Schumann's life and art in relationship to his mental disturbance, I would consider that his career as composer was, comparatively speaking, a happy outcome of his illness. After having tried his wings as writer and as lawyer, he decided to become a pianist. In order to do away with one of the technical problems of every pianist—how to accomplish independence in action of the fourth and fifth finger—he built a queer little device, such as only a schizoid person would evolve, and practiced on it with fanatical determination until he had ruined the function of his fourth and fifth fingers, thus bringing to an end any possible career as a pianist. From what is known of Schumann's history and of the few recitals he gave, it could be assumed that he would not have become too successful a concert pianist anyhow because of his schizoid lack of contact with and interest in his audience. Certainly, Schumann's mental difficulties were responsible for the fact that the world is the richer for one more great composer, whatever the expense to his contemporaries in the loss of a pianist.[11]

To add a few more examples of those people greatly handicapped in mind, but with equally great assets, the development of which

[10] Those readers who are musically interested may have learned to appreciate these songs in recent years while hearing them sung by Marian Anderson.

[11] For biographical data about Robert Schumann, see Wasiliewsky, Fuller Maitland, or Patterson. For his letters see: *The Life of Robert Schumann Told in His Letters,* translated by May Herbert, 1902, and *Letters of Robert Schumann,* translated by Hannah Bryant, 1907.

is due to their handicaps, let us take first the inarticulate, at times practically mute, schizophrenic dancer Nijinsky. He used bodily movement instead of spoken words, which failed him, as a means of self-expression in the highest style of the art. Most readers, at least those who are interested in the art of dancing, may remember some of the delightful performances by this schizophrenic artist which carried him to worldwide fame—"Le Spectre de la Rose," "Afternoon of a Faun," "Les Sylphides," and so on. The nature of his mental illness may be considered as one of the very sources of the impressive specificity of his art.[12]

Psychiatric experience teaches that there is in general a connection between schizophrenia and the choice of dancing as an artistic expression. For example, several of the most talented students of Mary Wigman's School of Dance, Dresden, had, as I know from personal experience, difficulties in living of the schizophrenic type. One of them, a resident of one of the war-torn southern European countries, had a mental break-down when the war conditions deprived her of the possibility of expressing herself to people by dancing, and recovered when she was able to resume her work and her art after the end of the war. Many institutions for the mentally disordered use artistic dancing successfully in the treatment of schizophrenics. I hope some artistic and psychological expert will find it worth his while, in the near future, to undertake further research on the problem of the fascinating relationship between schizophrenia and the dance.

To conclude the consideration of famous people whose assets were in causal connection with their mental difficulties, let me discuss a few people whose accomplishments were not in the field of the arts.

Clifford Beers emerged from the serious experience of many years of mental illness and hospitalization with the writing of his autobiography, *A Mind That Found Itself*, a classic among the biographies of the mentally disturbed. Sensitized by his own ex-

[12] Nijinsky, Romola, *Nijinsky*, Simon and Schuster, New York. Haskell, Arnold, and Nouvel, Walter, *Diaghileff, His Artistic and Private Life*, Simon and Schuster, New York.

perience to the needs of the mentally ill and to the necessity for preventive measures in this field, he became the founder first of the mental hygiene society in his home state, Connecticut, and, subsequently, the founder of the American and later of the international mental hygiene movements. He also interested Henry Phipps in donating the funds for the first psychiatric hospital connected with a medical school in this country. Thus, he became, in spirit, one of the co-founders of the Henry Phipps Psychiatric Clinic, Johns Hopkins Medical School in Baltimore.[13]

Anton T. Boisen, formerly a research associate at the Chicago Theological Seminary and chaplain at Elgin Hospital, recovered from several severe schizophrenic episodes, which he masterly describes in his most worth while theological and philosophical study, *The Exploration of the Inner World.* His experience as a psychiatric patient and as a theologist led him to promote clinical psychiatric training of theological students, he, himself, being the first one to get such training. He felt that psychiatric training was desirable for students of theology, because, with such training, future ministers were better equipped to help their parishioners if they got into emotional difficulties and, even more so, because he knew that a person who is trained in the right approach to the emotional problems of the mentally sick will automatically be better equipped to understand the emotional vicissitudes in the lives of the mentally healthy. In other words, Anton Boisen operated on the thesis that the difference between the mentally healthy and the mentally disturbed is one of degree only.

In addition, Boisen has published a number of most interesting contributions to the psychopathology of the mental disturbance which he himself had to undergo, and to the correlation between psychiatric and religious experience which was the background of his own creative development.[14]

[13] Beers, Clifford, *A Mind That Found Itself,* Longmans Green and Company, New York.

[14] Boisen, Anton T., *The Exploration of the Inner World,* Willet, Clark, Chicago 1936. Types of Dementia Præcox—A Study in Psychiatric Classification, PSYCHIATRY (1938) 1:233-236. Economic Distress and Religious Experience—A Study of the Holy Rollers, PSYCHIATRY (1939) 2:185-194. The

One more little known but great personality should be mentioned among those who recovered from severe mental disturbance and succeeded in making an asset of their experience: the anonymous "Late Inmate of the Glasgow Royal Asylum for Lunatics at Gartnavel," to whom I owe, by the way, the title of this paper. In his booklet, *The Philosophy of Insanity,* he expresses as early as 1860, when prejudice against mental illness was still overwhelmingly greater than it is now, his conviction that the difference between the mentally healthy and the mentally disturbed is one of quantity only. His own experience as an inmate of a mental hospital helped him, for instance, to come to as wise and modern a conclusion as the following: "What constitutes insanity?" he asks. "This is a question not easily answered, for the line which separates sanity from insanity is invisible, and there are as many kinds and degrees of the disease as there are sufferers."

"I am, and have been for years," he says in another place, "intimately acquainted with men, indeed I number some of them among my particular friends, whose advice on many subjects I would ask and take, and yet they are subject to delusions which totally unfit them, and, to all appearance, will ever unfit them, from residing outside the walls of a lunatic asylum." And at another place, "Of all men we [that is, those who have been mentally disturbed] should be the first to put, wherever it can bear it, a charitable construction upon the motives and actions of others—the last to judge, the last to condemn. The very brute extracts wisdom from suffering—why should not we? The dog burns his foot, and ever after looks askance at the fire."

In the spirit of such insight, the great anonym writes down what he remembers from the time of his own mental illness and of his hospitalization, fully aware of a definite purpose: "I purpose to note down," he says, "a few of my recollections concerning my thoughts and actions while under the influence of the disease, in the hope that they may be useful to those whose business it is to

---

Form and Content of Schizophrenic Thinking, PSYCHIATRY (1942) 5:23-33. Religion and Personality Adjustments, PSYCHIATRY (1942) 5:209-218. These are only some of the great number of Boisen's contributions.

watch over the insane, and a warning to those who, through ignorance or recklessness, abuse their minds, till the tortured spirit, like a fire-begirt scorpion, turns upon itself and stings." At another place: "This subject is to me decidedly painful, but I do hope that my treatment of it may be a means of encouraging friends to persevere in their attention to relatives who are thus afflicted, and in this hope I have told my plain truthful story, and who knows but that it may tend to soften the prejudices which almost everyone entertains against such as I; and I may add, for the consolation of the afflicted and their friends, that a fit of insanity does not necessarily permanently injure either the feelings, or the intelligence of the person, after the fit has passed." [15]

I have said that I borrow the title for my paper from the above quoted author. Yet he called his booklet "The Philosophy of Insanity," and I call my paper "Remarks on the Philosophy of Mental Disorder." This difference in wording is not only a formal one but also one of content. When psychiatrists talk about insanity, it has more or less the connotation of incurability; the expression "mental disorder" is therefore preferable, for even serious mental disturbances can potentially be treated successfully with intensive psychotherapy, it is now believed.

This leads me to discuss the first of the four statements on which I planned to elaborate in this paper, that severely mentally disturbed people can be approached with the methods of modern intensive psychotherapy.

Until about twenty years ago, it was the conviction among psychiatrists and psychoanalysts, guided by such classical teachers as Kraepelin and Bleuler and psychoanalysts as Fenichel and Schilder, that psychotherapy with seriously disturbed—psychotic—persons

[15] I have quoted verbatim from this precious little book because it was out of print at the time this paper was being written; it is now being reprinted by Greenberg, New York. *The Philosophy of Insanity—By a Late Inmate of the Royal Asylum for Lunatics at Gartnavel;* Maclachlan and Stewart, Edinburgh; Houlston and Wright, London; William Love, 40 St. Enoch Square, Glasgow; 1860. It contains so much of the wisdom which modern psychiatrists have still to learn and to teach today, 86 years after the anonymous former inmate of a mental hospital learned it from his own experience and felt called upon to teach it.

could not be done.[16] Freud predicted in 1904 that it might be possible to treat the severely mentally disordered with intensive psychotherapy if, despite basic difficulties as he saw and outlined them in 1914, psychoanalytic technique could be successfully adapted to their specific needs.[17]

Since then the attitude of many psychotherapists has changed. Under the leadership of Adolf Meyer, William Alanson White, and above all, Harry Stack Sullivan in this country, a number of American psychoanalysts and psychotherapists with psychoanalytic orientation have done intensive psychotherapy with psychotics, especially in the psychoanalytical hospitals—Chestnut Lodge (D. M. Bullard), Forest Sanitarium (J. Steinfeld), Menninger Clinic, The Haven (L. Bartemeier) and others.[18]

[16] Kraepelin, Emil, *Clinical Psychiatry,* New York, William Wood Company, 1904; pp. 21-29. Bleuler, Eugen, *Dementia Præcox,* Leipzig and Vienna, Franz Deuticke, 1911. Fenichel, Otto, *Outline of Clinical Psychoanalysis,* New York, W. W. Norton and Company, 1934; pp. 313-362. Schilder, Paul, *Introduction to a Psychoanalytic Psychiatry,* New York, Nervous and Mental Disease Publ. Co., 1928.

[17] Freud, Sigmund, *On Psychotherapy* in *Collected Papers,* Vol. I, London, Hogarth Press, 1924, and *On Narcissism—An Introduction, Collected Papers,* Vol. IV, London, Hogarth Press, 1925.

[18] Meyer, Adolf, *The Nature and Conception of Dementia Præcox,* in Dementia Præcox Monograph, Boston, Gorham Press, 1911. White, William Alanson, *Medical Psychology—The Mental Factor in Disease,* New York, Nervous and Mental Disease Publ. Co., 1931; *Outlines of Psychiatry,* New York, Nervous and Mental Disease Publ. Co., 1935. Sullivan, reference footnote 2, see Therapeutic Conceptions, pp. 87-117; Modified Psychoanalytic Treatment of Schizophrenia, *Amer. J. Psychiatry* (1931) 11:519-540.

In European countries, Federn of Vienna, Fairbairn of Edinburgh, Ernst of London, Hollos of Budapest, and Boss of Zurich were among those who tried modified psychoanalytic psychotherapy with hospitalized psychotics. Federn, Paul, The Analysis of Psychotics, *Internat. J. Psychoanal.* (1934) 15:209-214. Fairbairn, W. R. D., A Revised Psychopathology of the Psychoses and Psychoneuroses, *Internat. J. Psychoanal.* (1941) 22:250-279; and Endopsychic Structure Considered in Terms of Object-Relationships, *Internat. J. Psychoanal.* (1944) 25:70-93. Boss, E., Personal Communication from Dr. Ruth Charlotte Cohn, New York, (Swiss literature not yet available). Eissler, Kurt R., Limitations to the Psychotherapy of Schizophrenia, PSYCHIATRY (1943) 6:381-391. Ernst, M. G., A Psychotherapeutic Approach in Schizophrenia, *J. Mental Sci.* (1940) pp. 668-674. Fromm-Reichmann, Transference Problems in Schizophrenics, *Psychoanalytic Quart.* (1939) 8:412-426; Recent Advances in Psycho-

By intensive — psychoanalytically oriented — psychotherapy, I mean communication between two people through spoken words, gesture, and attitude, the psychiatrist and the psychiatric patient, with the goal that both may learn to understand the troublesome aspects of the patient's life and bring them and their hidden causes to the patient's awareness, so that his living may be facilitated and so that his difficulties in living may be alleviated, if not eliminated. In order to accomplish this goal, the patient must verbalize his problems to and investigate them with another trained and experienced person, the psychiatrist. As he does so, he may be freed from his difficulties in living to the extent to which he will be able to become aware of, and therefore capable of, handling his interpersonal relationships.[19] The psychiatric predecessors thought that it was not possible to realize such a procedure with seriously mentally disordered people, because they felt first, that no workable doctor-patient relationship—"transference"—could be established with the psychotic; second, that most of his communications were not understandable to the psychiatrist; and third, that the psychotic's tendency toward health and his wish for change was not sufficient to work with it.

As I have shown in the introductory fragment of psychotherapeutic contact with the catatonic woman poet, the assumption that such rapport cannot be established is untenable. The error in judgment of the classical psychiatrists seems to have been due to the withdrawn, detached, and sometimes aggressively hostile attitude which many mentally disturbed people show. This attitude was considered to be the result of a primary impenetrable grandiose self-engulfment—"narcissism." Modern psychiatric research shows that the seclusive, haughty, seemingly unapproachable attitude of these people is a secondary result of very early serious warping in their relationships with the people significant in their environment in infancy and childhood, with more or less consistent subsequent thwarting pressure in the same direction until they eventually break

analytic Therapy, PSYCHIATRY (1941) 4:161-164. [Editor's Note: Recent Advances in Psychoanalytic Therapy is included in this volume.]

[19] Sullivan, reference footnote 2.

down. It is in order to forego the repetition of further painful interpersonal experiences that these people withdraw into the detachment and regress to the infantile, self-sufficient attitude which prevented the older psychiatrists from trying to reach them.

In addition, these psychiatrists were hesitant to cope with the sometimes active assaultiveness of the inarticulate psychotic which seemed unpredictable and not understandable to them. Since modern psychotherapists have learned to understand the background of the psychotic's seclusive attitude from his early history, and have learned that his communications can be understood in principle, they are able to establish a workable doctor-patient relationship with him.[20]

Let me illustrate by telling how the initial rapport with the catatonic woman poet was established. We had our first interview while the young woman was still greatly disturbed, suicidal and actively assaultive, hallucinated and delusional. She opened the conversation by saying, "Dr. Bullard [the superintendent of the hospital] says I should talk with you; maybe the two of us could hit it off all right; and my brother [a psychiatrist] says that you have written something about people like myself, so that he thinks you will be able to understand me. By the way, could I read it? And my parents brought me all the way North from Argentine because they want me to be treated in this hospital." Realizing that this was the girl's way of testing out whether or not I intended to deal with my superintendent's patient, or with the sister of a colleague of mine, or with the daughter of her parents, who would pay the bills, or with herself in her own right, I responded that neither Dr. Bullard nor the patient's brother or parents would decide whether or not she and I could get along with one another, that we had to try to find out in our own right whether each of us felt that we could

[20] Fromm-Reichmann, Transference Problems in Schizophrenics, reference footnote 18; reference footnote 1. Hollos, J., *Hinter der gelben Mauer*, Bern, Huber. Schwing, G., *Ein Weg zur Seele des Geisteskranken*, Bern, Huber. Sullivan, Affective Experience in Early Schizophrenia, *Amer. J. Psychiatry* (1927) 6:468-483; Research in Schizophrenia, *Amer. J. Psychiatry* (1929) 9:553-567.

talk to one another and understand each other's language,[21] and whether she would feel that I could be of use to her in understanding and alleviating her difficulties. The girl's question as to whether she should read my publications was answered in the negative, for it did not necessarily follow that I would understand her difficulties because I had understood those of others. This elimination of the interference of any third person, with the establishment of our professional relationship and the definition of the goal of such a relationship, made it possible for the patient to talk to me immediately about her complaints. This she indicated by then asking whether I could explain to her why it was that she felt "so hazy and dizzy" all the time, and whether I could tell her what to do about it. Thus a workable relationship was established with a seriously disturbed, catatonic person.

The same can be done with even very hostile and inarticulate people. Several years ago, a very disturbed, inarticulate young male patient was on the disturbed ward of this hospital. He had been seen for regular psychotherapeutic interviews over a long period of time by one of our male physicians. During this time, I had only seen him casually, passing the time of day with him when I came to visit other patients on the ward. As the progress of this young man was not deemed satisfactory, change to a female psychotherapist was decided upon. When first I invited myself to a psychotherapeutic interview with the young man, he became violently assaultive and refused to see me. All I could do to protect myself was to retire quickly. Was this a not-understandable or an unpredictable response on the part of the patient? I did not think so. For a year or longer, I had paid no special attention to him. All of a sudden, I got good and ready to speak to him without being given the opportunity by him to explain the reasons. Why should he be ready to have us talk to one another just because I was? Realizing that his reluctance was justified and that, being the inarticulate patient he was, he could not express it other than in assaultive action, I subsequently went to see him daily for 3 months, telling him outside the door of his room that I came on the ward to see

[21] The patient was in full command of the English and Spanish languages.

him, and only him, and that I was waiting for him to become ready to give us a chance to try useful therapeutic interchange. After 3 months, he invited me in, confirmed my interpretation of his previous reluctance, and a workable relationship was established.

The second reason which prevented classical psychiatrists from believing that intensive psychotherapy with psychotics could be done successfully—namely, that the communications of the mentally disturbed were not understandable and perhaps meaningless—has been refuted by implication in what has been said thus far. If the concept is correct, that the psychotic's mental experiences and modes of expressing them are different only in degree and not in kind, his communications must, in principle, be as meaningful and potentially understandable as are those of the "healthy." The previously discussed parallels between dreams and psychotic productions and the preceding examples of establishing contact between two psychotics and myself bear witness to this.

Hence, the psychiatrist has to listen to the communications of the mentally disturbed and try to understand them irrespective of whether or not he can always grasp their meaning. If he cannot understand them, he still owes the respect to the mentally disordered person to know that his communications are practically always self-meaningful. The psychiatrist as the participant observer in the psychotherapeutic interchange with the psychotic must have a well-developed self-respect. If he has, he can afford acceptance of the fact that the mental patients can convey ideas to him which make no sense to the psychiatrist who is supposed to be "in his right mind,"—ideas which are evidently meaningful to the patient who is allegedly "out of his mind." This is where classical psychiatrists and psychoanalysts failed their psychotic patients. If the modern psychotherapist is able to accept this experience without any lowering of his security, psychotherapeutic collaboration between him and his patient will be possible. It is not necessary for the psychiatrist to understand the meaning of everything that the mentally disordered patient tries to convey to him. In his dealings with neurotics, he does not grasp the meaning of every dream which the neurotic may report; nor do "healthy" people "understand" all that is said to one another. However, in either situation, the psychiatrist is required to realize that the productions are potentially meaningful. The following are a few examples, illustrating the difference between ways of communication of the mentally disturbed and the mentally healthy.

One of the central pathogenic problems of the catatonic woman poet was an unrecognized jealousy of her baby sister, which was greatly justified by the preference given to this newcomer by her environment, but of which the patient was totally unaware. Various therapeutic efforts to make her see it had not been acceptable to her. One day Margherita discovered that I had just gotten a new history of art. I asked her whether she wished to look up something in it, and she answered by showing me some reproductions of the work of the painter Cézanne. Being sure that her choice was not accidental but quite meaningful, yet not knowing what the meaning might be, I asked her whether she had ever seen any of Cézanne's original paintings, upon which she told me the following story: When she was 17 or somewhat younger, her parents had taken her, the younger sister, and one brother to Madrid, where the family had seen some of Cézanne's originals. When they arrived at the Spanish border two days before reaching Madrid, her brother who had to attend to their *triptyques,* left the car in which they were traveling, on what appeared to be an abandoned railroad track. Suddenly, a train approached on this track. Instantly, Margherita moved to the driver's seat, turned on the ignition, and moved the car off the track just in time. The first thing that came to her attention afterwards was that her parents had grabbed the younger sister and were bestowing affection upon her as a sign of their great relief. Hearing this story, I was supposed to guess by implication that Margherita's parents, in their happiness at seeing the younger sister safe, had forgotten to thank Margherita whose presence of mind had saved the lives of the whole family. This was the patient's way of admitting to the psychiatrist that she had at last become aware of her jealousy of the younger sister,—an awareness which henceforth could be used for therapeutic purposes.

Another example of the psychotic's particular means of communication: one day, towards the end of the treatment, Margherita and I read and discussed some of her favorite poetry as a means of finding out about some emotional experiences of hers which were expressed in the poetry. At one point, I failed to hear her convey signs of her apprehension in terms of one of the poems. I only realized it afterwards, when I noticed an expression of utter sadness and disappointment upon her face. I apologized for my lack of alertness, stating that I realized such failures in alertness to be inevitable at times in our psychotherapeutic dealings and encouraging her to make me aware of them, if she could, whenever they occurred. The next day, Margherita brought me a little gift, stating that this was to express her appreciation for our discussion of the poetry. Realizing that a schizophrenic, as a rule, will not bother to account for the plausibility of his actions, I knew that this was not the real reason for Margherita's having brought the gift. I was supposed to guess that what she really was grateful for was my frank admission of my failure in alertness.

So much for the means of expression of the mentally disturbed and the psychiatrist's potential ability to understand.

As to the lack of a tendency towards health which made classical psychiatrists despair of trying to do verbalized psychotherapy with the mentally disordered, it was shown that there is a tendency towards health in every human being, as discussed in the section on the two-sided motivation of mental symptoms. I maintain with Sullivan that there is as much of a tendency towards health in the mentally or physically ill as there is a tendency towards intake of food and liquids in the hungry and thirsty.[22] In some mental patients, a spontaneous wish for change and recovery is found. In others, such a wish can be aroused on the basis of their tendency towards health, unless life has so little in store for them that they cannot be expected to become interested in being able to cope with its vicissitudes.

There is, however, one imperative presupposition to be entertained by any psychotherapist who wants to be useful to the

[22] Sullivan, reference footnote 2.

mentally disordered in their rehabilitation. He must have sufficient insight into and respect for the special needs of the specific personalities of these people to realize that he is not called upon to guide them toward adjustment conforming with the conventionalities of the culture. To a mentally disturbed person, recovery means being sufficiently aware of his previous difficulties in interpersonal relationships so that he may become able to reach out for that which means security and satisfaction to him, be it ever so different from the conventional patterns of interpersonal relationships in his culture.

Most justifiably, there has been much discussion about the as yet deplorably small number of recoveries of the mentally disordered under intensive psychotherapy. This has chiefly been attributed to lack of psychiatric skill and knowledge. It is my conviction and the conviction of my psychiatric friends that the greater responsibility must be referred to the sad fact that most psychiatrists have more respect for the society which pays them for their services than for the patients who need their help and guidance. These psychiatrists work, advertently or inadvertently, toward the recovery of a mental patient in terms of a conventional adjustment to society rather than in terms of his individual needs.

The schizophrenic woman poet, for example, from whose treatment history many examples in this paper are taken, was not treated with the goal of having her make an adjustment to the social standards and requirements of her family group, much less to living with her parents, whose main interest was playing a rôle in "society" in the capital city of their country. Nor was the appraisal of her state of mental health made dependent upon the question of whether or not this schizoid personality, with her great legitimate need for privacy, and at times aloneness, would make a successful marital adjustment. Treatment came to an end when she knew enough about her early and present interpersonal relationships to be able to get along with people when she met them as a social human being, instead of evading them because she dreaded them as she had done previously. She has been able to form some relationships of durable intimacy, and she has found security in these relationships, in her creative work, and in some worth-while pastimes.

Now to come to the discussion of my fourth and last point: the influence of one's dealings with the mentally disturbed on one's contacts with the emotionally healthy. When one realizes how many mentally sick or mentally handicapped persons are able to convert their previous liabilities into really worth-while assets, once they have succeeded in turning the destructive aspects of their difficulties in living into constructive aspects of life, the attempt at trying to help these people to attain such goals appears most gratifying even though at present psychiatrists are not at all successful in their therapeutic efforts with all of them.

There are other reasons which make the dealings of the so-called healthy with the mentally disordered most worth while. If psychiatrists could learn to apply the sensitive and cautious, yet spontaneous, respectful and alert considerateness, which is required in their dealings with the schizophrenic, to their relationships with their fellow men in general, it would constitute a most rewarding improvement of human relationships in this culture.

If society could learn something from the schizophrenic's lack of any need or wish for plausibility or magic use of apologetic rationalization, it would make for much greater directness and frankness in human interrelationships.

Mentally disturbed persons who have withdrawn their interest from their environment are refreshingly abhorrent of all kinds of cultural compromises; hence, they inevitably hold the mirror of the hypocritical aspects of the culture in front of society.

For all these reasons, it can be exceedingly valuable to deal with psychotic people for all those psychiatrists who are willing to learn from their psychotic fellow men. Considering relationships with mental patients from this viewpoint, it is no overstatement to say that the mentally sick, who allegedly have lost their minds in their interpersonal struggles, *may* be useful to the mentally healthy in really finding *their* minds which are all too frequently lost, as it were, in the distortions, dissociations, the hypocritical adaptations, and all the painful hide-and-seeks which modern culture forces upon the mind of man.

However, this may become possible *only* if "mentally disturbed" and "mentally stable" people are no longer considered different in kind but only in degree, and if no moral disqualification is attached to mental disorder. Then and then only will so-called healthy but too well adjusted people become capable of hearing with respect, and with a consequent gain in growth, maturation, and inner independence, the message which comes to them from some of the culturally uncompromising and mentally disordered persons—a message none the less valuable because at times the price of their nonconformity is painful episodes of mental disturbance.

NOTES ON INVESTIGATION, THERAPY, AND EDUCATION IN PSYCHIATRY AND THEIR RELATIONS TO SCHIZOPHRENIA

Harry Stack Sullivan

THE TASK which the Program Committee has given me is not unwelcome but my efforts to discharge it can scarcely be more than diagrammatic.* Even at that, there may be good reason, these days, for psychiatrists to see if they can make succinct and meaningful statements of the basic assumptions on which they operate and for other psychiatrists to see if they can discover wherein these succinct statements of the colleagues leave them uncertain or uninformed. It is the time, of all time, for psychiatrists not alone "to become observant of their observing" [1] but to become aware of the implicit assumptions which guide them in their work of being a psychiatrist.

Psychiatry has to be considered as a science, and as art and technology. As science, psychiatry is primarily concerned either with elucidating more or less inadequate and inappropriate patterns of living or with various other matters.

As art and technology, psychiatry is (1) primarily concerned with participant observation and influencing of patients in the direction of improved patterns of living; or (2) chiefly occupied with discharging a duty to society in significant contradistinction to the patient, a person whose living in society has become more or less

* [Editor's Note: The reference is to a symposium on schizophrenia as part of the program of the tenth annual meeting of the Medical Society of St. Elizabeth's Hospital, Washington, D. C., May 2 and 3, 1947.]

[1] A Note on the Implication of Psychiatry, the Study of Interpersonal Relations, for Investigations in the Social Sciences. *Amer. J. Sociol.* (1937) **42**: 848-861.

intolerable to the group; or (3) a combination of the first two; or yet (4) while perhaps giving lip service to the first or the second, is primarily concerned with the satisfaction and security of the practitioner.

I am keenly interested in the science of psychiatry as first defined and many of you must of necessity be much concerned with the third rubric of its art and technology.

Psychiatry as a science of living has its field of data at the level of performance as a person among persons, personifications, and the institutions, customs, conventions, and the like, described as the culture-complex or social order.

This in no way reduces the relevance to psychiatry of studies which are addressed to uncovering (1) the physical and physiological factors that enter into the living of a person among people; or (2) the history, organization, and functional significance of the social order or social orders in which the person lives with others; or (3) any special area of data abstracted for scientific study from the large contexts—such as neurophysiology, speech, marital disharmony, crime and its management, or even the training of psychiatrists.

The invention of a new mathematical operation may be of some importance for the science of psychiatry—witness, somewhat tangentially, factor analysis.

A history of the idea of God, especially if relatively comparative in approach so that the idea of immanent power or *manna* is clearly distinguished, may well have importance for the science of psychiatry.

It is, in a word, quite possible that any serious study of anything which is a part of living, human or of multicellular organisms, *under certain circumstances inhering in the formulation of the study and its results,* may be tributary to the science of psychiatry.

Let me rest this aspect of the matter with the comment that the imposition upon research in the other fields of the conditions which would insure a measure of relevance to psychiatry would not, in a vast number of instances, greatly complicate the research, but this is beyond the competence and interest of the investigator.

For this reason, the utility of a vast amount of biological and social science research continues to be small, and this misfortune is as evident at the level of biography as it is at that of physiology.[2]

Research is relevant to psychiatry when it studies an aspect of living under such conditions that it gives valid information on man's performance *as a person among* persons. The most frequently imperative of these conditions at the human level is the necessity that the research be a *participant* observing.

The science of psychiatry and the technology based on that science, keeping to the definition of my current interest in both, *must* grow in richness of validly formulated statements about interpersonal relations and the developmental evolution of abilities and disabilities for such relations. This central disciplinary field *can* be enriched by results from a vast number of tributaries.

The psychiatrist has to recognize among the data to which he has to attend certain ways of living to which we refer as *schizophrenic states*. To be a scientific psychiatrist, he has to seek to improve the relevance and other validity of his formulations about participating in the schizophrenic ways of living. He may do this by neurophysiological research, by anthropological field work, by research in the development of speech "habits," or by inventing hypotheses *and operations* in line with them in almost any field of human life. But for ready returns from his work to his disciplinary field of psychiatry it is best that he shall have some acquaintance with the characteristics of the schizophrenic way of living.

While I hold that there is much more of the essentially human in everyone than there are significant novelties, and I am quite sure that everyone has had extensive experience with all the processes in interpersonal relations which we encounter in the schizophrenic way of life, I also realize that the untutored investigator is at an extreme disadvantage in utilizing his experience with some

[2] I cannot resist the opportunity to mention at this point an observation called to my attention by Dr. David Rioch concerning the theory entertained to explain the better treadmill performance of sympathectomized than entire dogs. The operation is thought to protect the dogs from wearing themselves out in the effort to "please" the experimenter.

of the processes which are conspicuous in participant observation of, or with, the schizophrenic patient.

Not but that the untutored are at remarkable disadvantage in the whole field of psychiatry if only because everyone has been moulded in directions which make scientific observation of human living difficult; but additionally the schizophrenic way of living includes processes with which each of us has been *forced* to become unacquainted, has been compelled to relegate to that part of his current living which goes on *outside* of alert awareness, often in one's sleep.

Under these special circumstances it might seem that the psychiatrist might well omit the study of schizophrenic ways of life from his earlier ventures in research. He might perhaps "concentrate" on "the neuroses" and leave "the psychoses" to his more ambitious colleagues. Such alleged performances are no novelty in the current scene; in fact, I believe that many of the colleagues have omitted the serious study of any and all ways of living, including most significantly their own.

But even in that field of psychiatric art which is chiefly concerned with making a living, it is at times quite vitally important that one be somewhat acquainted with the schizophrenic ways of life. One may otherwise come to be in bad repute as a psychiatrist, with corresponding unfavorable effects on one's satisfactions and security; and persons who are manifesting the paranoid states which are often sequential on schizophrenic episodes are dangerous people to involve in any confidence game, or with whom to have professional dealings for which one is ill-trained.

The psychiatrist as scientist or as practitioner can no more safely omit the study of schizophrenic ways of living than can he neglect the relationship of developmental age and experience, or of experience and understanding, or of motive and intention.

How does the psychiatrist learn about the schizophrenic—and every other—way of living? One way, of course, is to have "been there," to have undergone in later life a schizophrenic episode. I cannot particularly recommend this potentially highly educative experience. Psychiatric technology cannot yet guarantee that you would return from that way of life to one more suited to philanthropic ambition. With the current vogues, you would quite as probably go on in life as a "result" of electroshock or lobotomy. And the mere "having been there" is not enough; not by any manner of means enough to confer scientific grasp on the schizophrenic way of living. As I have said, as I see it everyone has at least potentially "been there" in regard to every process important in living. What then is missing and in need of remedy by training in psychiatry?

At the present juncture in my psychiatric thinking—which is concerned much more with practical possibilities than with ultimate desiderata—the answer to the question runs somewhat as follows.

The work of the psychiatrist is not the recognized goal of anyone's early training for life among others. In a transitional state of a culture-complex, everyone is, as it were, educated to *need* a psychiatrist; psychiatrists' children in the main being no exception.

Even as this is true, it is equally evident that there are significant differences in the outcome of early training with respect to one's aptitudes and handicaps for subsequent training to be a psychiatrist.

There is such an accumulation of handicap in the case of some people that it is relatively impractical to undertake their training. These are in general people who are quite content with themselves, the present and their foreseen probable future. These genuinely complacent people can scarcely be said to have promise for psychiatry.

Many people who "sound like that" are, however, still excellent prospects, for their seeming complacency merely shows their skill at concealing anxieties about their personal present and future. As a person interested in psychiatric education, I have nothing against candidates who can, as it were, contain their uncertainties in interpersonal relations and conceal their vulnerability to others.

If one is not "too good to become better" in his private assessment of his living with others, *and if* he has undergone the education which gives him some grasp on the mere biology of living, then the problem of training him to be a psychiatrist becomes one of curriculum and technique—in the ultimate analysis, personnel who live adequately and appropriately the requirements of a satisfactory curriculum.

The training of a satisfactorily characterized candidate follows three lines.

One has to become acquainted with *frames of reference* by which to organize observational technique and thought.

One has to accumulate *experience* in discovering that to which observational technique and thought may apply usefully.

One has to learn to orient one's observing and thinking to successful *participation* in the therapeutic and other situations which make up the psychiatric way of life.

The training of the psychiatrist cannot be separated into neat compartments. One cannot secure much profit from didactic instruction without opportunity for assessing one's information by practical efforts. This does not reduce the importance of an organized curriculum, of an integrated program of learning.

Present practice makes it mandatory that a candidate for psychiatry shall spend some time in a junior position on the staff of a hospital for the mentally disordered. Here, he will at least "get used to" the more seriously disturbed sorts of psychiatric patients. To enter upon the practice of psychiatry without this familiarity is, in my opinion, grossly unwise.

I think that the candidate who has to spend 12-18 months in this "getting used to" more gravely disturbed ways of life is entitled to learn in the process something more useful than uninformed opinion to the effect that "There is nothing in psychiatry but a lot of words. One psychiatrist's opinion is as good as another's. No two psychiatrists agree about anything," and the like.

Fortunately, even if his formulable profit from residence in the psychiatric hospital is lamentably small, the residency is almost never a total loss. The mere undergoing of the experience widens one's horizon regarding human phenomena, and a wide horizon in this particular is a very real asset.

A great deal could be done to make internship and residency in the hospital for the mentally disordered a valuable part of graduate training. This would call for the prior orienting of the hospital's staff to the obvious benefits of coherent views, concerted effort, and reasonable collaboration in recognizing and formulating uncertainties.

A very great number of institutional psychiatrists have had little or no opportunity to become acquainted with more of psychiatry than its aspect as art and technology for discharging a duty primarily to society and but indirectly and secondarily to the patient. An often ignored but none the less remarkable proportion of them have come to manifest great skill in discharging these duties. This skill is in no way diminished by being poorly formulated, if not often actually misunderstood, by its possessor.

It is only in the last decade or so that we have found reasonably secure foundations on which to build a science of psychiatry which would be just that, and not a system of impressive platitudes or an exercise in tautology. The public prestige of exact science has meanwhile become enormous, and medicine itself has come to feel proud of the achievements of its laboratory substrates.

I wonder how many uncomfortable psychiatrists who have mixed up their feeling of personal worth with their often unfortunate verbiage have paused to notice the demonstrable competence of the average specialist in other fields of medical practice.[3]

There is call for a great effort to make psychiatrists' experience and information much more readily assimilable to the candidates associated with them in hospitals and clinics.

As it is now, the more serious phases of psychiatric training begin after one has "gotten acquainted with" institutional patients. It may take the form of apprenticeship learning of an empirical art. It may take the form of learning a science and the technology clearly derivative therefrom. Perhaps in most cases today it is a blend of both.

[3] A spread of this harmless exercise might have a salutary effect on the psychiatric "leaders" who now cultivate income and deference by genuflecting before the posteriors of medical Pooh-Bahs while poking cheap fun at serious workers in psychiatry and tediously iterating *as* psychiatry select items from the earlier textbooks.

The Council of Fellows ultimately responsible for psychiatric training as it is conducted in the Washington School of Psychiatry hold that "no person may be entrusted with responsibility for therapeutic intervention in difficulties of living who shall not have undergone a searching scrutiny of his personal history, liabilities, and assets from a therapeutic standpoint." This refers to an intensive study of the candidate himself as a subject for psychiatric participant observation. It has close historical relation to the procedure called in some circles the candidate's "training psychoanalysis."

This training which starts in an intensive evaluation of the candidate as a participant in scientific personality study, as a center of increasing awareness in a prolonged and specially constituted interpersonal situation, seems to me to be the only way to teach psychiatric scientific method. This does not mean, however, that it is always or now even often successful in that respect. I surmise that our efforts thus far have usually taught an empirical technique which often "works" in benefiting patients, instead of a precise method which would work much better far more quickly and the applicability of which would be far less a peculiar function of the particular psychiatrist. However imperfect the current results, the trend is demonstrably in the right direction, which is perhaps as much as can be expected in current affairs human, though I, for reason of dubious longevity, would like to see the other quality of the vector multiply.

The intensive study of personality is prolonged participant observation; subject-person and psychiatrist take active part in it. It seeks, whether training or treatment—if there be such a valid distinction—to uncover and explore inadequate and inappropriate processes in interpersonal relations, but such discovery requires frames of reference and a great deal of data to which they are usefully relevant.

One of the most profoundly important of these frames of reference is the theory of *anxiety* and the *self-system*. Every instance of intensive personality study includes a multitude of data on *security operations*—efforts to escape or to minimize anxiety in the doctor-patient relationship. Until doctor and patient have come to formulate the more recurrently significant of these, there may be very little except security operations, and no material training or treatment.

The theory of the self-system indicates that to the very extent that two people are the products of *the same* culture-complex, they will, other circumstances not intervening, experience anxiety and manifest security operations under exactly comparable interpersonal influences, and will be all but unable to notice these phenomena and to observe and analyze the pattern of activity concerned in terms of the pursuit of a goal which is not approved culturally—or the cultural acceptability of which is not recognized because of actually immaterial considerations.[4]

Two qualifications of this statement may well be considered. One pertains to the "sameness" of cultural ingredients integrated in the self-systems. This is often a matter of nuances rather than gross, easily describable, convictions about *right* ways of thinking and doing. Many children are taught not to steal, but there are family differences in defining the object-ownership relations violation of which constitutes stealing. I need scarcely stress the difference, for example, between objects owned by your next door neighbor and those owned by the power company, or a railroad, or the government; or the difference in "moral compulsion" about returning borrowed money and borrowed books.

It is hard for many candidates to learn to investigate apparent identities and differences in the culture incorporated in themselves and others, so that they can avoid the errors of precise parallelism *and* those arising from acting on assumed parallelism when there is *material* difference. Some of the people to whom we refer carelessly as "typical extroverts" are so lacking in observational acumen in this particular that they live on the assumption that all really decent people "know" right and wrong precisely as do they. Any-

---

[4] Some of the ability of "born" therapists resides in their freedom to notice and communicate this very consideration, the *immaterial* character of some of the self-system interventions "in" their patients. To the extent that they can do this, they are of significantly different background *or* they have "caught on to," recovered from, the relevant irrationality of the common culture—as a result of particularly fortunate experience and successful self-scrutiny.

one sufficiently motivated and skillful enough to invite attention to a difference is peculiar and of dubious personal worth.

The other important consideration to be kept in mind about people closely similar in particular details of background is the great difference in susceptibility to anxiety which they manifest in superficially similar situations. Many factors enter into determining one's vulnerability to anxiety and the intensity of anxiety which one will experience on a particular occasion. The psychiatrist can take nothing for granted in this connection; he simply has to explore and map out the areas in his relations with the patient which are marked by anxiety—and the intervention of security operations connected with it. He has to participate in a way that, no other consideration taking precedent, the changing therapeutic situation moves *away from* anxiety rather than towards increased anxiety. If he does not, communication is apt to become nil.

Insensitivity to interventions of the self-system is the bane of all psychiatric work and the central defect in incompetent work with conspicuously obsessional or schizophrenic people. I hope you will realize that this insensitivity *works both ways*. The psychiatrist, if ill-trained, may be all but a compendium of unwitting security operations, so vulnerable to anxiety that no patient can "tell him" a great deal of what is the matter. Many a supposedly well-trained psychiatrist becomes involved with certain of his patients in an unending, unrecognized, contest of security operations—which certainly seems natural to the patient, and as certainly does him no good.

In the case of those who have come to a schizophrenic way of living, any blundering in this region of anxiety and security operations is apt to foreclose the possibilities of therapeutic intervention. The doctrine of "the narcissistic neurosis" arose from this. To those who can reasonably aspire to becoming psychiatric *scientists* let me say that there is no purely psychiatric research except it be therapeutic. No one can secure data on interpersonal relations by the route of uncorrected error. Disastrous mistakes in the handling of particular schizophrenic patients are inevitable. These mistakes contribute data only in so far as they lead to demonstrably successful modification of an attempt at *the same operation* in relationship with another patient. In psychiatry, one learns from one's mistakes by discovering reasonably probable evidence of wherein there was a mistake, and this is not done by untested cogitation. Much less, indeed, is it achieved by *post hoc* face-saving verbalisms.

In my opinion, no other group of people are so vulnerable to simply disastrous interventions of anxiety in the more lucid intervals during which communication is possible, than are the schizophrenics. The possibilities of therapeutic intervention in schizophrenic situations are, therefore, to an extraordinary extent a simple function of the psychiatrist's skill at avoiding incidental, unintentional, collision with the patient's self-system. With the bitterest feeling about the human costs involved, I have to say that the testing ground of one's psychiatric skill lies in this area of distorted interpersonal relations.

Let me return now to the training of the psychiatrist to competence even with schizophrenics. I want first to round out the present picture; I want then to venture into the troublesome field of possible improvements.

After one has experienced useful participant observation of one's living with one's training psychiatrist for long enough, the present pattern of training requires one to enter into a more complex relationship; namely, that of supplementing one's "personal" work by undertaking simultaneously the treatment of a patient *under supervision* by another psychiatrist. One is expected to report at frequent intervals all that one can of what seems to be going on in the doctor-patient relationship. If one is adequately advanced in one's personal training, what one has to report is apt to be susceptible of grasp by the supervisor and reasonably probable in some of its implications.

The supervising psychiatrist may be able to assist in two ways. From greater experience in therapy, he can often see much more of the probable pattern of action towards favorable change and then alert the candidate to therapeutic possibilities, what seems to be standing in the way of their realization, and what can be done

—and avoided—in facilitating them. From deeper understanding of interpersonal relations, he can sometimes discover unnoticed, unresolved handicaps of the candidate, and use the supervisory situation to give meaning to a statement of what seems to be missing in the personal work of the candidate with his training psychiatrist. Both these contributions are in a measure inevitable, if the supervision is justified, but the first is usually the more conspicuous—chiefly because the candidate knows that he needs it, and there is no time for the inquiry which would be required to make the second gain certain.

Once in this phase of the training, the candidate is expected to supervise work on at least two patients, and to succeed in these cases to the satisfaction of the supervising psychiatrists. In the meanwhile he shall be participating in technical seminars with other candidates of roughly equivalent experience under leadership of thoroughly trained psychiatrists who have shown aptitude for conducting seminars; as well as continuing didactic instruction in theory, the history of techniques, and the more important collateral disciplines.

This is a crude sketch of the present picture. It leaves a good deal unsaid about training and it says nothing about the extraordinarily miscellaneous results that are actually achieved. Everything from uncovering and realizing genius to its utter discouragement can come from it. Much more generally, it elevates usually gifted people from extremely uneven dealings with people to rather dependable competence with some of the more justifiable classes of people. In general, it somewhat rehumanizes the products of current medical educational procedure. But that it usually leaves a good deal to be desired, I should think no informed person would argue.

One of the but slowly to be remedied deficiencies in psychiatric education is that of *personnel*—remember always that it is personnel who manifest and communicate grasp on theory and technical skill. Modern psychiatry did not rise suddenly into lucid totality. The personnel who can be considered to embody its present state did not begin their psychiatric work imbued with it. Every one of them

has come to it by revising their prior convictions on the basis of
information and belief born of capacity to recognize the better, of
freedom from personal necessity to resist change. None too many
of them have been able to take time out of their busy professional
life to reconsider their current theoretical and technical positions,
and to delete from their current performances all errors and irrelevancies which have carried over from their past.

This deficiency may be different in degree from its parallel in
any of the fundamental sciences and great technologies, but it is in
no sense a peculiarity of psychiatry.

One of the most damnable deficiencies of psychiatric education,
from distant start in premedical work to the end of all formal training, is the fantastic time taken to acquire anything useful because
of the great amount of one's lifetime spent to no or to remotely tan-
gential purpose.

I have said long since what I have to say about the unwisdom of
nonmedical "psychiatrists." [5] The years have brought no change in
this conviction, although the exigencies of war have led many to
accept compromises. I would still have those who intervene in serious disorders of living well grounded in human biology, pathology,
and general medicine *and* the study of cultural and social psychology, as well as thoroughly trained in the theory and practice
of psychiatry. But I think it is no longer in any sense tolerable that
the career of psychiatrist be considered an unfortunate accidental
outcome of medical education, as it unquestionably still continues
to be. People often *seek* to be psychiatrists before entering medical
school. More and more of them will appear. Why is not education
modernized so that they shall have every facility for reaching this
goal, instead of astonishing handicap?

I have suggested the deficiency in returns from postgraduate
time necessarily spent in the hospital for the mentally disordered.
It may be that a sort of extension work can be done here profitably,
and that the prospective National Institute of Mental Health will
have far-reaching remedial effects in this connection.

[5] Intuition, Reason, and Faith. An editorial. PSYCHIATRY (1939) 2:129-132,
especially the last full paragraph on page 131.

I want now to discuss—from a purely personal view—some ideas about improving the returns on graduate training in psychiatry after the above mentioned pattern of, for example, the Washington School.

The first deficiency which calls for correction is orienting the candidate clearly towards the task that is to be accomplished. A remarkably varied group of preconceptions about the nature of one's personality, now presumably to be studied intensively, are brought to the work. They all imply something of possible and impossible, and fortunate and undesirable results from the work.

I define personality in this connection as *the relatively enduring patterns of recurrent interpersonal relations which make up a person's living*. I expect the candidate to be fairly well acquainted with some of these patterns, but to be relatively or utterly oblivious to others; so that the information which he can communicate at the start of the work is bound to be incomplete and thus essentially misleading.

I realize also that anything which he can communicate in the early stage of our relationship is (1) strongly influenced by anticipations of its effect on me as he more or less dimly, but certainly inadequately, foresees it, and is (2) at best of value only in forming surmises to be entertained for the time being.

In the phase of *formal inception* of our relationship, its ostensible goal has to be dicussed explicitly, a prospective patient being led to state an adequate reason for seeking psychiatric help; a prospective training candidate, an adequate reason for seeking aid towards this sort of career. Neglect of this has been singularly costly; with unwilling or "uncooperative" patients, I have learned the wisdom of "telling them" wherein I observe their need for psychiatric help, wherein I see that their performances are obviously inadequate and inappropriate to the situation in which they are involved. This step in creating a workable relationship is simply never to be taken for granted.

An adequate reason for seeking *my* aid in pursuit of the goal of psychiatric competence is not a mere simple function of the candidate. It involves something more than the demonstrated abilities and impressive life experience of the candidate, and his expressing expectations which I consider reasonably related thereto. It involves my surmise that no important pattern in his recurring interpersonal relations is one to participating in the successful exploring of which I have thus far proven inadequate. If the more simply personal factors do not seem promising, I may discourage the pursuit of the goal; if the interpersonal relation seems too heavily freighted, I must recommend some other training psychiatrist. In the first instance, the advice is open to review by other psychiatrists. In the second instance, there is nothing practicable except referring the candidate to someone else.

Following the justified inception of the relationship there comes the phase of *reconnaissance* in which the candidate is expected to tell what he can of how he came to be who he is. This is a matter of securing an outline history of his known and easily recollectible interpersonal situations in more or less chronological order and with easily accessible impressions of their important influence on the course of his living. The data are not expected to be produced in exact order of occurrence, although towards the close of this phase an outline history of significant places, persons, and notable events by date of the year and age of the patient may well be requested.

The interrogation which underlies the reconnaissance is calculated to give a reasonably dependable impression of the person's developmental opportunities and gross handicaps, stage by stage—infancy, childhood, the juvenile era, preadolescence, early and late adolescence. It need scarcely be said that any formal rigidity in accumulating the data, as for example, by following a list of questions, is often defeating of the purpose.

The so-called method of *free association* is introduced at the points in the reconnaissance at which recall of important data fails; not by discussing it as such, but by indicating that whatever comes to the mind may prove relevant. I shall digress from the order of the discussion at this point to say that "free association" as a practical psychiatric method rests on the demonstrable phenomenon that *given a personally significant problem* to deal with, personal data for the solution of which are not immediately accessible for recall, the ensuing flow of covert processes which can be recited in speech, *if so expressed without noted reservations,* tend immediately or presently—perhaps on considerably subsequent occasion—to elucidate the relevant data in a newly meaningful way. Without the setting of specific meaningful goals to be achieved, "saying every littlest thing that comes to your mind" is apt to result in impossibly complex performances only now and then amenable to useful elaboration. The "good sense" of the patient may make this *all too free* "association" useful; the psychiatrist can scarcely be excused for leaving the usefulness of time and effort to such an uncertain influence.

The final steps in the phase of reconnaissance are the psychiatrist's *summary of impressions gained* and the patient's or candidate's subsequent, not interrupting, corrective discussion of these impressions. The invariable inclusion of these two steps goes far to make the difference between scientific study of personality and a blind-leading-the-blind through a phantasmagoria of misunderstandings and magic formulae to an unhappy conclusion in mutual deception or mutual despair.

A very great deal could be said on the subject of the psychiatrist's summary. I have to say that the summary is to be couched in terms which do not precipitate very severe anxiety and aggravate the mental disorder uncovered, unless critical clinical judgment indicates the necessity for this always riskful step. The thing of all things which must be true of the summary, however, is that it must in its very organization and verbiage teach the meaning of personality study above indicated. It emphasizes the presumptively relatively enduring patterns of recurrent interpersonal relations uncovered in the reconnaissance and communicates the idea of their historical development from earlier patterns. It omits a great deal of confusing or complicating details; it seeks to be succinct but comprehensive with respect to the centrally significant *more adequate* and strikingly inadequate and inappropriate of these patterns. And it is always to be followed by serious attention to the subject-person's emendations, criticisms, and corrections. When these are relevant and material, the summary is to be recast appropriately. When they are carefully judged to be principally security operations manifesting some of the very difficulties in living touched on in the summary, they are stated to be open to this surmise and the summary is considered to stand as a working hypothesis with which to begin the next phase of the work.

I believe that only widely experienced psychiatrists should depend solely on their own judgment in preparing these summaries of reconnaissance in the case of candidates for training. A review of the data with a thoroughly experienced supervising psychiatrist sometimes provides along with the summary a promptly effective strategy for further study when otherwise the actual prospects are not at all cheerful.

I believe that no candidate who has progressed to doing treatment work under supervision should be permitted to omit this step of communicating a summary of his impressions to his patient as a preliminary to the phase of the work next to be discussed. He will be learning to reconnoiter and to summarize more helpfully for many a year to come, but he will not even be learning to be a scientific technologist until he has accepted the demanding necessity of this expressed summary as a precaution against slipshod and shoddy work.

The third and usually almost fantastically time-consuming phase of personality study is the *detailed inquiry*, about the varied and often intricately interrelated processes on which I can scarcely take time now to comment. I want instead to discuss some simple practical measures to improve the returns on time and effort spent in this phase. As a preliminary to this let me say that one of three cases seems usually to apply to each interview in the detailed inquiry. In the first case, patient and psychiatrist have some however different ideas of what is being dealt with. In the second, the psychiatrist at least is quite sure that something, even if something currently relatively unformulable, is struggling towards clarity. In the third case, the psychiatrist can only by unwarranted faith maintain any conviction that he knows what, if anything, is actually under way.

The psychiatrist in the second case must be alert to its transformation into the first or the third case. In the latter eventuality, he should promptly intervene to reestablish consensually valid work. This may cost him, on occasion, the discovery that he has failed in alertness or interpretive skill. I have undergone this repeatedly, invariably to the patient's benefit, as well as my own.

The more novel recommendation which I would like to have tried out pertains primarily to the first case, and incidentally to the second. I believe that candidates in training should be required to submit written summary reviews of their progress and current preoccupation at rather regular intervals, the actual length of which intervals might vary from person to person in direct relation to the characterizing central difficulty in communication, but in no case be longer than three calendar months or thirty actual hours of effort.

These reports would be submitted to the training psychiatrist for discussion with the patient, after their prior discussion by the training psychiatrist with the supervising psychiatrist if such there be, or with a psychiatrist designated by the training authority as Supervisor of Intensive Training in case the work is not being supervised individually.

I can foresee a number of arguments against adopting such an innovation, some of which may have a measure of intrinsic validity. With the emergency character of the present situation in psychiatry, I think that the conservation of training psychiatrists' time in terms of candidates' results per hour has become imperative, and that this innovation might well be given a trial.

Among the objections which might be offered to adopting such a scheme are some which arise from Freudian thinking in terms of *transference* working-through of *infantile sexuality* problems, Œdipus relationship, and the like, which may be presumed to be complicated by the known intervention of supervisory personnel, with increase in difficulty in overcoming the *resistance*. Others might take the form of expecting increased difficulty in accomplishing needed *therapeutic* ends because of an overemphasis of the training aspect. The theory of *parataxic distortions* [6] seems to dispose of the first group of these objections; and the proper early orientation of the candidate, of the second.

Were this innovation to be adopted, I believe one would soon discover that an even more startling deviation from conventional practice is in order; namely, early change of some few candidates to other training psychiatrists, and the early termination of training efforts in the case of a few of these. It is only by the test of training activity that the impracticality of continuing some candidates is certainly discoverable and, under existing circumstances, we are wasting a good deal of training psychiatrists' time on relatively forlorn hopes which might be the better for prompt guidance away from an unpromising career.

There is some hardship in changing from one to another training psychiatrist, but surely there is also hardship in spending a great many months to accomplish very little—not to mention the hardship to other candidates in having to wait many months to get started on their intensive personality study. The matter is at base one well-known to all institutions of higher education; and the proposed solution, only a form of the most usual one.

[6] See *Conceptions of Modern Psychiatry*—reprinted with a new foreword by the author, and a criticism of the theory by Patrick Mullahy. The William Alanson White Psychiatric Foundation, 1947.

CHANGING CONCEPTS
OF HOMOSEXUALITY
IN PSYCHOANALYSIS

Clara Thompson

THE TERM "homosexual" as used in psychoanalysis
has come to be a kind of wastebasket into which
are dumped all forms of relationships with one's own sex. The word
may be applied to activities, attitudes, feelings, thoughts, or repression of any of these. In short, anything which pertains in any way
to a relationship, hostile or friendly, to a member of one's own sex
may be termed homosexual. Under these circumstances, what does
an analyst convey to himself, his audience, or his patient when he
says the patient has homosexual trends? It does not clarify much
in his own thinking, nor convey a definite idea to his audience.
When he uses the term in talking with the patient, his words—instead of being helpful—often produce terror, for in ordinary speech
the word "homosexual" has a much more specific meaning, and in
addition a disturbing emotional coloring.

In view of the general confusion, it has seemed to me worth
while to review the whole subject, trace the various psychoanalytic
ideas about homosexuality, and, finally, describe the status of the
concept today.

Freud, in accordance with his libido orientation, considered unconscious homosexuality something basic and causal in neurosis,
while more recent analysis has led to the conclusion that homosexuality is but a symptom of more general personality difficulties.
Instead of being the basic problem in a given case, it is but one
of the manifestations of a character problem and tends to disappear
when the more general character disturbance is resolved. From

Freud's point of view, unconscious homosexuality is to be found in everyone. It is a part of the original libido endowment. According to him, it may exist in three different forms. There is latent homosexuality, repressed homosexuality, and overt homosexuality. Latent homosexuality apparently exists in everyone, although perhaps the amount varies from one person to another. It is not necessarily pathological. Freud assumes it may either find expression in pathological difficulties or in sublimation. Psychoanalysis has to deal with homosexuality as a problem only in its repressed or overt forms. If the use of the term were limited to these two forms, there would be less confusion, although even here Freud speaks of repressed homosexual trends in situations where the sexual content in the usual limited sense of the term does not exist.

Freud's view of the matter is based on his concept of bisexuality. According to him a part of the original libido endowment is allocated to homosexuality. This libido apparently cannot be converted into heterosexual libido. The two remain distinct and are a part of the original bisexuality. In the course of development, one of the two wins out, and the loser either becomes sublimated or is the foundation for the formation of neurotic difficulties. So in Freud's theory unconscious homosexuality is an important ingredient of basic personality structure. It has never been clear to me under what conditions Freud thought these unconscious tendencies became conscious or overt.

The inverted Edipus complex is presented as the starting point of homosexual development. In some situations also a regression to narcissism is thought to favor the development of homosexuality, since loving a member of one's own sex may be thought of as an extension of love of oneself. However, even if one accepts Freud's formulation, this description does not explain the dynamics of the process. It is still necessary to know what specific life experiences produced the inverted Edipus or the regression to narcissism, and why regression to narcissism does not always produce overt homosexuality. Freud suggests that a possible determinant may be varying strengths of original homosexual endowment. Resort to constitution as an explanation very often simply means—the necessary information is not yet available.

One confusion in the literature arises from the fact that cases are sometimes reported as examples of homosexuality where no clear-cut sexual relation existed, but only a strong neurotic dependency on a member of one's own sex was demonstrated. One is left to assume that there is no difference in the dynamics of such a case and one with definite overt manifestations. As far as I know, there has been no analytic data in the classical school on what produces the final violation of cultural taboo when the person accepts an overt homosexual way of life, except the very general idea that such a person has a weak superego, that is, he is unable to control the direction of his libido drives.

If Freud's basic theory of personality is questioned, that is, that the character structure is the result of the sublimation of sexual drives, the problem of repressed and overt homosexuality has to be approached differently. When the libido formula is discarded, it is much easier to see that homosexuality is not a clinical entity. There is no clear-cut situation in which it invariably occurs. It appears as a symptom in people of diverse types of character structure. The simple division into active and passive types does not cover the picture, nor are these distinctions always clear-cut. For example, the same person may be active with a younger partner and passive with an older one. The personality type who happens to have made an overt homosexual adjustment in one case may be almost identical with the personality type who under very similar circumstances makes a heterosexual choice in another case. Robbins [1] describes the competitive and exploitative personalities as characteristic of homosexuals. However, as is well known, competitive and exploitative heterosexual situations are also very frequent. So the specific choice of the sex object is not explained in Robbins' paper.

One can agree with Freud that all people are not only bisexual but polysexual in the sense that they are biologically capable of being sexually roused by either sex, or in fact by a variety of other

[1] Robbins, Bernard S., Psychological Implications of the Male Homosexual "Marriage," *Psychoanalytic Rev.* (1943) 30:428-437.

stimulants. Many people tend to form a more or less lasting attachment to the partner in their sexual pleasure. In childhood before the taboos of adults are imposed, a state of uncritical enjoyment of body stimulation exists. When the pleasure is shared, it may be shared with either sex depending to a great extent on propinquity or availability.

On the basis of the early childhood example, it would be interesting to speculate about what might happen if a person could continue his development in a culture with no sex restrictions. It is possible that most children would eventually develop a preference for the biologically most satisfactory type of sexual gratification and that that would prove to be found in the union of male and female genitals. If it should be found that heterosexual activity eventually became the preferred form of sex life, would this mean that the other forms had been repressed? If the culture were truly uncriticizing, repression would be unnecessary. Homosexuality would disappear when more satisfactory gratifications were available. It might reappear if the heterosexual possibilities were withdrawn. In other words, it is probable that on the physiological level uninhibited humans would get their sex gratification in any way possible—but if they had a choice, they would choose the most pleasurable. However, most sexual relationships, in addition to the physiological gratification of lust, have meaning also in interpersonal terms. The relationship as a whole has significance. The value of the relationship in turn affects the satisfaction obtained from the sexual activity. Except in some situations, to be described presently, in which the choice of a homosexual love object is determined by environmental limitations, it would seem that the interpersonal factors—that is, the type of relationship, the nature of the dependency, the personality of the love object—cannot be overlooked in determining whether the choice is a heterosexual or a homosexual way of life. Before discussing this in detail, it would be well to look at some of the varying degrees of acceptability of homesexuality in our own society.

Some form of sexual restriction is found in most cultures. There is a preferred and acceptable form of sexual behavior while other forms of sexual gratification are in varying degrees of disrepute—some being absolutely forbidden and punishable, others simply less acceptable. It is obvious that under these circumstances no individual is free to choose. He has to cope with the danger of ostracism if he is driven towards a culturally unacceptable form of sexual behavior. This is definitely one of the problems associated with overt homosexuality in our culture, especially in the case of men.

Freud believed one important distinction between a repressed and an overt homosexual was that the former had a stern superego and the latter a weak superego. This is too simple a statement of the problem, for among overt homosexuals one finds, in addition to the psychopaths who answer to Freud's description, those people who suffer from [stern or severe] superegos and are genuinely unhappy about their condition; others who accept their fate with resignation but feel handicapped; and still others who have lost all sense of self-esteem and think of their sexual behavior as but another evidence of their worthlessness. Also some more fortunate cases through protected circumstances have not happened to come in contact with the more criminal psychopathic elements in homosexual groups, especially in large cities, and because of their isolation or discreet living have not been made acutely aware of society's disapproval. These homosexuals do not feel great conflict about their relationship, although in other respects they are not lacking in a sense of social responsibility, that is, they do not have weak superegos, to use Freud's term.

Women are most frequently found in the last-named situation. This brings us to a consideration of the difference between male and female homosexuality, at least in this culture. Women in general are permitted greater physical intimacy with each other without social disapproval than is the case with men. Kissing and hugging are acceptable forms of friendly expression between women. In America a father is often too self-conscious to kiss his own son, while mother and daughter have no such inhibitions. Ferenczi [2]

[2] Ferenczi, S., *Sex in Psychoanalysis;* Boston, Richard G. Badger, Gorham Press, 1922. See chapter 12, "The Nosology of Male Homosexuality."

pointed out that in our culture compulsive heterosexuality is one outgrowth of the taboo on even close friendship with one's own sex. It is obvious that in the case of women there is a much more permissive attitude about friendship with one's own sex and therefore about overt homosexuality. Until recent times there was a much stronger taboo on obvious nonmarital heterosexual situations. Two overt homosexual women may live together in complete intimacy in many communities without social disapproval if they do not flaunt their inversion by, for example, the assumption of masculine dress or mannerisms on the part of one. Sometimes even if they go to this extreme they are thought peculiar rather than taboo. On the other hand, two men attempting the same thing are likely to encounter marked hostility.

Perhaps this difference in the attitude of society has a deep biological origin, to wit: two women may live together in closest intimacy with kisses, caresses, and close bodily contact without overt evidence of sexual gratification; two men in the same situation must know that they are sexually stimulated.

Whether this biological factor contributes to the increased tolerance for female homosexuals or not, there are other factors which definitely contribute to making the situation more normal in women. Earlier in the discussion I pointed out that in situations of limited choice a person makes the best of the sexual partner available. If there is a wide range of choice, a person chooses the most desirable. Circumstances producing privation—such as army life in remote places—may make strange creatures attractive as sex objects. However, in general men encounter fewer external causes of deprivation than women. So when a man becomes an overt homosexual it is almost always because of difficulties within himself. Of these society is not tolerant. It tends to label the man as weak. Women are more frequently in an isolated situation with regard to heterosexual possibilities than men. Age and physical unattractiveness handicap women more. More conventions surround her search for a partner so that even when young and attractive she may find herself for long periods without socially acceptable means of meeting men. Thus strong external difficulties often lead relatively mature women into homosexual relationships, whereas overt homosexuality in the male is usually an expresison of grave personality disorder. I do not wish to imply that there are no severely disturbed homosexual women, but rather that society's tolerance may be traced to the greater proportion of fairly healthy homosexual women.

The different cultural attitudes towards the sissy and the tomboy again show society's greater tolerance for the female homosexual type. When a boy is called a sissy, he feels stigmatized, and the group considers that it has belittled him. No such disapproval goes with a girl's being called a tomboy. In fact she often feels considerable pride in the fact. Probably these names get their value from childhood ideas that courage and daring are desirable traits in both sexes. So the sissy is a coward, a mamma's boy, and the tomboy is a brave girl who can hold her own with a boy her size. These attitudes probably become a part of later attitudes toward homosexuality in the two sexes.

The attitude towards homosexuality in Western society may be summed up as follows: In most circles it is looked upon as an unacceptable form of sexual activity. When external circumstances make the attainment of a heterosexual choice temporarily or permanently impossible, as with women or with men in isolated situations, society is more tolerant of the homosexual situation. Also character traits usually associated with the homosexual affect the degree of disapproval of the individual invert. Thus the tomboy receives less contempt than the sissy.

People who for reasons external to their own personality find their choice of love object limited to their own sex may be said to be "normal" homosexuals, in the sense that they utilize the best type of interpersonal relationship available to them. These people are not the problem of psychopathology.

The question which concerns psychotherapists is what kind of inner difficulty predisposes a person to the choice of overt homosexuality as his preferred form of interpersonal relationship. When no external limitations are in evidence, is there any one predisposing factor or may it appear in a variety of interpersonal difficulties? Is it an outgrowth of a definite personality structure or do accidental factors add it to an already burdened personality? Or are there in each case definite tendencies from early childhood leading in the direction of homosexuality? It is possible that each of these situations may occur as a predisposing background, and that in each case the meaning of the symptom of homosexuality is determined by the background. In short, homosexuality is not a clinical entity, but a symptom with different meanings in different personality set-ups. One might compare its place in the neurosis to that of a headache in various diseases. A headache may be the result of brain tumor, a sinus, a beginning infectious disease, a migraine attack, an emotional disturbance, or a blow on the head. When the underlying disease is treated successfully, the headache disappears.

Similarly, overt homosexuality may express fear of the opposite sex, fear of adult responsibility, a need to defy authority, or an attempt to cope with hatred of or competitive attitudes to members of one's own sex; it may represent a flight from reality into absorption in body stimulation very similar to the auto-erotic activities of the schizophrenic, or it may be a symptom of destructiveness of oneself or others. These do not exhaust the possibilities of its meaning. They merely represent situations which I have personally found in analyzing cases. The examples indicate the wide scope of difficulties which may find expression in the symptom.

The next concern is to determine if possible why this symptom is chosen as a solution of the difficulty. Can one invariably show in a given person tendencies which can clearly be traced from childhood, predisposing to homosexuality?

In many cases this seems to be true. In our culture, most children grow up in very close relationship to two people of opposite sexes. It is clear that a child has a distinct relationship to each parent and that sexual interest and curiosity play some part in this, although there are usually more important factors. The relationship is to a great extent molded by the role of that parent in the child's life. For example, the mother is usually more closely associated with the bodily needs than is the father. The father's function varies more widely. In some families he stands for discipline, in others he is the playmate, in others he shares the care of the child with the mother. These facts influence the child's reaction to the parent. In addition, the child has a relationship to the parent in terms of the kind of person the parent is. He early learns which parent wields the power, which loves him more, which is the more dependable, which one can be manipulated best by his techniques, and so on. These facts determine which parent the child prefers and where his allegiance lies. A very important determining influence in the development of homosexuality is the child's awareness that his sex was a disappointment to his parents or to the more important parent, especially if their disappointment leads them to treat the child as if he were of the opposite sex. However, none of these considerations invariably produce homosexuality in the adult. Girls whose parents wished them to be boys may grow up without any special interest in their own sex. Boys with gentle motherly qualities often marry and find satisfaction in mothering their own children without ever having gone through a struggle against homosexuality. If the father happened to be the strongest, most loving and constructive influence in a boy's life and the mother failed him badly, the boy may become a homosexual, but it is equally probable he will seek a woman of his father's personality type; or if he is more seriously damaged, he will be driven to marry a woman with a destructive influence on him somewhat in the pattern of his mother, or he may even become involved in a homosexual relation with a destructive man. In the same manner one can take up all the possible personality combinations found in parents and show that they in themselves do not predetermine the choice of the sex of the later partner.

Sexual relationships seem to be determined along two main lines. There is the constructive choice where mutual helpfulness and affection dominate the picture, and there is the destructive choice where one finds himself bound to the person whom he fears and who may destroy him—the moth and flame fascination. There are of course many in-between situations where, for example, the partnership is on the whole constructive but has some destructive elements, and so on. This distinction cuts across sex lines. There are both types of heterosexual relationships and both types of homosexual ones.

It is therefore necessary to look further for definite predetermining factors in the formation of the symptom of homosexuality. Two other considerations are important in this respect—the degree of personality damage and the role of accidental factors. People who have been greatly intimidated or have a low self-esteem and therefore have difficulties in making friends and being comfortable with other people have a tendency to cling to their own sex because it is less frightening. They feel understood by people like themselves. There is not the terrifying unpredictability of the unknown. Moreover, relationship with the opposite sex makes greater demands—the man is expected to support the woman, a woman is expected to have children. Also the frightened woman fears to test whether she is sufficiently attractive to win a man, and the frightened man fears he may not be sufficiently successful to attract a woman. However, the above considerations do not invariably produce homosexuality, for the fear of disapproval from the culture and the need to conform often drive these very people into marriage. The fact that one is married by no means proves that one is a mature person.

A homosexual way of life also attracts people who fear intimacy and yet are equally afraid of loneliness. As already mentioned, one's own sex is less frightening because it is familiar. The relationship looks less permanent, less entrapping, as if one could get away at any time. To be sure, the appearance of freedom often proves deceptive, for neurotic attachments with either sex have a way of becoming binding through neurotic dependencies. Among men the fear of the struggle for existence tempts a certain number to become dependent financially as well as otherwise on another man.

Thus far I have shown that various personality problems may find partial solution in a homosexual symptom, but nothing has been shown as specifically producing homosexuality. Some writers have laid great stress on the importance of early seduction by homosexuals, and many homosexuals attribute their way of life to such experiences. However, many people have such experiences without becoming homosexual. It is probable that a homosexual experience to a boy who is already heavily burdened, fears women, and feels unequal to life may add the decisive last touch to his choice of neurosis. Yet a similar seduction of a boy not afraid of life is but an incident in the process of investigation of life, and he simply goes on to master new experiences. Homosexual play is known to be very frequent in pre-adolescence and causes no serious disturbance in the majority of children.

Perhaps because of Freud's great emphasis on the sexual origin of neurosis and perhaps also because of the strong cultural disapproval, therapists are likely to think of homosexuality as a more fundamentally significant symptom than it really is. It seems certain from analysis in recent years that it is a problem which tends to disappear when the general character problems are solved.

Even as a symptom, homosexuality does not present a uniform appearance. There are at least as many different types of homosexual behavior as of heterosexual, and the interpersonal relations of homosexuals present the same problems as are found in heterosexual situations. So the mother-child attachment is sometimes found to be the important part of the picture. Frequently competitive and sado-masochistic feelings dominate the union. There are relationships based on hatred and fear and also relationships of mutual helpfulness. Promiscuity is possibly more frequent among homosexuals than heterosexuals, but its significance in the personality structure is very similar in the two. In both the chief interest is in genitals and body stimulation. The person chosen to share the experience is not important. The sexual activity is compulsive and is the sole interest. In fact in much activity carried on in movies, the partner is not even clearly seen and often not a word is exchanged.

At the other extreme is the homosexual marriage, by which I mean a relatively durable, long-term relationship between two people—a relationship in which the interests and personalities of each are important to the other. Here again we may find all of the pictures of a neurotic heterosexual marriage, the same possessiveness, jealousies, and struggles for power. The idea may be at least theoretically entertained that a homosexual adult love relationship can exist. Adult love seems to be a rare experience in our culture anyway and would doubtless be even more rare among homosexuals, because a person with the necessary degree of maturity would probably prefer a heterosexual relation unless external circumstances in his life made this impossible.

So the actual choice of homosexuality as the preferred form of interpersonal relations may have different origins in different cases, as I have indicated. If it is caused by some one specific situation or combination of circumstances, that has not yet been discovered.

Even though the specific cause for homosexuality cannot be found, the specific needs which it satisfies can be examined. Obviously it gives sexual satisfaction, and for a person unable to make contact with the opposite sex, this is important. Also, because it requires a partner, it helps cope with the problem of loneliness and isolation. The very fact of belonging to a culturally taboo group has its satisfactions. One can feel defiant, brave, and strong, and as a member of a band united against the world, lessen the feeling of ostracism. I have spoken earlier of other satisfactions, such as financial support— especially in the case of some male homosexuals—and freedom from responsibility.

An overt homosexual way of life can play a constructive or destructive role in the personality. It may be the best type of human relation of which a person is capable and as such is better than isolation. This would apply especially to the mother-child type of dependencies found in homosexuals of both sexes. Or it may be an added destructive touch in a deteriorating personality. In no case will it be found to be the cause of the rest of the neurotic structure —the basic origin of the neurosis—although after it is established, it may contribute to the problems. As in the case of other symptoms in neurosis, psychoanalysis must deal primarily with the personality structure, realizing that the symptom is a secondary development from that.

PSYCHOLOGICAL ASPECTS
OF OBESITY

Hilde Bruch

A CLINICIAN of the last century divided obesity into three stages, known respectively as the enviable, the comical and the pitiable. This is unusual language for medical classification. It illustrates well the peculiar place which obesity occupies in medicine. Obesity is not an illness, nor is it a malformation. It is here included in a program on disorders of metabolism and the endocrine glands. To a large extent this association must be considered as an expression of conformity with traditional concepts concerning the etiology of obesity. Recent studies, embodying clinical as well as experimental work, bring little if any support to the view that obesity is caused by primary metabolic or endocrine disturbances; although it may happen, of course, that a person suffering from a true endocrine disorder is also obese. For those rare cases in which there is a localized organic lesion the disturbance seems to lie in central nervous regulatory mechanisms. For the great majority of fat people there is no uncontested evidence of any specific physiologic disturbance that could be regarded as the cause of obesity.

Yet there are few conditions which cause such a distortion of the body and make a person as conspicuous as does obesity. All gradation exists and the border between the normal state of blooming good health and the abnormal state of disfiguring obesity is not at all distinct. Obesity becomes a medical problem in a strict sense only when it interferes with the well-being and efficiency of a person. Frequently it is a serious hazard to health when it is combined with other disorders such as diabetes, hypertension, orthopedic and cardiac conditions, to mention just a few. I do not wish to enumerate the many associations and interactions between obesity and other clinical disorders. Without complications, obesity *per se* becomes a physical encumbrance only in its more extreme forms.

It has been said that there are few bodily conditions that cause quite as much unhappiness and misery as the unlovely state of corpulence. The suffering of the obese person is of a different order from that in other physical ills. It is not experienced as pain or bodily discomfort, but in a person's relationship to his fellow men. In this sense obesity belongs to the group of social and psychological disorders.

This fact that obesity becomes abnormal through its social connotations is well illustrated by the different prestige value which it carries with different people and at different historical times. With our present day attitude, for instance, it would be difficult to consider any stage of obesity as enviable. Western culture on the whole has ridiculed and despised fatness. Ancient Cretan mosaics depict women of great slimness with wasp-waists. Little wonder that the classical Greeks, their cultural successors, credited them with the knowledge of the "ideal drug"—a drug which would keep a person slim however much he ate.[1] According to an old source,[2] "Roman mothers, during the Empire, starved their daughters to make them slender as rushes and eligible in the marriage market."

On the other hand (I quote from the same source) "The Tunisians have a curious custom of fattening up their young ladies for marriage. A girl, after she is betrothed, is cooped up in a small room. The food used for this custom, worthy of barbarians, is a seed, which is of an extraordinary fattening quality; and Mr. Mungo Park tells of African mothers who cram meat down the throats of their daughters, that they may please the princes who range the great desert.

"We learn from Erasmus that the Gordii carried their admiration so far as to advance him to the throne who was the fattest and most corpulent. And Bernier informs us that the Emperor of Mogul is an-

[1] W. Durant, *The Life of Greece;* New York, Simon and Schuster, 1939.
[2] W. Wadd, *Cursory Remarks on Corpulence* (third edition); London, J. Callow, 1816.

nually weighed upon his birthday; when, if it appears that since his former weighing, he has made any considerable acquisition of flesh, it is matter of public rejoicings throughout his whole dominions."

These are just a few examples of extremes in evaluating obesity as a social asset or as a liability—and they are partly based on hear-say tales of old travelers. Modern anthropologists have confirmed the existence of fattening houses in some African tribes and the fact that being fat may convey high prestige on certain people or pro-fessions. No systematic study has been made, as far as I know, of the question as to under what cultural conditions obesity adds to the re-pute of a person and under what circumstances it becomes a humili-ating burden. It seems to be uncommon for obesity to be considered without special emotional significance or with indifference.

Even in our Western culture, with its general low esteem for fat-ness, variations in the evaluation of obesity occur as the beauty ideal changes. It is little more than a generation ago that an eminent French physician complained that "there can be no doubt that in order to have 'un décolleté impressive' each woman considers herself duty bound to be fat around the neck, the shoulders, and the arms. But it is just these places where fat accumulates with the greatest difficulty. One can, therefore, be sure that the abdomen, hips, thighs and lower extremities of a woman with well padded beautiful neck and shoulders, are in a state of hopeless adiposity. . . . As to treat-ment, she cannot achieve a reduction of the waistline for which she clamors without sacrificing, in her spirit, the upper parts of the body. It is a true sacrifice to the fashionable demands. . . . Thus one finds esthetic and social factors which are active enough to make women persist in being obese!"

This statement sounds so alien to us and as though from a differ-ent era that one has to look twice at the title page of the book from which the paragraph was taken to make sure that it was published in Paris in 1911.[3]

Even now, and I am speaking of contemporary observations in New York City, a wide range exists in the emotional appraisal of obesity. Opinions vary all the way from the sophisticated remarks

[3] F. Heckel, *Les grandes et petites obésités;* Paris, Masson et Cie., 1911.

of Ogden Nash that "Some ladies smoke too much and some ladies drink too much and some ladies pray too much, but all ladies think that they weigh too much"—to the undisputable dictum of the mother of a fat boy that her family thinks the bigger he is the better he is!

These remarks on the wide range of social and emotional evaluation of obesity are intended as a background for the present topic. If we speak of psychological aspects of obesity it is well to remember that the remarks apply only within the cultural and social setting in which observations have been made, and only to that fraction of the large number of fat people who come for treatment.

I shall discuss the problem from three different angles, namely, (1) the psychological aspects of being obese, (2) the psychological aspects of becoming obese, and (3) the psychological aspects of treatment. This third section will also deal with the psychological attitude of the physician in regard to the diagnosis and treatment of obesity.

PSYCHOLOGICAL ASPECTS OF BEING OBESE

A vivid description of the mental suffering of fatness was given by Banting in his famous "Letter on Corpulence, Addressed to the Public," published in 1863.[4] He complains: "No man laboring under obesity can be quite insensible to the sneers and remarks of the cruel and injudicious in public assemblies, public vehicles, or the ordinary street traffic; nor to the annoyance of finding no adequate space in a public assembly if he should seek amusement or need refreshment, and therefore he naturally keeps away as much as possible from places where he is likely to be made the object of the taunts and remarks of others."

Since Banting's time obesity has vastly increased in its negative rating as an object of ridicule and humiliation. This is particularly true for young obese people. They feel more or less excluded from the activities of their age group and thus fail to develop interests and social skills necessary for success and happiness in adult life. The fear of embarrassment, of making a spectacle of themselves by expos-

[4] W. Banting, *Letter on Corpulence Addressed to the Public;* New York, Mohum, Ebbs and Hough, 1864.

ing their unshapely figures, is so great that many obese young people become withdrawn and seclusive. They give up whatever sport and physical activities they had previously enjoyed, then they avoid larger groups and finally they even stay away from friends in order not to embarrass them, as they say, by their ungainly company. The preoccupation with weight and appearance may become so grave that it overshadows all other feelings and actions. Everything is experienced in terms of "weight" and "figure." People are classified into fat and non-fat with a feeling of contempt and hatred for the fat ones and of envy and hopeless inferiority in relation to the slender ones. Many of the personality features of obese people, their shyness and over-sensitivity, their easy discouragement in the face of difficulties or when confronted with the slightest rejection, their tendency to depressions and their phlegmatic manner may be considered sequels to their constant concern with the impression they make on account of being obese—at least it might appear so.

The practical consequences of this preoccupation with their appearance are also serious. The young fat girl who feels unattractive has little prospect of getting married, particularly if she is so convinced of being rated only according to her size that she will not even permit herself to get interested in men. For many young people the fact of being fat stands like an insurmountable obstruction in the road toward a cherished professional goal. Again I wish to add, at least it appears so.

There are, on the other hand, many fat people who deny any difficulties in living on account of their obesity. They are cheerful and unconcerned, easygoing and friendly with everybody. They seem to confirm the popular opinion that a fat man is a jovial good fellow. There may be fat people amongst us who really are content and unconcerned. They are not likely to come to medical attention, at least not for the treatment of obesity. In those happy-go-lucky fat people whom I have had the opportunity to observe, the joviality and often boisterous cheerfulness was nothing but a thin veneer put on for the benefit of the public, a compensatory defense against underlying feelings of unhappiness and futility.

The really puzzling aspect of the psychology of obese people, who blame all their misery and failures in life on "being fat," is their seeming unwillingness or inability to do something about it. Ordinarily, if one recognizes the source of one's suffering, one will bend every effort to remove it. Not so the obese person. On the contrary, their very reactions to being fat contain all the elements which go toward making the condition progressively worse. If one learns to understand fat people more intimately, it gradually appears that their tremendous size, which they so loudly bemoan, is not without a positive emotional meaning for them. This is more easily recognized when dealing with obese children who say quite frankly, "I would want to lose weight but I do not want to be skinny." Usually their mothers share the anxiety about losing weight. It seems that in the insecure and unstable relations to the surroundings, physical size and bulkiness convey a feeling of strength, safety and power to the timid fat child. The heavy layers of fat seem to act as protective walls against an outer world which the fat person often experiences as unfriendly and threatening. Sometimes the very unattractiveness of obesity serves a definite emotional purpose. It offers a seemingly obvious reason for avoiding situations which might provoke fear and anxiety. Many fat young girls, though outwardly very concerned about not getting married, nevertheless persist in remaining fat because it is a protection against men and sex and the responsibilities of adult womanhood which they dread even more than the disgrace of being fat.

Such an ambivalent attitude towards themselves and their condition can be recognized in many psychological reactions of obese people. The more familiar one becomes with their problems the less clear-cut are the issues. What on first impression looks like an understandable reaction to being fat reveals itself as intimately interwoven with the emotional problems of becoming obese. The withdrawal from all social contacts, which fat people so readily explain as due to their obesity, is usually quite out of proportion, and it often precedes or coincides with the development of obesity. I mentioned before the low prestige value of obesity in our society. This unfriendly attitude of the environment, however, is really nothing in comparison with the contempt and self-hatred that many fat people express towards themselves. There is no denying that obesity is a psychological handicap, but mainly in the sense that it becomes the focus of a derogatory attitude towards one's self which is the much more fundamental disturbance and which plays an essential rôle in the very development of obesity.

THE PSYCHOLOGICAL ASPECTS OF BECOMING OBESE

In order to understand the development of obesity, it is necessary to make a clear distinction between the mechanism of becoming fat and the stimulus that sets the mechanism into operation; or, to express it differently, between the "how" and the "why."

As to the "how" there is no doubt left that obesity is the result of a positive energy balance, that means a person becomes fat when his caloric intake is greater than his energy expenditure. In most obese people this is brought about through a combination of over-eating and inactivity. From a caloric point of view the large food intake is usually of greater importance than the saving in energy expenditure through inactivity.

There is really nothing noteworthy about the fact that a person who persistently and grossly over-eats grows fat, particularly if at the same time physical exercise is decreased. Under normal conditions a decrease in activity is associated with a reduction of appetite. The unexplained question is *why* this normal regulation is disturbed in obesity. This question becomes answerable if we turn from physiological to psychological considerations. Eating and exercise, physiologically represented as calories in the energy balance, are at the same time very important aspects of a person's behaviour. A systematic inquiry into the living habits of many obese people has revealed that these functions are endowed in the obese with an emotional meaning different from the normal. Food has an exaggerated positive value for the obese person. It stands for love, security, and satisfaction. Muscular activity and social contacts, on the other hand, are associated with the concept of danger, threat and insecurity. The simultaneous occurrence of love of food and avoidance of activity becomes thus comprehensible.

Eating and activity acquire this peculiar emotional significance in a family setting which, though not specific, is characteristic for obesity. The typical obese family is of small size. Quite often it is the youngest or an only child who becomes obese. Fathers usually play a subordinate rôle in the emotional life of the obese family. The mothers are dominant in their influence and have a particularly close hold on the potentially obese child. Many mothers live out their own problems and frustrations in these children. They cannot give their children respect as individuals nor permit them independence and the dignity of personal achievement. These mothers try to realize in their children their own dreams of a life of luxury and idleness of which they themselves may have felt deprived. Their expression of affection is over-feeding the child and sparing him the necessary tasks of doing things for himself. The mother's attitude towards the obese child is like that toward an inanimate and prized possession, one to which they give the very best of care in order to retain it. A characteristic aspect of this possessive attitude is the frequently expressed wish for a daughter instead of a son, because these mothers feel that a daughter represents a more permanent possession than a son. In bringing up their sons they give them the rôle of a daughter in their emotional life. The "feminine" characteristics of obese boys seem to be related to this attitude of the mother. There certainly is no evidence that it is an expression of gonadal dysfunction.

Mixed with the expression of affection, which over-protectiveness and over-feeding represent, is an underlying hostility which many mothers feel in relation to the fat child. Far-reaching protective measures are devised to spare the mother the anguish of her own anxiety for the safety of the child, even though these measures interfere with the child's normal psychological growth and social adjustment. At the same time the mother is irritated by the demands which this excessive care makes upon her. She nags and criticizes the child and often resorts to beating him in order to find relief from her own exasperation. Yet in her heart she wants to retain his affection and loyalty, and food is a constant bribe with which she keeps him close and dependent. As long as the child is young there is prestige for her in having a well-fed child. As the child grows older and the obesity becomes a handicap, the mother is likely to be the first to nag and belittle him for his awkward appearance and to berate him for his greediness.

The family frame of obese children thus reveals influences which lead to inactivity and over-eating and distort their personality maturation. The most serious aspect in this mal-development is the interference with the development of an adequate sense of security, competence and worth-whileness. The obese child grows up with a fundamentally low self-esteem and with the conviction of his helplessness in a world which has been represented to him as a dangerous place in which he is lost without a protecting mother. Such an attitude toward life makes an individual a constant victim of uncertainty and anxiety. His only defense against this anxiety is to turn back to mother; and since the mother has been a person who was unable to give of herself but had appeased all his needs with the offering of food, food becomes his weapon against anxiety and source of comfort in periods of emotional stress. For many obese people eating is the only known source of comfort and satisfaction. Other sources of satisfaction, comfortable relations to people and the realization of inherent creative and constructive abilities, have remained seriously crippled under the unfavorable influences of his upbringing.

The first systematic inquiries into the emotional background of obesity were made on obese children.[5] Numerous observations on obese adults show that there are amazingly little differences between the psychological problems of children and adults.[6] As a matter of fact, failure to develop true emotional adulthood is an outstanding feature of obese people. This means that in the course of development the necessary emotional changes which "growing up" implies have not taken place, because every change means abandoning of

[5] H. Bruch and G. Touraine, The Family Frame of Obese Children, *Psychosomatic Med.* (1940) 2:141. Bruch, Obesity in Childhood and Personality Development, *Amer. J. Orthopsychiatry* (1941) 11:467.

[6] T. A. C. Rennie, Obesity as a Manifestation of a Personality Disturbance, *Diseases of the Nervous System* (1940) 1:8. H. B. Richardson, Obesity as a Manifestation of a Neurosis, *Med. Clinics of North America* (September 1946). Richardson, Obesity and Neurosis, *Psychiatric Quarterly* (July 1946). A. Schick, Psychosomatic Aspects of Obesity, *Psychoanalytic Rev.* (1947) 34:173.

old satisfactions, a step which obese people are reluctant to take. The obese adult, like the fat child, is emotionally immature, passively dependent and helpless in meeting the exigencies of life. He seeks comfort in overeating in the face of failure and of frustrating experiences.

A woman of thirty described this misuse of food in periods of emotional stress as follows: "Sometimes I think I'm not hungry at all. It is that I am just unhappy in certain things—things I cannot get. Food is the easiest thing to get that makes me feel nice and comfortable. I try to reason with myself and tell myself that these problems cannot be solved by eating." She was one of the many fat people who succeeded in showing a fairly complacent attitude towards the world during the daytime but who became tense and anxious when alone at night. As she describes it, "I think then that I am ravenously hungry and I do my utmost not to eat. My body becomes stiff in my effort to control my hunger. If I want to have any rest at all—I've got to get up and eat. Then I go to sleep like a new-born baby."

The comparison to a "new-born baby," that is, an infantile type of reaction, is a fitting description and may well be applied to the inability of fat people to tolerate frustration or postponement of satisfaction. Though most marked in relation to food, it can be recognized in many other aspects of their behavior. Fat people are described as placid and submissive and this is often correct as far as outward behavior goes. Their fundamental attitude towards life is demanding and they do not tolerate denial of their wants. Since the genuine solution of life situations is not always available or would entail an effort on their part, food is resorted to over and over again as a substitute satisfaction.

Many of the personality features are not limited to obesity but are met with in other forms of emotional mal-development and neurosis. The specific aspect of obesity is the utilization of food for obtaining immediate gratification or as defense against anxiety. This perverse indulgence in food is often followed by a sense of guilt and moral inferiority which in turn leads to more eating. Unless this cycle is interrupted a person will persist in being fat however much he wants to reduce his weight. I just wish to add that obese people may suffer from many other symptoms which are commonly recognized as neurotic manifestations.

PSYCHOLOGICAL ASPECTS OF TREATMENT

Awareness of the underlying psychological factors leads to an understanding of the question why obesity has always presented such a baffling therapeutic problem. Viewed as a disturbance in energy balance, the treatment of obesity should be a very simple task. Reduction of the food intake and increase in exercise should and actually does accomplish a corresponding loss in weight. There is only one difficulty which makes the physiological prediction so uncertain in its clinical application. The fat patients just will not adhere to the perfect, well-balanced reducing diets which we prescribe, nor do they follow our advice for more active participation in social life that should make for their greater happiness and better adjustment.

It was this notoriously poor cooperation, particularly flagrant in the case of obese children and their parents, that prompted us at Babies Hospital to inquire into the life stories and living habits of fat people. This investigation had been at first part of a study on the endocrine factors in obesity. The observations on the growth and development of obese children which we made in the course of the investigation, stood in striking contrast to the then current assumption that hypothyroidism or hypopituitarism, or even hypogonadism were causative factors in obesity.

Looking upon the obesity problem from a historical point of view, one is truly amazed to find that the quintessence of the cause and cure of obesity had been known since the time of antiquity. It seems that it was the application of the knowledge in the treatment of fat people which so often was found to be disappointing. The continued effort to understand this discrepancy seems to have led to many ludicrous theories about the cause, and to elaborate but useless programs of treatment of obesity. In a booklet called "Cursory Remarks on Corpulence; or Obesity Considered as a Disease: with a Critical Examination of Ancient and Modern Opinions, Relative to its Causes and Cure," published in London in 1816, the author, William Wadd,

Surgeon,[7] summarizes the therapeutic practices of the ancient past and of his own time by saying: "The person who depends solely on the benefit to be derived from the use of any of them, will find himself grievously disappointed." He mentions as remedies the chewing of tobacco, fennel water, acids of various kinds, soap, eating of much salt to increase the absorption of fat by producing thirst, etc. Wadd proceeds to outline a plan of treatment which would be useful today even though his theories on nutrition and metabolism may sound quaint. He understood very well the reasons for the many fanciful regimes which he discards as useless: "The idea of a specific is peculiarly flattering to a patient, for whilst it encourages an implicit reliance on a single remedial process, it tends strongly to shake his confidence in the slow and disagreeable operation of diet and regimen. A gentleman who was fond of good living, and found himself becoming more corpulent than he thought convenient, having heard of the salutary effects of Mr. Wood's regimen, ordered his cook to prepare the miller's pudding, which he ate with great regularity every day after his usual dinner."

He further explains: "Many would willingly submit to any violent remedy, so that an immediate benefit could be produced; but unless the disease speedily gives way, they despair of success; consider it as unalterably connected with their constitution, and of course, return to their former habits." Wadd's remarks are as pertinent today as they were in his time. It seems that each generation has to rediscover the simple basic facts about causes and cure for obesity. Fifty years later Banting in his Letter to the Public [8] reported how he had been searching for help for many years, consulting one "high orthodox authority (never an inferior adviser)" after another and how he received many conflicting and abstruse prescriptions, all in vain, until he found the "excellent adviser" in whose honor he publishes the account of his cure which he calls "simply miraculous." Banting exclaims, "Oh! that the faculty would look deeper into and make themselves better acquainted with the crying evil of obesity—that dreadful

[7] Reference footnote 2.
[8] Reference footnote 4.

tormenting parasite on health and comfort. Their fellow men might not descend into early premature graves, as I believe many do, from what is termed apoplexy, and certainly would not during their sojourn on earth, endure so much bodily and consequently mental infirmity."

The diet which Banting outlined has been included under his name in medical textbooks. Its main features, the elimination of bread, butter, sugar, beer, and potatoes are in good agreement with the diet which we would calculate today. Yet the search for more specific explanations and more specific treatment of obesity has continued, and we are just now emerging from the promise and allure of miracles to be worked by endocrine treatment.

This repetitious cycle of overlooking plain facts about obesity and of clinging to high-sounding theories may be understood if we take psychological factors into account. The correction of faulty eating habits is a central problem in treatment. Yet the importance of overeating has been most often overlooked in the medical treatises on obesity. The occurrence of alimentary obesity, the simple or exogenous as it has been called, has never been entirely denied and it has been included in the medical classification of obesity only to be cast aside as not quite worthy of serious scientific endeavor.

One of the reasons for this neglect of over-eating may be found in the fact that obese patients usually are very vague when asked about their eating habits. They just do not tell us how much they eat, sometimes in good faith because to them it is not "too much," more often because they are ashamed to admit it. If obesity on the whole has been looked upon in our society as a problem with little dignity, this is even more the case for the moral evaluation of over-eating or gluttony. Over-eating is looked upon as a moral weakness and self-indulgence. Even physicians may express a sarcastic attitude. I quote from the monograph of a modern writer: "There is only one kind of alimentary obesity, and there are only two adjectives which can suitably be used to describe it, namely contemptible and disgusting. Every degree of alimentary obesity is contemptible, because it denotes self-indulgence, greed and gormandizing; and most are disgusting because they represent an unsightly distortion of the human form divine, and a serious impairment of the intellectual faculties." [9] Little wonder that this doctor, who I am sure wants to treat his patients with respect and human understanding, has to find other causes for obesity and sets out to prove that most patients are fat from "causes which are endocrine and not alimentary."

The obese patient is more than ready to accept such a so-called scientific diagnosis. It makes him the victim of some mysterious fate and he himself does not need to exert any effort or to assume responsibility for a change in his living habits. As we have seen, the basic attitude toward life of a fat person is passive and demanding and he expects to have everything done for him. His ideal of treatment is something, anything, that will melt his fat away without effort on his part such as the "ideal drug" of the ancient Cretans, the secret of which was lost already to the old Greeks—if such a drug ever existed. It sounds too much like wish-fulfillment in the Golden Age for fat people.

Even if such a drug existed, the best it would accomplish would be a purely symptomatic treatment producing "thin fat people." By this expression I mean to say that if the fundamental attitude and life habits of fat people remain unchanged they will regain the lost weight—if not immediately, then as soon as they are faced with problems that challenge their low capacity for independent decisions and achievement.

The basis of rational treatment of obese patients is an understanding of and respectful attitude towards their genuine problems. If an obese patient is approached with a respectful tolerance, particularly in regard to the fact that he over-eats, he is not only more frank in giving information but his efforts at reducing will be more genuine and lasting. While on a reducing diet he needs the sympathetic support of a physician who will also help him to gain insight into the nature of his real problems. This can best be accomplished by regular and continuous contact. Prescription of a diet alone is rarely sufficient. The dependent attitude of an obese patient is as much a fact of his existence as his over-eating. If we are aware of this problem

[9] L. Williams, *Obesity;* Oxford University Press, 1926.

we can utilize his visits to help him to achieve greater independence.

If, in order to insure regular visits to the office, some prescription is given, this will not interfere with a rational psychological approach as long as the drug is not presented as a magic pill that will do the job. There seem to be some drugs on the market which are said to have a curbing influence on the appetite and they might therefore be of direct additional help. There is, however, strong psychological objection against the use of endocrine products for treatment of so-called sexual mal-development in obese boys.[10] Cases in which there is true indication for such treatment are so exceedingly rare that they can be neglected for our discussion. In a very large number of obese pre-adolescent boys who are made the object of such therapeutic zeal, there is no medical justification whatsoever for exposing the family to unnecessary expense and the young patient to the emotional trauma of being branded as suffering from an essential physiological deficiency. Such young people are already handicapped by grave adjustment problems due to the difficulties of their background and the embarrassment of being fat. The additional psychological trauma of such unwarranted diagnosis and treatment further aggravates the situation since it seems to confirm their worst fears about being inadequate for life.

SUMMARY

I have presented herewith a concept which treats obesity as the somatic expression of a mal-development in personality maturation. The large physical size represents symbolically the need and desire for strength and security which the fat person lacks in his human relationships. The bodily expansion may be looked upon as a vicarious expression of a thwarted personality development. The leading traits which collaborate in the production of obesity, namely, over-eating and under-activity, have in themselves a high emotional significance. They serve as a defense against anxiety and give a semblance of satisfaction which the obese person has not learned to achieve in more constructive ways.

[10] Bruch, Obesity in Relation to Puberty, *J. Pediatrics* (1941) 19:365.

A modern writer [11] expresses the inner awareness of a fat person that his creative potentialities are locked within him, far out of reach, by saying: "Imprisoned in every fat man, a thin one is wildly signaling to be let out." This seems to me to express the essence of the obesity problem.

[11] Palinurus (Cyril Connolly), *The Unquiet Grave;* New York and London, Harper Brothers, 1945.

WHY CULTURAL
ANTHROPOLOGY NEEDS
THE PSYCHIATRIST

Edward Sapir

UNTIL not so many years ago cultural anthropology and psychiatry seemed miles apart. Cultural anthropology was conceived of as a social science which concerned itself little, if at all, with the individual. Its province was rather to emphasize those aspects of behavior which belonged to society as such, more particularly societies of the dim past or exotic societies whose way of life seemed so different from that of our own people that one could hope to construct a generalized picture of the life of society at large, particularly in its more archaic stages of development. There was little need in the anthropology of a Tylor or Frazer to ask questions which demanded a more intimate knowledge of the individual than could be assumed on the basis of common experience. The important distinctions were felt to be distinctions of race, of geographical setting, of chronology, of cultural province. The whole temper of cultural anthropology was impersonal to a degree. In this earlier period of the development of the science it seemed almost indelicate, not to say indecent, to obtrude observations that smacked of the personal or anecdotal. The assumption was that in some way not in the least clearly defined as to observational method it was possible for the anthropologist to arrive at conclusive statements which would hold for a given society as such. One was rarely in a position to say whether such an inclusive statement was a tacit quotation from a primitive "John Doe" or a carefully tested generalization abstracted from hundreds of personal observations or hundreds of statements excerpted from conversations with many John Does.

Perhaps it is just as well that no strict methodology of field inquiry was perfected and that embarrassing questions as to the factual nature of the evidence which led to anthropological generalizations were courteously withheld by a sort of gentlemen's agreement. I remember being rather shocked than pleased when in my student days I came across such statements in J. O. Dorsey's "Omaha Sociology" as "Two Crows denies this." This looked a little as though the writer had not squarely met the challenge of assaying his source material and giving us the kind of data that we, as respectable anthropologists, could live on. It was as though he "passed the buck" to the reader, expecting him by some miracle of cultural insight to segregate truth from error. We see now that Dorsey was ahead of his age. Living as he did in close touch with the Omaha Indians, he knew that he was dealing, not with a society nor with a specimen of primitive man nor with a cross-section of the history of primitive culture, but with a finite, though indefinite, number of human beings, who gave themselves the privilege of differing from each other not only in matters generally considered as "one's own business" but even on questions which clearly transcended the private individual's concern and were, by the anthropoligist's definition, implied in the conception of a definitely delimited society with a definitely discoverable culture. Apparently Two Crows, a perfectly good and authoritative Indian, could presume to rule out of court the very existence of a custom or attitude or belief vouched for by some other Indian, equally good and authoritative. Unless one wishes to dismiss the implicit problem raised by contradictory statements by assuming that Dorsey, the anthropologist, misunderstood one, or both, of his informants, one would have to pause for a while and ponder the meaning of the statement that "Two Crows denies this."

This is not the place to introduce anything like a complete analysis of the meaning of such contradictory statements, real or supposed. The only thing that we need to be clear about is whether a completely impersonal anthropological description and analysis of custom in terms which tacitly assume the unimportance of individual needs and preferences is, in the long run, truly possible for a social discipline.

There has been so much talk of ideal objectivity in social science and such eager willingness to take the ideals of physical and chemical workmanship as translatable into the procedures of social research that we really ought not to blink this problem. Suppose we take a test case. John Doe and an Indian named Two Feathers agree that two and two make four. Someone reports that "Two Crows denies this." Inasmuch as we know that the testimony of the first two informants is the testimony of all human beings who are normally considered as entitled to a hearing, we do not attach much importance to Two Crows' denial. We do not even say that he is mistaken. We suspect that he is crazy. In the case of more abstruse problems in the world of natural science, we narrow the field of authority to those individuals who are known, or believed, to be in full command of techniques that enable them to interpret the impersonal testimony of the physical universe. Everyone knows that the history of science is full of corrective statements on errors of judgment but no value is attached to such errors beyond the necessity of ruling them out of the record. Though the mistaken scientist's hurt feelings may be of great interest to a psychologist or psychiatrist, they are nothing for the votaries of pure science to worry about.

Are correspondingly ruthless judgments possible in the field of social science? Hardly. Let us take a desperately extreme case. All the members of a given community agree in arranging the letters of the alphabet in a certain historically determined order, an order so fixed and so thoroughly ingrained in the minds of all normal children who go to school that the attempt to tamper with this order has, to the man in the street, the same ridiculous, one might almost say unholy, impossibility as an attempt to have the sun rise half an hour earlier or later than celestial mechanics decree to be proper. There is one member of this hypothetical society who takes the liberty of interchanging A and Z. If he keeps his strange departure from custom to himself, no one need ever know how queer he really is. If he contradicts his children's teacher and tries to tell them that they should put Z first and A last, he is almost certain to run foul of his fellow beings. His own children may desert him in spite of their natural tendency to recognize parental authority. Certainly we should agree that this very peculiar kind of a Two Crows is crazy, and we may even agree as psychiatrists that so far as an understanding of his aberrant fantasies and behavior is concerned, it really makes little difference whether what he is impelled to deny is that two and two are four or the order of the letters of the alphabet as a conventionally, or naturally, fixed order.

At this point we have misgivings. Is the parallel as accurate as it seems to be? There is an important difference, which we have perhaps overlooked in our joint condemnation. This difference may be expressed in terms of possibility. No matter how many Two Crows deny that two and two make four, the actual history of mathematics, however retarded by such perversity, cannot be seriously modified by it. But if we get enough Two Crows to agree on the interchange of A and Z, we have what we call a new tradition, or a new dogma, or a new theory, or a new procedure, in the handling of that particular pattern of culture which is known as the alphabet. What starts as a thoroughly irresponsible and perhaps psychotic aberration seems to have the power, by some kind of "social infection," to lose its purely personal quality and to take on something of that very impersonality of custom which, in the first instance, it seemed to contradict so flatly. The reason for this is very simple. Whatever the majority of the members of a given society may say, there is no inherent human impossibility in an alphabet which starts with a symbol for the sound or sounds represented by the letter Z and ends up with a symbol for the vocalic sound or sounds represented by the letter A. The consensus of history, anthropology, and common sense leads us to maintain that the actually accepted order of letters is "necessary" only in a very conditional sense and that this necessity can, under appropriate conditions of human interrelationship, yield to a conflict of possibilities, which may ultimately iron out into an entirely different "necessity."

The truth of the matter is that if we think long enough about Two Crows and his persistent denials, we shall have to admit that in some sense Two Crows is never wrong. It may not be a very useful sense for social science but in a strict methodology of science in general it dare not be completely ignored. The fact that this rebel,

Two Crows, can in turn bend others to his own view of fact or theory or to his own preference in action shows that his divergence from custom had, from the very beginning, the essential possibility of culturalized behavior. It seems, therefore, that we must regretfully admit that the rebel who tampers with the truths of mathematics or physics or chemistry is not really the same kind of rebel as the one who plays nine-pins with custom, whether in theory or practice. The latter is likely to make more of a nuisance of himself than the former. No doubt he runs the risk of being condemned with far greater heat by his fellow men but he just cannot be proved to contradict some mysterious essence of things. He can only be said, at best, to disagree completely with everybody else in a matter in which opinion or preference, in however humble and useless a degree, is after all possible.

We have said nothing so far that is not utterly commonplace. What is strange is that the ultimate importance of these commonplaces seems not to be thoroughly grasped by social scientists at the present time. If the ultimate criterion of value interpretation, and even "existence," in the world of socialized behavior is nothing more than consensus of opinion, it is difficult to see how cultural anthropology can escape the ultimate necessity of testing out its analysis of patterns called "social" or "cultural" in terms of individual realities. If people tend to become illiterate, owing to a troubled political atmosphere, the "reality" of the alphabet weakens. It may still be true that the order of the letters is, in the minds of those relatively few people who know anything about the alphabet, precisely what it always was, but in a cultural atmosphere of unrest and growing illiteracy a Two Crows who interchanges A and Z is certainly not as crazy as he would have been at a more fortunate time in the past. We are quick to see the importance of the individual in those more flexible fields of cultural patterning that are referred to as ideals or tastes or personal preferences. A truly rigorous analysis of any arbitrarily selected phase of individualized "social behavior" or "culture" would show two things: First, that no matter how flexible, how individually variable, it may in the first instance be thought to be, it is as a matter of fact the complex resultant of an incredibly elaborate cultural history, in which many diverse strands intercross at that point in place and time at which the individual judgment or preference is expressed [this terminology is *cultural*]; second, that, conversely, no matter how rigorously necessary in practice the analyzed pattern may seem to be, it is always possible in principle, if not in experiential fact, for the lone individual to effect a transformation of form or meaning which is capable of communication to other individuals [this terminology is *psychiatric* or *personalistic*]. What this means is that problems of social science differ from problems of individual behavior in degree of specificity, not in kind. Every statement about behavior which throws the emphasis, explicitly or implicitly, on the actual, integral, experiences of defined personalities or types of personalities is a datum of psychology or psychiatry rather than of social science. Every statement about behavior which aims, not to be accurate about the behavior of an actual individual or individuals or about the expected behavior of a physically and psychologically defined type of individuals, but which abstracts from such behavior in order to bring out in clear relief certain expectancies with regard to those aspects of individual behavior which various people share, as an interpersonal or "social" pattern, is a datum, however crudely expressed, of social science.

If Dorsey tells us that "Two Crows denies this," surely there is a reason for his statement. We need not say that Two Crows is badly informed or that he is fooling the anthropologist. Is it not more reasonable to say that the totality of socialized habits, in short the "culture," that he was familiar with was not in all respects the same entity as the corresponding totality presented to the observation or introspection of some other Indian, or perhaps of all other Indians? If the question asked by the anthropologist involved a mere question of personal affirmation, we need have no difficulty in understanding his denial. But even if it involved the question of "objective fact," we need not be too greatly shocked by the denial. Let us suppose that the anthropologist asked the simple question, "Are there seven clans or eight clans in moiety A of your tribe?", or words to that effect. All other Indians that he has asked about this sheer question of "fact" have said eight, we will assume. Two Crows claims there are only seven. How can this be? If we look more closely to the facts, we should undoubtedly find that the contradiction is not as puzzling as it seems. It may turn out that one of the clans had been extinct for a long time, most of the informants, however, remembering some old man, now deceased, who had been said to be the last survivor of it. They might feel that while the clan no longer exists in a practical sense, it has a theoretical place in the ordered description of the tribe's social organization. Perhaps there is some ceremonial function or placement, properly belonging to the extinct clan, which is remembered as such and which makes it a little difficult to completely overlook its claims to "existence." Various things, on the other hand, may be true of Two Crows. He may have belonged to a clan which had good reason to detest the extinct clan, perhaps because it had humiliated a relative of his in the dim past. It is certainly conceivable that the factual non-existence of the clan coupled with his personal reason for thinking as little about it as possible might give him the perfectly honest conviction that one need speak of only seven clans in the tribe. There is no reason why the normal anthropological investigator should, in an inquiry of this kind, look much beneath the surface of a simple answer to a simple question. It almost looks as though either seven clans or eight clans might be the "correct" answer to an apparently unambiguous question. The problem is very simple here. By thinking a little about Two Crows himself, we are enabled to show that he was not wrong, though he seemed to disagree with all his fellow Indians. He had a special kind of rightness, which was partly factual, partly personal.

Have we not the right to go on from simple instances of this sort and advance to the position that any statement, no matter how general, which can be made about culture needs the supporting testimony of a tangible person or persons, to whom such a statement is of real value in his system of interrelationships with other human beings? If this is so, we shall, at last analysis, have to admit that any individual of a group has cultural definitions which do not apply to all the members of his group, which even, in specific instances, apply to him alone. Instead, therefore, of arguing from a supposed objectivity of culture to the problem of individual variation, we shall, for certain kinds of analysis, have to proceed in the opposite direction. We shall have to operate as though we knew nothing about culture but were interested in analyzing as well as we could what a given number of human beings accustomed to live with each other actually think and do in their day-to-day relationships. We shall then find that we are driven, willy-nilly, to the recognition of certain permanencies, in a relative sense, in these interrelationships, permanencies which can reasonably be counted on to perdure but which must also be recognized to be eternally subject to serious modification of form and meaning with the lapse of time and with those changes of personnel which are unavoidable in the history of any group of human beings.

This mode of thinking is, of course, essentially psychiatric. Psychiatrists may, or may not, believe in cultural patterns, in group minds, in historic tendencies, or even missions; they cannot avoid believing in particular people. Personalities may be dubbed fictions by sociologists, anthropologists, and even by certain psychologists, but they must be accepted as bread and butter realities by the psychiatrist. Nothing, in short, can be more real to a psychiatrist than a personality organization, its modification from infancy to death, its essential persistence in terms of consciousness and ego reference. From this point of view culture cannot be accepted as anything more than a convenient assemblage, or at best total theory, of real or possible modes of behavior abstracted from the experienced realities of communication, whether in the form of overt behavior or in the form of fantasy. Even the alphabet from this standpoint becomes a datum of personality research! As a matter of fact, the alphabet does mean different things to different people. It is loved by some, hated by others, an object of indifference to most. It is a purely instrumental thing to a few; it has varying kinds of overtones of meaning for most, ranging all the way from the weakly sentimental to the passionately poetic. No one in his senses would wish the alphabet studied from this highly personalistic point of view. In plain English, it would not be worth the trouble. The total meaning of the alphabet for X is so very nearly the same as that for any other individual, Y, that one does much better to analyze it and explain its relation to other cultural patterns in terms of an impersonal, or cultural, or anthropological, mode of description. The fact, however, that X has had more difficulty in learning the alphabet than Y, or that in old age X may forget the alphabet or some part of it more readily than Y, shows clearly enough that there is a psychiatric side to even the coldest and most indifferent of cultural patterns. Even such cold and indifferent cultural patterns have locked in them psychiatric meanings which are ordinarily of no moment to the student of society but which may under peculiar circumstances come to the foreground of attention. When this happens, anthropological data need to be translated into psychiatric terms.

What we have tried to advance is little more than a plea for the assistance of the psychiatrist in the study of certain problems which come up in an analysis of socialized behavior. In spite of all that has been claimed to the contrary, we cannot thoroughly understand the dynamics of culture, of society, of history, without sooner or later taking account of the actual interrelationships of human beings. We can postpone this psychiatric analysis indefinitely but we cannot theoretically eliminate it. With the modern growth of interest in the study of personality and with the growing conviction of the enormous flexibility of personality adjustment to one's fellow men, it is difficult to see how one's intellectual curiosity about the problems of human intercourse can be forever satisfied by schematic statements about society and its stock of cultural patterns. The very variations and uncertainties which the earlier anthropologists ignored seem to be the very aspects of human behavior that future students of society will have to look to with a special concern, for it is only through an analysis of variation that the reality and meaning of a norm can be established at all, and it is only through a minute and sympathetic study of individual behavior in the state in which normal human beings find themselves, namely in a state of society, that it will ultimately be possible to say things about society itself and culture that are more than fairly convenient abstractions. Surely, if the social scientist is interested in effective consistencies, in tendencies, and in values, he must not dodge the task of studying the effects produced by individuals of varying temperaments and backgrounds on each other. Anthropology, sociology, indeed social science in general, is notoriously weak in the discovery of effective consistencies. This weakness, it seems, is not unrelated to a fatal fallacy with regard to the objective reality of social and cultural patterns defined impersonally.

Causation implies continuity, as does personality itself. The social scientist's world of reality is generally expressed in discontinuous terms. An effective philosophy of causation in the realm of social phenomena seems impossible so long as these phenomena are judged to have a valid existence and sequence in their own right. It is only when they are translated into the underlying facts of behavior from which they have never been divorced in reality that one can hope to advance to an understanding of causes. The test can be made easily enough. We have no difficulty in understanding how a given human being's experiences tend to produce certain results in the further conduct of his life. Our knowledge is far too fragmentary to allow us to understand fully, but there is never a serious difficulty in principle in imputing to the stream of his experiences that causative quality which we take for granted in the physical universe. To the extent that we can similarly speak of causative sequences in social phenomena, what we are really doing is to pyramid, as skillfully and as rapidly as possible, the sorts of cause and effect relations that we are familiar with in individual experience, imputing these to a social reality which has been constructed out of our need for a maximally economical expression of typically human events. It will be the future task of the psychiatrist to read cause and effect in human history. He cannot do it now because his theory of personality is too weak and because he tends to accept with too little criticism the impersonal mode of social and cultural analysis which anthropology has made fashionable. If, therefore, we answer our initial question, "Why cultural anthropology needs the psychiatrist," in a sense entirely favorable to the psychiatrist, that is, to the systematic student of human personality, we do not for a moment mean to assert that any psychiatry that has as yet been evolved is in a position to do much more than to ask intelligent questions.

CULTURAL COMPLEXITY AND PSYCHOLOGICAL PROBLEMS

Ernest Beaglehole

IT HAS been customary among anthropologists, psychologists, and psychiatrists to assume that primitive or pre-literate societies do not display a complexity of social organization that is supposed to be characteristic of Western European societies. Because of this assumption it is often suggested that primitive societies provide a sort of laboratory condition whereby many of the theories of the social scientist or psychologist may be checked, overhauled and generally brought to the touchstone of widely gathered fact. Our own society, so runs the argument, is but one of many different possible and existing social forms. What we call human nature may be, after all, only the psychology of man in Western European society. Let us test this view, the argument continues, by studying human nature in the uncomplex, simpler societies. Then with all the facts at our command, gathered as they are from societies simple and complex, we should be able to come to terms with the problem of what really constitutes human nature.

It is perhaps unnecessary to document in detail this commonly used argument. To clarify it, however, two references chosen almost at random may be given. Thus Dr. Margaret Mead tells us that the psychologist interested in human experiment must study "quite simple peoples, primitive peoples, whose society has never attained the complexity of our own." [1] In the complicated civilizations of

[1] Mead, Margaret, *From the South Seas;* New York, Morrow, 1939 (1072 pp.). This and the following quotations are all from the Introduction, pp. 1-13. The point is also stressed again in the same book, beginning on page 200, where Dr. Mead gives an excellent, but one feels, somewhat unreal description of the actual choice dilemmas facing the large majority of children in the large majority of sub-cultures in this country.

Europe or the East, she says, "years of study are necessary before the student can begin to understand the forces at work in them." Even European peasant communities, though they may present a way of life that is simple, nevertheless, "belong essentially to the historical tradition to which the complex parts of European or American civilization belong." Neither complex civilization nor peasant community can compare therefore for purposes of "experiment" with less complex primitive groups "who have had thousands of years of historical development along completely different lines from our own, whose language does not possess our Indo-European categories, whose religious ideas are of a different nature, whose social organization is not only simple but very different from our own." The fundamental structure of such a primitive group, suggests Dr. Mead, can be mastered by a trained student in a few months. Once this fundamental structure is understood, concludes the argument, everything is plain sailing and the way is clear for the fruitful examination of psychological problems.

Psychiatrists have also argued along these lines. Thus Laubscher, in his study of the major psychoses among the Southeastern Cape Bantu, Cape Province, South Africa,[2] is faced with the problem of offering an explanation for a very high incidence of schizophrenia among native patients in his mental hospitals. He argues that constitutional factors must be more important than psychological conflicts in causing this disease on the explicit grounds that Bantu social life is more simple and less complex than European social life. The Bantu, that is, suffer more from schizophrenia than do Europeans; but Bantu society is, by Laubscher's assumption, a simple society; hence it has few conflict situations; therefore psychological motivations can only be of slight significance in causing schizophrenia. Such reasoning may be impeccable according to every canon of logic. But the minor premise that would make the reasoning both valid and true is just the one that may need a query.

Sometimes the argument in favor of the relative simplicity of life among the primitives is given a slightly different turn. Mental dis-

[2] Laubscher, B. J. F., *Sex, Custom and Psychopathology;* London, Routledge, 1937 (xv and 347 pp.); pp. 220-256.

ease, it is said, is increasing in our own society. This can be due only to the fact that more and more people in Western European culture are finding life too complex for them. Faced with this complexity the individual flies from reality into the breakdown of a major psychosis. Conversely, a major psychosis is rare among primitives. This can be due only to the fact that primitive life presents few conflicts and hence rarely presents situations solvable only by a retreat into psychoses.

Many of the facts, however, on which this second type of argument is based seem of such character that they do not actually support the conclusion inferred. Thus in regard to our own society, a recent survey shows that in New York State, 1910–1936, apart from certain disorders like cerebral arteriosclerosis and alcoholic insanity the incidence of which has generally increased, there has been a very slow constant decrease in the rate for general paresis, and, more generally, a slight increase in the past twenty-five years in both the first admission and total admission for all mental diseases to the New York State mental hospitals. Expanded hospital facilities to reduce overcrowding, more liberal admission policies to the hospitals, and the fact that the average resident in New York State is both older and more likely to be an urban resident than the average resident of 1910, are all factors that must be taken into account in evaluating the reality of such increases as are apparent. Similarly the mental stress and turmoil of the first World War and of the recent depression may have increased unhappiness in our society, but the strains and tensions have not been sufficiently acute to lead to an increased rate of hospitalized mental disease.[3] In other words, our own society may be complex but there seems extremely little evidence for the Cassandra-like view that its complexity is becoming so acutely felt as to lead more and more individuals into mental disease as a way of escape.

It is unfortunate that when we come to study the converse side of this argument, that is, the mental disease situation in primitive com-

[3] The above generalizations are abstracted from pages 137-150 of the recent study of Landis, Carney, and Page, James D., *Modern Society and Mental Disease;* New York, Farrar and Rinehart, 1938 (xii and 190 pp.).

munities, the evidence at present available is both scanty and often downright conflicting. Thus Laubscher notes an extremely high incidence of dementia præcox, a very low incidence of manic-depressive insanity among his Cape Bantu. Winston, on the basis of Dr. Margaret Mead's data, suggests a high incidence of insanity in Samoa—about 10 per 10,000—as compared with a 1930 to 1934 admission rate per 10,000 of 7.8 in England, 5.9 in Norway and 7.8 in Belgium.[4] On the other hand, figures for the native Fijian suggest an insanity rate in 1936 of about 1.6 per 10,000 over the eleven year period from 1925 to 1936.[5] Seligman, finally, in his study of abnormality in New Guinea advances the opinion that insanity is unknown among natives untouched by European cultural influences but that psychotic conditions may become manifest in native groups which are in increasing contact with European culture.[6] The second part of Seligman's conclusion is doubtless true. The first part may be subject to question.[7] One would be inclined therefore to sum up the position by stressing the fact that mental disease is not unknown in primitive societies, that its incidence seems to vary within wide limits and that in no way does it seem possible to draw any correlation, even the roughest, between the relative complexity or simplicity of a society and the incidence of major mental disorders.

An exception to this generalization, however, would be a recent statement by Róheim which concludes that "primitive tribes with primitive culture are less inclined to neurosis and psychosis than civilized mankind."[8] Róheim advances little statistical material in support of this statement. It is rather the conclusion of a long chain

[4] Winston, Ellen, Alleged Lack of Mental Diseases among Primitive Groups. *Amer. Anthrop.* (1934) 36:236-237; and reference footnote 3; p. 144.

[5] Beaglehole, Ernest, Culture and Psychosis in New Zealand. *J. Polynesian Soc.* (1939) 48:144-155—in particular pp. 145 and 151.

[6] Seligman, C. G., Temperament, Conflict and Psychosis in a Stone-Age Population. *Brit. J. Med. Psychol.* (1929) 9:187-202.

[7] See reference footnote 5—p. 153—where a brief attempt is made to evaluate some of the complex factors involved. Reference may also be made to John Gillin's survey of Personality in Preliterate Societies. *Amer. Sociological Rev.* (1939) 4:681-702.

[8] Róheim, Géza, Racial Differences in the Neurosis and Psychosis. PSYCHIATRY (1939) 2:375-390; Quotation from p. 390.

of inferences based mainly on suppositions relating to the evolutionary history of mankind and on certain psychoanalytic interpretations of abnormal behavior some of which, as Róheim admits, do not as yet command universal agreement among psychoanalysts. Without in any way decrying the scientific value of the deductive development of hypotheses, one feels that hypothetical inferences in regard to primitive abnormalities must be sustained by wide appeal to facts, some of them probably of a statistical nature, before Róheim's conclusion can be regarded as even provisionally valid.

On the basis of these preliminary doubts it seems legitimate to ask several questions about the whole concept of cultural complexity and its relation to psychological studies. Not with a view to giving a final answer to the questions, but for the purpose of suggesting that the meaning of this concept of complexity might well be clarified before we proceed further with comparative psychological studies. The questions, then, that may be asked are: how complex, relatively, is our own society? How simple, or uncomplex, relatively, is a primitive society? What are the criteria for cultural complexity or cultural simplicity? Is there any correspondence between the relative complexity or simplicity of a culture and the relative complexity or simplicity of cultural—psychological—problems?

In seeking therefore to clarify the concept of complexity it is necessary to distinguish between what may be called objective complexity and subjective or participation complexity. By objective complexity is meant roughly the degree of complexity observable in the organization of any social structure or in the total structure of any culture when that society or culture is viewed formally, from the outside as it were, with a view to analyzing both the structural interrelation of elements and their formal functioning. Parenthetically it should here be stated that by Cohen's principle of polarity both simplicity and complexity involve each other when applied to any significant entity—they are distinct, opposed yet inseparable; hence, if at times the adjective "relative" is omitted when referring to the two concepts of simplicity and complexity it is not because one takes them to be real contradictories but merely to avoid repetition. Formal criteria of structural simplicity or complexity would include such factors as largeness of scale, degree of differentiation, extensiveness or intricacy of organization, degree of integration, degree of reciprocity, scope of coördination, number and elaboration of associations, interests, purposes, institutions, etc. All or any of these criteria could be applied to given social structures to determine degree of complexity.[9] Judged by such criteria or by others of similar nature one takes it to be self-evident that Western European culture or the culture of the United States or France or England is more complex than the culture of Samoa or the Hopi or the Bantu. It is well to remember, however, even in this context that, whereas primitive cultures are generally integrated on a geographical basis, the numerous social units that together make up a modern Indo-European culture, tend to stratify themselves, even though they may be of the same time and place, in terms of different standards, motivations and interests.[10] When, therefore, we compare civilized with primitive, we tend to compare a vaguely uniform cosmopolitan culture whose total patterns in their very complexity and heterogeneity are probably known to no living man with the culture of a geographically located, primitive tribe, all of whose patterns may be known to a few tribesmen at least. Whereas a more valid comparison might be made of individually known with individually known. Then we would compare the complexity of the culture of the rural poultry farmer in Windsor, California, with that of the corn-growing Hopi, or the complexity of the culture of the Kwakiutl nobleman with that of a wealthy English aristocrat, the culture of an American factory operative with that of a Dahomean commoner. It is hard to prove either way, but it is at least open to query whether the formal structure of

[9] Another criterion that might well be kept in mind would be the distinction between cultures on the basis of their apparent "interest" in formalizing and formulating the patterns of the culture. Linton draws a useful contrast here between the legalistic, consciously verbalizing cultures of West Africa and the non-generalizing-of-pattern culture of say the Plains Comanche—a personal communication; see Linton, Ralph, *The Study of Man*; New York, Appleton-Century, 1936, (ix and 503 pp.)—in particular pp. 259-260.

[10] Ruth Benedict has stressed this point in her *Patterns of Culture*; New York, Houghton Mifflin, 1934 (291 pp.)—in particular p. 230.

the culture of the Western European expressed in this way is more complex than that of his primitive counterpart.

It is when we consider subjective complexity of culture, however, that the real vagueness of the concept of complexity is evident. Assuming that one society is structurally more complex than another, does this complexity have any particularly complex reverberation in terms of individual participation in this culture—in terms, that is, of the meanings and symbolisms that make up the content of culture for the individual? The answer is, one suspects, in the negative. In other words, no matter how apparent an objective complexity, the individual will give meaning to his cultural forms on the basis of a psychological awareness that is everywhere in every society limited and defined by inertia, custom and habit. From this point of view, complexity of social structure is one thing, and of a very different nature from complexity as the individual experiences these same social patterns and participates in his culture.

One criterion, among many, for determining subjective complexity might be the number of choice situations which confront the individual in his daily living. By such a criterion it is common to judge the Western European as living in a thoroughly complex culture. And it is true that by placing a mythical American in turn in all possible or imaginable situations where freedom of choice is theoretically possible in our culture, difficulty and complexity of choices would become so incredibly monstrous as almost to freeze the imagination. On the other hand when semblance of flesh and blood is given this American he is immediately defined as a participant in a particular and relatively specific sub-culture, a man, say, of particular age, life history, economic status and the rest, for whom a theoretic boundlessness of choice has dwindled until freedom of choice is almost an illusion and where choice occurs, it is so narrowly defined by habit, custom, social pressures and other factors, that it hardly ranks as choice at all.[11]

[11] The point may well be made in this connection that my references to the patterns of sub-cultures in our own society are not without factual foundation. They are based on discussions with post-adolescent college and graduate students of both sexes, and adults of varying and various ages in adult education classes—probably some 200 in all. Hence my material, though not strictly

An example or two may make the meaning clearer. A farmer who decides to join a Federal soil conservation scheme has, in order to secure monetary benefits, the theoretical choice of planting half-a-dozen different species of grass or participating in twenty or more different works projects. Practically this wide freedom of choice does not appear to him as a troublesome freedom. He plants the grass seed which his farm advisor recommends and draws money for installing in his fields a second-hand bathtub as his contribution to water preservation. Again, in another altogether different aspect of human life, one might well feel that the Western European lives in a complex culture because he has a theoretically almost unlimited choice of a marriage mate as compared with the Australian aboriginal Kurnai tribesman who is so entangled in the complexities of his eight-class marriage system that there may be but one mate in his whole tribe whom he may legitimately marry or even no one at all. But a theoretical freedom of choice for the Western European hardly means this in practice. His choice of a mate is limited by many factors—class and caste considerations, racial prejudices, parental control, accidents of personality development, and so on, for the factors are endless—so much so that again effective choice may hardly function as choice at all. Even if he is worried by this situation he can always take refuge in the thought that although he may be in no better plight than the aborigine, at least the romantic love concept of his culture gives a justification similar to the eight-class system elsewhere. "You are the only girl in the world" or "We were made for each other since time began" run the popular song-philosophies. They at least never let the singer subscribe to the doctrine that freedom of choice is other than the politest of fictions.

---

quantitative, is none the less not purely imaginative. On pages 175 to 176 of *Middletown in Transition,* the Lynds talk of baffled highschool children and their parents suffering from uncertainties and tensions caused by a widening contact with different, unevenly sanctioned group choices. Documentation to support the existence of these tensions in Middletown is extremely scanty. The reader of the book therefore remains unclear as to the factual basis of the Lynds' inferences on this topic. Lynd, R. S., and Lynd, H. M., *Middletown in Transition: a Study in Cultural Conflicts;* New York, Harcourt, Brace, 1937 (xviii and 604 pp.).

Finally, does the invention of contraceptives mean freedom of choice over the begetting of children—a freedom unknown to the primitive? The widespread and increasing use of such an invention together with the increasing costs of bearing and raising children and the insistent philosophy of the advertiser of consumer goods all suggest that for most, the problem of choice is not particularly acute and is left, practically, for chance or accident to decide. In other words most modern inventions—refrigerator, radio, telephone, automobile, hot-water boiler and the rest—which objectively appear to increase the complexity of social structure seem to operate in such a fashion as to make the personal life of the individual more simple and un-complex. There is always a transition period of course, when new habits are necessary and changes in social forms necessitate new individual adaptations. But the incidence of these changes is sof-tened in its impact on the many sub-cultures of Western European culture. We may be living in an era of unprecedented social change. Most of us would be unaware of this fact, as far as our personal lives are concerned, unless social scientists and newspapers had not un-consciously conspired to drum the facts into our heads. As it is they rarely get past our heads. Our day-to-day living is rarely affected by such remote control. We do not in fact choose to choose. Among the apparent choice situations so temptingly spread before us, we are ascetic in our choices, if not in the other pleasures of life.

On the other hand when we look more closely at the life of the primitive from this point of view one of the most striking things about this life seems to be both the theoretical and practical multi-plicity of choice situations. Perhaps this is largely due to the fact that in the average primitive community there is involved on the part of the ordinary culture participant a face-to-face contact and a personal responsibility that permeates almost every aspect of culture functioning. The Californian lettuce picker has little responsibility as far as his job is concerned. His life is simple on almost every plane and this simplicity extends even to the act of losing his job. The worker in a company steel town has often lost even the per-sonal interest in his job and his freedom of choice is largely illusion.[12] By contrast, the Hopi farmer, for example, must plan and plant and grow, meeting the challenge of insect pest and adverse season, as well as all the personal demands of his relatively complex economic and religious culture. Again, the Polynesian fisherman-cultivator has a personal responsibility for securing food aided only by his skill and ability to make quick day-to-day decisions regarding wind and tide and hurricane and a multitude of adverse environmental forces. Admittedly he has the help of tradition, magic, religion, the support of his fellows. But the choices and the decisions that face him seem many more, and more important than those confronting a subsidy- and bounty-nursed American farmer. With Hopi, Polynesian or American there probably operates the human tendency to simplify life as much as possible, to rely upon the flywheel of habit in order to keep the social and human machine running without too many back-fires or breakdowns. The suggestion is, however, that the life of Hopi or Polynesian is lived at a higher level of participation complexity because freedom of choice cannot be so limited and defined as in the case of the American farmer or factory operative.

In our own society, to stress for a moment the life of the American farmer's sub-culture for comparison with the Hopi, we are often accustomed to think of the farmer's occupation as "chancey" and fraught with many important day-to-day decisions. But as Veblen noted many years ago, in connection with his studies of the machine technology, "even in work that lies so near the fortuities of animate nature as dairying, stock breeding and the improvement of crop plants, a determinate, reasoned routine replaces the rule of thumb. By mechanical control of his materials, the dairyman, for example, selectively determines the rate and kind of the biological processes that change his raw material into finished product." [13] Veblen goes on to show that in the same fashion this pre-determined control has taken much of the chance out of stock breeding and plant breeding.

[12] Plant's comments on the effects of industry on personality are apposite here. Plant, James Stuart, *Personality and the Cultural Pattern;* New York, The Commonwealth Fund, 1937, (441 pp.)—see pp. 390-401.

[13] Veblen, Thorstein, *The Theory of Business Enterprise;* New York, Scribner's, 1927 (vii and 400 pp.)—footnote 1, p. 6.

From this point of view agricultural research works towards effective technological control of biological factors "with a view to eliminating fortuitous, disserviceable and useless elements from the processes of agricultural production and so reducing these processes to a calculable expeditious and wasteless routine." [14] With this scheme of operations one may well compare the rule of thumb plus chance, plus magic sort of farming or gardening upon which most primitives have to depend for their economic welfare.

It is from this point of view also that one feels a little uneasy about Sapir's distinction between cultures genuine and spurious— our own, spurious; primitive or folk cultures, genuine. If, to repeat, one compares the vague cosmopolitan culture of the United States with that of a primitive people, then the distinction is probably valid. But if one compared the functioning cultural unit in our own society, one of its many sub-cultures, that is, with folk culture, much of the point of difference seems to disappear. Linton has phrased the same contrast in terms of his distinction between culture patterns on the basis of their being universals, specialties, alternatives or individual peculiarities: the folk or primitive culture has many universals and few alternatives; modern civilizations have few universals, many alternatives. [15] Again it would seem as if the valid comparison should be not between "modern civilization" and savage, but between defined sub-culture within our own society and primitive culture.

In the discussion so far it must be admitted that one side to the comparison has been primitive society in a relatively static condition. In many cases, of course, today the pressures of culture contact together with a high rate of selective borrowing are accelerating the normally very slow rate of culture change. Where this acceleration occurs it is also expectable that the number of choice situations for the primitive will increase. As Mead notes for Samoa many of the deviant girls in Samoan society are deviants because they wish to exercise untraditional choices, choices, that is, which they are encouraged to make by a Christian missionary educational system

[14] Reference footnote 13.
[15] Reference footnote 9; pp. 272-275 and 283-287.

superimposed upon native Samoan culture.[16] Culture contact situations, however, do not necessarily in themselves produce these multiplied choices for the primitive. Thus Erikson in his study of Sioux education notes that the process of acculturation has brought with it a wide discrepancy between the values of democratic ideology and those of the old Indian society. Many Indian parents are puzzled by this ideological chasm. Sioux children on the other hand, respond to the conflict of standards with "unbelievable stoicism . . . Indian children can live for years, without open rebellion or any signs of inner conflict, between two standards which are incomparably further apart than are those of any two generations or two classes in our culture." [17] On the Polynesian island of Pukapuka, a somewhat similar situation has been observed. Culture contact has brought to the Pukapukans a rather strict, Puritan morality which is entirely alien to the native morality of adolescent and post-adolescent sex experimentation. Theoretically the cultural situation today is one marked by an extreme conflict of moral standards. Practically, however, there is no obvious conflict over a multiplicity of choices. Young people follow traditional native morality. When they reach the stage of considering marriage seriously, and finally do marry, they become church members. This involves among other obligations, the obligation to accept and practice the official Puritan moral standard of the missionized culture. The response to the culture contact situation is thus the cultural elaboration of an unofficial dual standard of morality; one unofficial or *sub-rosa* standard for the young adult, a directly contrasting standard for those who are married and church members. Church members complain and gossip about the moral values of youthful non-church members but make little attempt to enforce the official moral standard of the culture. Young adults go blithely ahead with their own way of life, little heeding the denunciations of pastor or deacon, secure in the knowledge that these denunciations are right and proper because they come from the appointed guardians of the newly established moral

[16] Reference footnote 1; p. 171.
[17] Erikson, Erik Homburger, Observations on Sioux Education. *J. Psychol.* (1939) 7:101-156; quotation from p. 124.

order. The elders for their part are content to denounce, because this is a function of their guardianship. They reserve active interference only for married church members who break the moral law on the theory that "youth will be youth and what does it matter anyhow?"

The processes of culture contact may therefore produce an overt clash of ideologies and values. Whether this is felt as a conflict situation, adding to the complexity of life, must always be decided by further examination of the situation produced by acculturation. Probably a subjectively felt conflict is the result of many general and particular causes whose operation may vary from one culture contact situation to another and which may also vary in incidence between the generation strata of the society. Further empirical analysis of acculturation in various parts of the world is necessary before such causative factors may be stated with definite assurance.

One may speculate quite fruitfully with the concept of participation-complexity, it would seem, in order to provide explanation for many of those Dionysian-like frenzies, those attempts to attain a divine madness, a spirit that destroys man's reason, which are so characteristic of many primitive societies. Man's life in primitive society, it may well be, is lived at a high pitch of emotional intensity. When he seeks for some experience that will lift him above his accustomed level of living he must develop the self-tortures of the Sun Dance or overcome, what is to the Kwakiutl, an intense repugnance to human flesh by eating of a human corpse in the fury of the Cannibal Dance. By contrast, man's life in the sub-cultures of Western European civilization is mostly a matter of rather drab routine, uncomplex, unexciting. Alcohol or the vicarious, and therefore painfully powerless, jolts of an average movie program or pulp magazine seem sufficient to stir up his emotions, for a time, to a level of pleasant excitement.

Examples of the type that have been already discussed could be multiplied many times over without perhaps giving much added support to the argument that has been advanced. Summarized again it is simply this: whatever differences of complexity there may be between the structures of our own sub-cultural variants on Western European culture and those of primitive societies, these differences do not necessarily operate functionally in the meanings that culture patterns have for the individual participating in European or primitive society. These meanings may be just as complex or even more so for the average Samoan or Eskimo as they are for the Greenwich villager or the poor white in Southerntown. And in parenthesis here one may note that the seeming simplicity of primitive social life is often unconsciously exaggerated by professional anthropologists who frequently claim that in a few months study of a primitive tribe they can understand the fundamental patterns of the society in question. Their word is not, in my opinion, to be doubted. But it is well to be aware of the fact that "fundamental" may mean either "most general" or "most basic." The general patterns of a strange culture are often the easiest to analyze. The basic motivations, on the other hand, are often the hardest, especially when one tries to hold steadily to a view of pattern, individual variation and personal meaning. By contrast, it would be easy for a visiting Martian anthropologist to understand the fundamental patterns of an American sub-culture after a few months study. One might well be forgiven, however, if one suspected that it would still need long years of patient study and participation before the majority of the patterns were clearly defined and their individual meaning known. A volume about a primitive tribe, even by the most highly trained specialist, barely skates over the surface of that tribe's culture. And, as Sapir once said of Middletown, not in criticism, but with just and proper evaluation, that book with all its detail would hardly rank as more than a footnote were each of us to verbalize our own knowledge of the contemporary American sub-culture in which we participate. Again the point may be put in question form: Are the simpler societies, so-called, really easier to comprehend in their totality of structure and functioning than an American sub-culture, or are we often content for many and various reasons in our study of a primitive society with a different level of understanding and comprehension? The answer this time is probably affirmative. After mastering a strange language, we often have to be satisfied with an understanding that is on the level of generalized pattern—fundamental, therefore, only in this sense; whereas a moment's reflection shows us that we have already this command of our culture and realize that our knowledge is still relatively incomplete.

If it is now granted that from a subjective viewpoint heterogeneity or homogeneity of culture, simplicity or complexity, are not dichotomous terms whereby an American sub-culture can be separated as if by a difference of quantity, or quality, or both from primitive societies, then what is the implication of this view for psychological studies? Just this: that for some kinds of psychological research, the point is immaterial. Studies of color vision for instance or of other simple sensory discriminations need to take cognizance of complicating cultural factors; measurement of other psychological functions such as emotion and intelligence are possible provided some valid accultural test is elaborated; developmental studies of child behavior can be made provided conditions render possible the use of necessary apparatus and the recording of exact age; materials may also be collected illustrative of the various phenomena which are described by social psychology; cross-section studies of abnormal behaviour and its symptomatology can be fruitfully made with primitive materials provided the cultural background is kept well to the fore. Studies of this kind and others can be made irrespective of whether any culture is judged to be simple or complex. Other kinds of psychological studies, however, have to be made with an ever-present awareness that, although the culture in which individuals are studied may be structurally simple, nonetheless problems of personality development may be just as complex to unravel and as hard to understand as in our own society. In other words just because the chosen society is simple, the psychology of the developing individual in that society is not necessarily simple and hence easy of understanding. It is in this connection that a somewhat chastening thought may serve as a warning: over the past forty years in our own society there has been a corps of numerous scientists—clinicians, laboratory specialists, psychologists, psychiatrists, educators—focussing attention and study upon problems of personality formation and development in the individual member of Western European culture. And yet he would surely be optimistic who suggested that by now the psychology of man in Western society was an open book for all to read. All feel today that, whatever is known, incalculably more yet remains to be known. Even the best psychologist is often sadly astray in puzzling out the psychology of one child's personality —even though it be his own; a science of child psychology is hardly yet at other than a descriptive stage with fundamental categories being refurbished every few years—which is not a matter for condemnation, of course; and practical programs for child training have a disconcerting way of reorientating themselves radically, as if in proof of the fact that child training today is still largely a matter of informed guess work. With all this, then, it is surely doubtful whether the usual study, of a primitive society, as it is at present conducted can bring back more than suggestions for the psychologist to arrange, as best he can, in terms of current theory.

One feels that this judgment applies both to much current research on personality in primitive societies and also to present attempts to carry out that most difficult of psychological jobs—the analysis of the psychology of a culture. Róheim has made attempts of this sort. His results are stimulating, perhaps, but hardly convincing. Others are working on what seems, to the nonanalyst at least, to be a more modest scale. From this work much is to be expected. The attempt however to psychoanalyze a primitive culture often appears to assume an initial cultural simplicity by virtue of which related patterns are coördinated on the basis of certain analytic hypotheses. If, on the other hand, primitive culture is not particularly simple then the task of the psychologist working with a culture that he may neither know nor "feel" at first hand is rendered increasingly difficult. The validity of his interpretations will have to be judged by the application of many criteria. Among these, some estimate of what the culture in question means subjectively to a participating member would appear to be significant.

The possibility of making such analytic interpretations of culture also raises a question of methodology. Assuming for instance that the hypothesis of an oral character seems the most plausible interpretation of certain Australian data and assuming also that no Australian aborigine would recognize such interpretation as having any meaning in his own experience, then would such meaning, inferred from cultural fact by an outside observer, be part of Australian culture? How far in other words is psychologist or anthropologist justified in reading into another culture meanings—interpretations or hypotheses—which have validity in terms of concepts derived from a "depth-psychology" of his own culture, but which would provoke no response or recognition in the individual member of that other culture? One would hesitate in the present state of psychological understanding even to guess at answers to such questions. Possibly analysis of culture in psychiatric or psychoanalytic concepts could be given ultimate validation only if psychoanalysis of individual members of such cultures revealed unconscious meanings or symbolisms in the individual that corresponded to, or otherwise had significance only in terms of, a previously made analytic interpretation of the culture as a whole. This might represent a methodologically sound position. But it makes one further assumption, namely, that it is possible to carry out a psychoanalysis of a member of a primitive tribe, using for this purpose the psychoanalytic technique as employed in our own society. Such an assumption seems doubtful.

Using the term with strict definition, the basis for the use of psychoanalytic technique appears to be in the possibility and necessity of building up a transference situation. Apart altogether from differing conceptualizations of what happens in the process of emotional transference it is known that the problem of overcoming resistances to transference is not merely a minor aspect of psychoanalytic treatment in our own culture where patient and analyst have been bred and born in roughly—but only very roughly—the same culture. The problem would surely become immeasurably more complex where the analyst-anthropologist tried to secure affective transference from a primitive tribesman. If, on the other hand, psychoanalysis is defined more loosely in terms of the application of a combination of case history and memory association techniques—with no attention paid to questions of transference—then it is again doubtful how far one could uncover unconscious symbolism and repressed personal meanings from the primitive.

The success of a psychoanalysis whether conceived widely or

narrowly depends finally upon linguistic factors. It presupposes and necessitates in the patient a high degree of facility and ability at verbalization—the sort of verbal ability that is only acquired in our own culture by long years of college or "bookish" education. Of the verbalization abilities of an average Semang or Eskimo or Papuan it would be difficult even to hazard a guess. Yet a valid and valuable depth analysis of a primitive would presumably depend upon this unknown quality. The further linguistic difficulty of bridging the gap between the language of analyst and patient is also no mean hurdle to overcome because it would raise a problem of communication that is surely different from, and other than, the necessity of common understanding which the anthropological field-worker can successfully establish through the use of vernacular, pidgin, or interpreters when kinship structure or lashing technique is the point of inquiry. When communication involves not only the idiomatic use of an established linguistic pattern but also an appreciation of personal meanings and emotional weightings given to certain items in this pattern of sound by the primitive patient, then the analyst from another culture has indeed assumed a task of somewhat heroic proportions. The trouble is that such analysis to be impeccable must be an all-or-none matter. Either the alien language must be thoroughly understood in general, particular and personal meaning, or else the results of analyses, though interesting, may well be suspect on the basis of an intelligible scientific methodology.

It is not my intention, of course, to disparage the valuable work that has already been done in exploring the limits of psychological research in primitive communities. This work had already broadened our scientific horizons immeasurably. It has provided the touchstone whereby many a theory has had to be sharpened, many a dogma discarded. But now such research has reached the stage of formulating major hypotheses of its own and it is becoming aware of the fact that, to repeat, simple or homogeneous societies do not mean simple psychological problems to study. Personality structure is just as complex, personality functioning just as various, personality prediction just as difficult in Africa or South America as it is in

Cambridge, Massachusetts—with this difference that in one case a lone worker is sometimes hopeful whereas in the other a corps of scientists is often in doubt.[18]

Pessimism has no more place in science than has optimism. A cold enthusiasm for the truth, as Boas has aptly put it, should be the scientist's working philosophy. As long as this kind of enthusiasm is shared by anthropologist and psychologist alike there should be no misjudgment of the issue. Whether the psychologist is interested primarily in children or in abnormals or in personality studies that may ultimately serve as focus for the development of a powerful social psychology, he should be aware of the fact that degree of cultural complexity may not correspond in the least to degree of psychological complexity. This is due ultimately to the fact that the individual, participating in his culture, is always giving personal meaning to the symbolism of his culture or sub-culture. These meanings can never be simple because each individual reworks the culturally given and provides with new emphasis the content that he absorbs. Anthropology, as Sapir has said, is constantly rediscovering the normal. And the normal is always complex whether it is the normal of Baffin Land or of Papua or again of a Monterey fisherman.

[18] It is significant of this trend that Dr. Margaret Mead notes that her future work will be coöperative "in which at least two, and sometimes six observers, armed with modern methods of recording, typewriters or stenotypes, miniature cameras and moving picture cameras, will bring a battery of observations to bear upon the behavior of native children or native mothers." Reference footnote 1; p. vii.

CERTAIN PRIMARY SOURCES AND PATTERNS OF AGGRESSION IN THE SOCIAL STRUCTURE OF THE WESTERN WORLD

Talcott Parsons

THE PROBLEM OF AGGRESSION

THE PROBLEM of power and its control is not identical with that of aggression.[1] Without any conscious intent on the part of one individual or collectivity to gain at the expense of another, or even any unconscious disposition to do so, there would still be important sources of instability in the rela-

[1] "Aggression" will here be defined as the disposition on the part of an individual or a collectivity to orient its action to goals which include a conscious or unconscious intention illegitimately to injure the interests of other individuals or collectivities in the same system. The term *illegitimately* deliberately implies that the individual or collectivity in question is integrated, however imperfectly, in a moral order which defines reciprocal rights and obligations. The universality of the existence of a moral order in this sense is a cardinal thesis of modern social science. This is not to say that world society constitutes one integrated moral order in this sense; on the contrary, the diversity of such orders is a primary problem of integration, but it is *not* as such the problem of aggression. Thus friction and hostility arising from lack of mutual understanding or mere thoughtlessness or insensitiveness to the position of the other party are not as such acts of aggression, although aggressive dispositions become attracted to these situations as fields of expression perhaps more readily than any others, because they are easier to rationalize.

The use of the term aggression here is thus narrower than in some psychological, particularly psychoanalytic, discussions. In particular "self-assertion," the "drive to mastery"—for example, of a technical skill—without meaningful hostility to others, will not be treated as aggression. It will not be an issue in the present analysis to decide as to whether, on deeper psychological levels, aggression, in the sense here meant, and nonaggressive self-assertion, or mastery, are fundamentally different or whether they derive from the same roots. On the level of *social behavior* the difference is fundamental, and that is what matters in the present context.

tions of individuals and social groups into which the use of power could and would play. There can, however, be little doubt that the widespread incidence of aggressive tendencies is the most important single factor in the dangerously disruptive potentialities of power relationships; and if these could be notably lessened, the prospects of effective control would be correspondingly enhanced.

Modern sociological and psychological analysis has greatly improved understanding of the factors and situations which produce aggressive dispositions. This understanding in turn carries with it the potentiality of devising and applying measures of deliberate control, although it is naive to suppose that control will follow automatically on knowledge of causes. Indeed the problem of utilizing what knowledge we have for control is so complex that no attempt will be made to deal with it in this brief paper which will be confined to sketching a few of the diagnostic considerations on which any program of control would have to be based. This is not to depreciate the importance of an action program, but is merely an application of the principle of the division of labor. It is better to do one thing reasonably well than to attempt too many things and do none of them well.

All social behavior, including the "policies" of the most complex collectivities like nation-states, is ultimately the behavior of human beings, understandable in terms of the motivation of individuals, perhaps millions of them, *in the situations* in which they are placed. Therefore the psychological level of understanding of individual motivation is fundamental to even the most complex of mass phenomena. At the same time, however, the complications and modifications introduced by the facts of the organization of individuals in social systems are equally crucial. If it were possible to arrive at a statistically reliable estimate of the average strength of aggressive tendencies in the population of a nation, it would *by itself* be worthless as a basis of predicting the probability of that nation embarking on an aggressive war. The specific goals and objects to which these aggressive dispositions are attached, the ways in which they are repressed, deflected, projected, or can be directly expressed according to the forces which channel or oppose them, and the structure of situations into which they come—all these are equally important with any aggressive potential in general in determining concrete behavioral outcomes. Indeed they may be far more important to understand, since many of these factors in aggressive behavior may be far more accessible to control than are the ultimate reservoirs of aggressive motivation themselves. The present analysis therefore will be largely concerned with the social structuring of aggression in Western society, rather taking for granted that there is an adequate reservoir to motivate the familiar types of aggressive behavior.

A few elementary facts about the psychology of aggression need, however, to be stated since they will underlie the analysis on the social level. There does not seem to be any very clear understanding of how far or in what sense aggressive dispositions in the sense here meant are inherited. It is, however, highly probable that there are very wide variations in hereditary constitution in this as in other respects and that the variations within any one ethnic population are far more significant than those between "races" or national groups. But whether on the individual or the group level, it is at least very doubtful how far anything like a human "beast of prey" by heredity exists. Ideas to that effect almost certainly contain far more of projection and fantasy than of solid empirical observation and analysis. Indeed there is much to be said for the hypothesis that aggression grows more out of weakness and handicap than out of biological strength.

Far more definite and clear is the relation between aggression on the one hand and insecurity and anxiety on the other. Whatever the hereditary potential, and whatever it may mean, there is an immense accumulation of evidence that in childhood aggressive patterns develop when security in some form, mostly in human relationships, is threatened, and when realistic fears shade over into anxiety of the neurotic type. This is a very complex field and only a few points can be brought out here.

Insecurity, as the term is used in psychology, certainly has a number of dimensions. One of the most important generalizations concerns the extent to which the specific patterning of reactions to insecurity, at least, is a function of the human relationships in which the child is placed rather than of its physical safety and welfare alone. One of the major human dimensions is unquestionably that of love or affection which in most social systems centers on the relationship of mother and child. The absolute level of maternal affection is undoubtedly of fundamental significance, but equally so is its consistency. The withdrawal of love to which the child has become accustomed, or ambivalence, however deeply repressed, may have devastating effects. Similarly, relative distribution of affection between siblings is important. Frustration through withdrawal, if not absolutely low-level or absent, undoubtedly is normally reacted to with aggression. A common example is provided by the fantasies of children that they will die or commit suicide so the parents will be sorry for their maltreatment.

Another major dimension of security touches expectations of achievement and of conformity with behavioral standards. Here two contexts seem to be particularly important as sources of anxiety and aggression. The first is the sense of inadequacy, of being expected to do things which one is unable to achieve, and thus incurring punishment or the loss of rewards. The second is the sense of unfairness, of being unjustly punished or denied deserved rewards. In both cases the comparative context is fundamentally important. Inadequacy is highlighted by the superior achievements of others with whom one feels himself to be in competition, and unfairness almost always involves specific examples of what is felt to be unjust favoritism toward others. Again in both cases the consistency of the standards which are held up to the child and of adults in applying them is crucial. In this general context the sense of inadequacy or injustice may generate aggressive impulses, on the one hand toward those who are held to have imposed such unfair standards or applied them unfairly, and on the other hand toward more successful rivals or beneficiaries of unfair favoritism.

Two further facts about these structured patterns of aggression in childhood are particularly important. First, they are rooted in normal reactions to strain and frustration in human relations at the stages of development when the individual is particularly vulnerable, since he has not, as some psychologists say, yet attained a strong ego-development. But unless they are corrected by an adequate strengthening of security, these reactions readily embark on a cumulative vicious circle of "neurotic" fixation. The child who has reacted with anxiety and aggression to inadequate or ambivalent maternal love builds up defenses against re-exposure to such frustrating situations and becomes incapable of responding to genuine love. The child who has felt inadequate in the face of expectations beyond his capacity to fulfill becomes neurotically resistant to stimuli toward even the achievements he is capable of and aggressive toward all attempts to make him conform. Unless re-equilibration takes place in time, these defensive patterns persist and form rigid barriers to integration in a normal system of human relationships. The result is that the individual tends either to react aggressively, without being able to control himself, in situations which do not call for it at all, or to overreact far more violently than the situation calls for.

The second important fact is a result of the conflict of the aggressive impulses, thus generated and fixated, with the moral norms current in the family and society and the sentiments integrated with them. In childhood the persons in relation to whom such affects are developed are primarily the members of the child's own immediate family. But solidarity with them and affection toward them is a primary ethical imperative in the society. Indeed it is more than an ethical imperative, since these attitudes become "introjected" as part of the fundamental attitude system of the child himself. The hostile impulses therefore conflict both with his own standards and sentiments and with the realistic situation, and cannot be overtly expressed, except under strong emotional compulsion, or even tolerated as conscious thoughts. They tend, therefore, to be dissociated from the positive, socially approved attitude system and "repressed." This repressed attitude system, however, persists and seeks indirect expression especially in symbolic form. This may be purely in fantasy, but there is one particularly important phenomenon for the present context, namely displacement on a "scapegoat." If the father or mother or sibling cannot be overtly hated, a symbolically appropriate object outside the circle of persons who must be loved is chosen and gratification of the impulse indirectly secured. Precisely because his aggressive impulses are repressed, the person is unaware of the fact of displacement and by rationalization is convinced that this is a reasonable reaction to what the scapegoat has done or is likely to do if given a chance. There can be no doubt but what an enormously important component of group hostility has this psychological origin and character.

THE KINSHIP SYSTEM

"Western Society" is a very complex entity with many different variations on national, regional, cultural, class, and other bases. There are, nevertheless, a small number of structurally distinctive features of it which, though unevenly distributed in different parts, are of such strategic significance for the whole that they can be singled out as presenting in the most accentuated form the problems which are crucial to the whole. These are, above all, those features associated with the development of the modern type of urban and industrial society, which is far more highly developed in the modern Western world than anywhere else or at any other period.[2]

In attempting to analyze the genesis and channeling of aggression in modern Western society, four aspects or structural-functional contexts appear to stand out as of paramount importance, and will be discussed in order. They are: First, the kinship system in its context in the larger society, since this is the environment in which the principal patterns in the individual personality become crystallized. Second, the occupational system, since this is the arena of the most important competitive process in which the individual must achieve his status. Third, the fundamental process of dynamic change by which traditional values and sentiments are exposed to a far more drastic and continuing disintegrating influence than in most societies. And fourth, the set of institutional structures through which aggression becomes organized in relation to a small number of structurally significant tensions, rather than diffused and dissi-

[2] Modern Japan and the Early Roman Empire are the two cases outside this sphere which have gone farthest in approaching the modern Western situation.

pated in an indefinite variety of different channels without threatening the stability of the social system as a whole.[3]

The dominant feature of the kinship system of modern Western urban and industrial society is the relatively isolated conjugal family which is primarily dependent for its status and income on the occupational status of one member, the husband and father. This role, however, is segregated from the family structure itself, unlike the role of the peasant father. Work is normally done in separate premises, other members of the family do not cooperate in the work process and, above all, status is based on individual qualities and achievements which specifically cannot be shared by other members of the family unit.

It follows that sons on maturity must be emancipated from their families of orientation and "make their own way in the world" rather than fitting into a going concern organized around kinship. Determination of occupational status by family connection threatens the universalistic standards so important to the system as a whole. Daughters become overwhelmingly dependent on their marriage to the right individual man—not kinship group—for their status and security. In practice their parents cannot greatly help them—marriage becomes primarily a matter of individual responsibility and choice.

This kinship system in its larger setting involves a variety of influences on the child which favor high levels of insecurity structured in relatively definite and uniform ways and correspondingly a good deal of aggression. In the first place, the affective orientations of the child are concentrated on a very small number of persons, particularly since the family size is likely to be small. Of

[3] The study which comes closest to the present attempt in approach and analytical method is Clyde Kluckhohn's *Navaho Witchcraft,* Papers of the Peabody Museum of American Archaeology and Ethnology, Harvard University, (1944) 22:no. 2. (see also the author's review, *Amer. J. Sociology* [1946] 51:566-569). Naturally because of the vast extent of Western society, the facts must be determined on a basis of broad general impressions rather than on specific field observation. This does not, however, invalidate the comparability of the two analyses. There is a very important sense in which nationalism in the Western world is the functional equivalent of Navaho witchcraft.

adult objects, particularly in the early years, the mother overwhelmingly predominates, because the care of household and children traditionally falls to her, and because the father is normally away from the household at work most of the child's waking hours. This creates a very high degree of sensitivity to the emotional attitudes of the mother and of vulnerability to anything disturbing about them. To reinforce this, most associations outside the immediate family in the neighborhood play group and school are those in which the child cannot take security of love and status for granted but is placed in competition with others either directly or for adult approval by the teacher and parents. The fact that his mother loves him does not solve his problems; he must stand on his own feet. Furthermore doing well in such situations is highly valued in the society, and this attitude is apt to be shared by the mother, so that her own love and approval tend to become contingent on the child's objective performance rather than unconditional as it is in many societies.[4] This love is therefore more acutely needed than in most societies and more precarious. The situation is favorable to a high level of anxiety and hence of aggression. But because of the very acuteness of the need for affection and approval, direct expression of aggression is more than normally dangerous and hence likely to be repressed.

On top of this situation come factors which are differential between the sexes and not only intensify insecurity but have much to do with the direction aggressive tendencies take. Our kinship situation, it has been noted, throws children of both sexes overwhelmingly upon the mother as *the* emotionally significant adult. In such a situation "identification" in the sense that the adult becomes a "role model" is the normal result. For a girl this is normal and natural not only because she belongs to the same sex as the mother, but because the functions of housewife and mother are immediately before her eyes and are tangible and relatively easily understood by a child. Almost as soon as she is physically able, the girl begins

---

[4] See Mead, Margaret, *And Keep Your Powder Dry*, N.Y., William Morrow, 1942, for a discussion of the pattern of "conditional love" and its consequences.

a direct apprenticeship in the adult feminine role. It is very notable that girls' play consists in cooking, sewing, playing with dolls, and so on, activities which are a direct mimicry of their mothers. But the boy does not have his father immediately available; in addition —especially in the middle classes, but increasingly perhaps in the lower—the things the father does are intangible and difficult for a child to understand, such as working in an office, or even running a complicated machine tool.

Thus the girl has a more favorable opportunity for emotional maturing through positive identification with an adult model, a fact which seems to have much to do with the well-known earlier maturity of girls. The boy on the other hand has a tendency to form a direct feminine identification, since his mother is the model most readily available and significant to him. But he is not destined to become an adult woman. Moreover, he soon discovers that in certain vital respects women are considered inferior to men, that it would hence be shameful for him to grow up to be like a woman. Hence when boys emerge into what Freudians call the "latency period," their behavior tends to be marked by a kind of "compulsive masculinity." They refuse to have anything to do with girls. "Sissy" becomes the worst of all insults. They get interested in athletics and physical prowess, in the things in which men have the most primitive and obvious advantage over women. Furthermore they become allergic to all expression of tender emotion; they must be "tough." This universal pattern bears all the earmarks of a "reaction formation." It is so conspicuous, not because it is simply "masculine nature," but because it is a defense against a feminine identification. The commonness with which "mother fixation" is involved in all types of neurotic and psychotic disorders of Western men strongly confirms this. It may be inferred also that the ambivalence involved is an important source of anxiety—lest one not be able to prove his masculinity—and that aggression toward women, who "after all are to blame," is an essential concomitant.

One particular aspect of this situation is worthy of special attention. In addition to the mother's being the object of love and identification, she is to the young boy the principal agent of socially significant discipline.[5] Not only does she administer the disciplines which make him a tolerable citizen of the family group, but she stimulates him to give a good account of himself outside the home and makes known her disappointment and disapproval if he fails to measure up to her expectations. She, above all, focuses in herself the symbols of what is "good" behavior, of conformity with the expectations of the respectable adult world. When he revolts against identification with his mother in the name of masculinity, it is not surprising that a boy unconsciously identifies "goodness" with femininity and that being a "bad boy" becomes a positive goal. It seems that the association of goodness with femininity, and therewith much of our Western ambivalence toward ethical values, has its roots in this situation. At any rate there is a strong tendency for boyish behavior to run in antisocial if not directly destructive directions, in striking contrast to that of preadolescent girls.

As would be expected if such a pattern is deep-seated and has continued for several generations, it becomes imbedded in the psychology of adults as well as children. The mother therefore secretly —usually unconsciously—admires such behavior and, particularly when it is combined with winning qualities in other respects, rewards it with her love—so the "bad" boy is enabled to have the best of both worlds. She may quite frequently treat such a "bad" son as her favorite as compared with a "sissy" brother who conforms with all her overt expectations much better.

It should be particularly noted that this is not the functionally dominant pattern of the adult masculine role. It combines an emphasis on physical prowess with a kind of irresponsibility. But the adult man predominantly gains his place by using his mind rather than his brawn and by accepting responsibility, not by repudiating it. There must, therefore, in a large majority of boys, be a further transition as they grow to maturity; they must come to value other lines of achievement and accept responsibilities. It is to be presumed that this transition in turn is not accomplished without further repressions. At least this "bad boy" pattern did permit a direct outlet

[5] In this she is followed by a teacher who in the United States is almost always a woman until quite a late stage in the process of schooling.

of aggression in physical terms, though to be sure this could not be directed against mothers. But the discipline of most adult masculine roles sharply limits that, although a sublimated form in competitive activities is still possible. It is, however, probable that this is one important source of a reservoir of latent aggression susceptible of mobilization in group antagonisms, and particularly war, because it legitimatizes physical aggression as such.

With girls the situation is different, but not intrinsically or necessarily more favorable. In childhood a girl has the opportunity to mature primarily through identification with the mother and hence introjection of the mother role pattern. But girls later face a situation of realistic insecurity which profoundly disturbs the continuity of transition to adulthood in this role. In many societies marriages are arranged by the older generation who are primarily concerned with providing good mothers for their grandchildren, and the qualities of this pattern are then a positive asset. But increasingly in Western society a girl must seek her fundamental adult security—which, inherently in the structure of the situation, depends overwhelmingly on her relation to the one particular man she marries—by direct appeal to the personal sentiments of men—and she must do so in competition with the other girls of her age group. Compared with the masculine problem of becoming established in a satisfactory occupational career line, it is a more severe type of competitive insecurity, because so much depends on the one step which is almost irrevocable and the average age of marriage is such that the occupational prospects of a suitor are necessarily still indefinite. In addition to this, she must compete for the personal favor of a young man who, in the nature of the influences to which he has been exposed, tends to be deeply ambivalent about the primary role his future wife is going to play, hence severely handicapped in making rational decisions on such matters.[6]

[6] An additional feature of this ambivalence not touched above concerns attitudes toward sex. The fact of the incest taboo plus the intensity of emotional concentration on the mother makes for strong inhibitions against sexual attachments, since the asexual relation to the mother becomes the ideal of love. The revolt against this attachment in the "bad boy" pattern thus very readily draws the attitude toward sex into the polarity, and sexual interests become

The undoubted predominant tendency in this situation is for the plane of competition in the process of selection of marriage partners to be deflected markedly from attraction to "good wives and mothers" (and husbands and fathers) toward an accent on "romantic love," certain rather immature types of sexuality, and "glamor"—the exploitation of certain specifically feminine assets of attraction.

Psychologically speaking, this situation implies two very fundamental sources of frustration for the growing girl. The first is the discovery of what is, in the relevant sense, "masculine superiority," the fact that her own security like that of other women is dependent on the favor—even "whim"—of a man, that she must compete for masculine favor and cannot stand on her own feet. This is a shock because in her early experience her mother was the center of the world and by identifying with her she expected to be in a similar position. Secondly, it turns out that the qualities and ideals which were the focus of her childhood identification and personality development are not the primary asset in solving her fundamental problem, are even to a degree a positive handicap. The severity and relative abruptness of this transition cannot but, in a large proportion of cases, be a source of much insecurity, hence the source of a high level of anxiety and of aggressive impulses. The primary source of this aggression is the sense of having been deceived, of being allowed to believe that a certain path was the way to security and success only to find that it does not seem to count. The aggression, it may be presumed, is directed both against men and against women: the latter because they are the primary "deceivers," they are not what they seemed to be; the former because it is they who seem to have forced upon women this intolerable fate of having to be two or more incompatible things. This undoubtedly underlies the widespread ambivalence among women toward the role of motherhood,

---

"bad" but attractive. Indeed frequently the hedonic aspect of sex becomes tinged with aggression; sexuality is, so to speak, a means of taking revenge on women for their maltreatment of boys as children. It is notable that the sentimentally idealized stereotype of the "good" woman is strikingly asexual. It may be presumed that this stereotype is largely the product of masculine fantasies.

which is a primary factor in the declining birth rate, as well as toward sexual relations and the role of being a woman in any other fundamental respect.[7]

The upshot of the above analysis is in the first place that the typical Western individual—apart from any special constitutional predispositions—has been through an experience, in the process of growing to adulthood, which involved emotional strains of such severity as to produce an adult personality with a large reservoir of aggressive disposition. Secondly, the bulk of aggression generated from this source must in the nature of the case remain repressed. In spite of the disquieting amount of actual disruption of family solidarity, and quarreling and bickering even where families are not broken up, the social norms enjoining mutual affection among family members, especially respectful affection toward parents and love between spouses, are very powerful. Where such a large reservoir of repressed aggression exists but cannot be directly expressed, it tends to become "free-floating" and to be susceptible of mobilization against various kinds of scapegoats outside the immediate situation of its genesis.

In addition to establishing the basis for the existence of a large reservoir of repressed aggression, the above analysis tells us something of the directions which its indirect expression may be likely to take and the "themes" of grievance which are most likely to arouse aggressive reactions. In the first place, Western society is one in which most positions of large-scale responsibility are held by men. In this connection the cult of "compulsive masculinity" cannot but be of significance. Western men are peculiarly susceptible to the appeal of an adolescent type of assertively masculine behavior and attitude which may take various forms. They have in common a

[7] In this and other previous discussions, emphasis has been deliberately placed on the negative aspect of the situation, the strains and their disruptive consequences. This is because present interest is in sources of aggression. The positive side is not evaluated; hence the reader should exercise great care not to take this discussion as a general appraisal of the emotional qualities of the Western kinship system. Furthermore it should go without saying that these patterns have a very unequal incidence in the population, ranging from virtual negligibility to pathological intensity.

tendency to revolt against the routine aspects of the primarily institutionalized masculine role of sober responsibility, meticulous respect for the rights of others, and tender affection toward women.
Assertion through physical prowess, with an endemic tendency toward violence and hence the military ideal, is inherent in the complex and the most dangerous potentiality.

It is, however, not only masculine psychology which is important
in this respect. Through at least two channels the psychology of
women may play in to reinforce this tendency. First there is undoubtedly widespread if repressed resentment on the part of women
over being forced to accept their sex role and its contradictory components. This is expressed in an undercurrent of aggression toward
the men with whom they are associated, which, given the latter's
hypersensitiveness toward women's attitudes toward them, can be
expected to accentuate the pattern of compulsive masculinity.

But this feminine resentment against men is only one side of an
ambivalent structure of attitudes. The situation by virtue of which
women have to accept an inferior position in crucial respects leads
to an idealization of precisely the extreme type of aggressive masculinity. It is quite clear that Western men are peculiarly dependent
emotionally on women and therefore feminine admiration of them
will powerfully stimulate any pattern of behavior which can evoke it.[8]

The childhood situation of the Western world also provides the
prototypes of what appear to be the two primarily significant themes
or contexts of meaning in which it is easiest to evoke an aggressive
reaction, since these are the contexts in which the people of the
Western world have been oversensitized by the traumatic experiences of their childhood.

The first of these is the question of "adequacy," of living up to
an acceptable standard of achievement or behavior. There is a tendency to be hypersensitive to any suggestion of inferiority or incapacity to achieve goals which have once been set. This in turn is
manifested in two ways of primary significance for present purposes.

[8] The indications are that this feminine admiration, not to say adulation, of
the "heroic" "He-man" pattern played a major role in the spread of the Nazi
movement in Germany.

On the one hand the peoples of Western society are highly susceptible to wishful and distorted beliefs in their own superiority to others, as individuals or in terms of any collectivity with which they are identified, since this belief, and its recognition by others, tends to allay anxiety about their own adequacy. On the other hand, since such a belief in superiority has compulsive characteristics, those who have to deal with such people find it "hard to take," even when the former have a highly realistic attitude. But it also stimulates a vicious circle of resentment on the part of those who, sharing the same hypersensitivity, are treated as inferior. It is, in other words, inordinately easy for either individual or group relationships in the Western world to become defined as relations of superiority and inferiority and to evoke aggressive responses, if the assumption of superiority is, even justly, questioned, or if, again even justly, there is any imputation of inferiority.

The second major context of meaning is that of loyalty, honesty, integrity, justice of dealing. Both in competition with others and in relation to expectations which he has been allowed to build up, the Western child has usually had the traumatic experience of disillusionment, of being "let down." The boy has not been allowed to emulate the ideal of his mother; when he has been "good," he has been punished rather than rewarded for it, and his "bad" brother has been preferred. The girl has found out both that her mother as a woman is an inferior being and that to be a "good woman," that is a mother, does not pay. These experiences are the prototype of a certain hypersensitivity to the question of whether others can be trusted either as individuals or collectivities. In sex relations there is a tendency to be compulsively preoccupied with the fidelity of the partner. In general there is an overreadiness to believe that the other fellow will attempt to deceive or injure one. Naturally, since this hypersensitivity is associated with repressed aggression, it is very easy for the aggressive impulse to be projected on the other party to the relation, producing the "paranoid" pattern of overreadiness to impute hostile intentions where they do not exist, or to exaggerate them grossly where they do. In its extreme form the rest of the world is apt to be seen as mainly preoccupied with plotting to destroy one or one's group. The Western tendency is to be "thin-skinned," unable to "take it," when frustrations must be faced and to place the blame on others when most of it belongs at home.

THE OCCUPATIONAL SYSTEM

The other most fundamental institutional structure of modern Western society, the occupational system, can for present purposes be dealt with much more briefly—especially since a good deal has been anticipated in dealing with kinship, the two being so closely interdependent. Its most essential feature is the primacy of functional achievement. This implies the selection of people on the basis of their capacities to perform the tasks, of innate ability and training, not of birth or any other antecedent element of status. It further implies the segregation of the technical role from other aspects of the incumbent's life most of which are, in the nature of the case, governed by other types of standards. This takes the form in the type case of physical segregation and of segregation of personnel and activity, so that it involves a distinct system of relationships. Finally, it implies a peculiar type of discipline in that any type of personal feeling which might come in conflict with these relationships is subordinated to the requirements of the technical task, which are often highly exacting and often narrowly specialized.

There is an inherently competitive dimension of the occupational system. Even when competitive victory is not as such a major direct goal, but rather is subordinated to functional achievement as such, a selective process, which among other things governs access to opportunity for all the higher achievements, is inherent in the system. A man has to "win" the competition for selection, often repeatedly, in order to have any opportunity to prove his capacity for the higher achievements. The inevitable result of the competitive and selective processes is the distribution of the personnel of the system in a relatively elaborate hierarchy of prestige which is symbolized and expressed in manifold ways.

It is furthermore relevant that in the aggregate particular roles, and still more organizations, undertake functions which are altogether unknown in simpler societies. Men are more frequently sub-jected to the discipline and strains of more exacting skills. But even more important are two other consequences. One is the involvement of people in systems of social relationships of very great complexity which, because of their newness and rapidly changing character, cannot be adequately governed by established and traditionalized norms. The other is the fact that explicit responsibility, in that great consequences hinge on the decisions and competence of individuals, is a far greater factor than in simpler societies. In view of what we know of the deep-seated tendencies to dependency and the psycho-logical difficulties involved in assuming responsibility, this is a fact of prime importance.

When these features of the occupational system are brought into relation to the personality structure discussed above, two classes of conclusions touching the problem of aggression appear to follow. The first set concerns the relation to the general levels of aggression in the society, the second the channeling of what exists into different actual and potential types and directions of expression.

Though it is difficult to arrive at more than a very rough judg-ment, it seems clear that the balance is rather heavily on the side of increasing rather than reducing the levels of insecurity and hence of anxiety and aggression—the foundations of which are laid in the process of socialization in the family. It is true that the wide field for competitive activity provides some outlets which are construc-tive for sublimating aggression by harnessing it to the motivation of constructive achievement, and at the same time "winning." But the other side of the medal is the condemnation of probably a consid-erably larger number to being "losers"—since success in such a system is to a considerable degree inherently relative—and thereby feeding any tendency to feel unduly inadequate or unjustly treated. At the same time, participation in the occupational system means subjection to a severe discipline. It means continual control of emotions so that repression and dissociation are favored rather than counteracted.[9]

[9] This discipline includes adherence to sharply objective standards in the face of the strains growing out of the emotional complexity of the system of social relationships of the work situation, and the additional strains imposed

Perhaps most important of all, however, the competitive process is governed by a rather strict code which is very often in conflict with immediate impulses. In particular it is essential to be a "good loser" and take one's misfortunes and disappointments with outward equanimity. This reinforces the need to repress feelings of resentment against unfair treatment, whether the feelings are realistically justified or not, and hence their availability for mobilization in indirect channels of expression.

The above considerations apply primarily to men since they are the primary carriers of the occupational system. Conversely, however, by the segregation of occupational from familial roles, most women are denied a sense of participation with *their men* in a common enterprise. Moreover, it is in the occupational sphere that the "big things" are done, and this drastic exclusion must serve to increase the inferiority feelings of women and hence their resentment at their condemnation by the accident of sex to an inferior role.

In respect to the channeling of aggression as distinguished from its absolute level, two things are of primary importance. First, if there are no reasons to suppose that, on the average, absolute levels are lowered, at the same time few direct outlets are provided for most types of aggressive impulse. Hence the general need for indirect channels of expression, particularly by displacement on scapegoats, is reinforced by experience in this sphere of life.

Secondly, it is above all in the occupational sphere that the primary institutionalization of the basic themes of the above discussion takes place—childhood is an apprenticeship for the final test which the adult world imposes on man. Ability to perform well and hold one's own or excel in competition is the primary realistic

---

by high levels of responsibility for those who have to assume it. In addition, the mobility which is inherent in such a system has two further significant consequences. Status is inherently insecure, in that it cannot be guaranteed independently of performance—to say nothing of the results of economic fluctuations in causing unemployment and the like. Then technological and organizational change, as well as promotion and job change of the individual, are also inherent and make it difficult to "settle down" to a complete emotional adjustment to any one stable situation; it is necessary to make continual new adjustments with all the attendant emotional difficulty.

test of adult adequacy, but many, probably the considerable majority, are condemned to what, especially if they are oversensitive,
they must feel to be an unsatisfactory experience. Many also will
inevitably feel they have been unjustly treated, because there is in
fact much injustice,. much of which is very deeply rooted in the
nature of the society, and because many are disposed to be paranoid and see more injustice than actually exists. To feel unjustly
treated is moreover not only a balm to one's sense of resentment,
it is an alibi for failure, since how could one succeed if he is not
given a chance?

Thus the kinship and the occupational systems constitute from
the present point of view a mutually reinforcing system of forces
acting on the individual to generate large quantities of aggressive
impulse, to repress the greater part of it, and to channel it in the
direction of finding agencies which can be symbolically held responsible for failure and for deception and injustice to the individual and to those with whom he is identified.[10] Perhaps the most
important mitigation of the general situation which the working of
the occupational system brings about is that occupational success
may do much to reduce the pressure toward compulsive masculinity. But the difficulty here is that sufficient success to have this effect
is attainable only to a minority of the masculine population. Lack
of it would seem to have the opposite effect, and this is just as
much a consequence of the system as the other.

The Structure of Group Hostility

The occupational system of the Western world is probably the
most important institutional "precipitate" of a fundamental dynamic
process, which Max Weber has called the "process of rationaliza-

[10] If anything, probably the kinship system has to absorb more strains originating in the occupational system than vice versa. In any case the effect of
these strains is to accentuate the sources of aggression inherent in the kinship
system rather than to mitigate them. This would appear to operate above all
through the influence on children of parents who themselves are showing the
effects of tension. In so far as a man "takes out" the frustrations of his occupational situation on his wife she may in turn "take it out" on the children.

tion." Through it, as well as other channels, this process has had a fundamental part in structuring attitudes in the Western world which is relevant to the problem of aggression and hence calls for a brief discussion.

The progress of science and related elements of rational thought is the core and fundamental prototype of the process. Science is an inherently dynamic thing. Unless prevented by influences extraneous to it, it will continually evolve. Moreover, unless science is hermetically insulated from the rest of social life, which is manifestly impossible, this dynamic process of change will be extended into neighboring realms of thought, for example, philosophical and religious thought, and in the direction of practical application wherever rational norms play a significant role in the determination of action. Hence through this dynamic factor, a continuing process of change is introduced, both into the primary symbolic systems which help to integrate the life of a society, and into the structure of the situations in which a large part of the population must carry on their activities.

The significance of this arises in the first place from the fact that there is much evidence that security in the sense relevant to this analysis is to a high degree a function of the stability of certain elements of the socio-cultural situation. This is true especially because certain aspects of the situations people face are involved in the actual and, as they feel it, prospective fulfillment of their "legitimate expectations." These expectations are, even apart from any neurotic distortions, apt to be highly concrete so that any change, even if it is not intrinsically unfavorable, is apt to be disturbing and arouse a reaction of anxiety. It should above all be noted that technological change inevitably disrupts the informal human relationships of the members of working groups—relationships which have been shown to be highly important to the stability and working efficiency of the participants.[11] On the other hand, the corresponding process of change on the level of ideas and symbols tends to disrupt established symbolic systems which are exceedingly im-

[11] Cf. Roethlisberger, F. J., and Dickson, William J., *Management and the Worker;* Cambridge, Harvard University Press, 1941.

portant to the security and stability of the orientation of people.

The weight of evidence seems to be that the amount of such change to which even the best integrated personalities can adapt without the possibility of upsetting the smooth functioning of personality is rather limited; but in proportion as there is a neurotic type of insecurity, there tends to be a compulsive need for stability in these respects. The capacity to adapt to both types of change is a function of "emotional maturity," and the above analysis has shown that there must be serious limitations on the levels of emotional maturity which most members of Western society can have attained. There seems, therefore, to be no doubt that the continuing incidence of dynamic change through the process of rationalization is one major source of the generalized insecurity which characterizes our society. As such it should also be a major factor in maintaining the reservoir of aggressive impulses at a high level. It is a factor so deep-seated in our society that it must be expected to continue to operate on a major scale for the foreseeable future; only profound changes in the whole social situation which would invalidate the greater part of this analysis would produce a situation where this would not be true.

It is not, however, the significance of the process of rationalization, as a source of quantitative addition to the reservoir of aggression, which is most important, but rather the way it operates to structure the direction of its actual and potential expression. It is a major factor in the polarization of attitudes in the society, especially as they are distributed between different groups in the population in such a way as to focus anxiety and aggression on a single structured line of tension.

It must be remembered that the incidence of the process of rationalization is highly uneven in the social structure. With respect to any given level of traditionalized values, symbols, and structuring of situations, there are always relatively "emancipated" and relatively traditional groups and sectors of the society. Certain of the emancipated groups, like the best of the professions for instance, become relatively well institutionalized so that the dynamic process of which they are agents is not so disturbing to them. They always, however, contain at least a fringe, if not more, where insecurity is expressed in compulsively distorted patterns of extreme emancipation which are highly provocative to the more traditionalized elements, which lead into a vicious circle in proportion as elements of both groups are compulsively motivated.

The process is, however, always tending to spread into the relatively traditionalized areas of the society and thereby tending to threaten the security of the population elements most dependent on traditionalized patterns. Partly these elements already have serious insecurities and are compulsively dependent on traditionalism; partly change introduces new insecurities. In either case, the result is to stimulate what has elsewhere been called a "fundamentalist reaction," a compulsively distorted exaggeration of traditional values and other related patterns.[12] This above all attaches to those elements of culture and society which are not so readily and in the same sense susceptible of rationalization as are the areas of science, technology, and administrative organization—namely, religion, family, class attitudes, the informal traditions of ethnic culture, and the like, where nonlogical symbolic systems are heavily involved.

The reverse side of the exaggerated assertion of these traditional patterns is the aggressive attack on the symbols which appear to threaten them, science as such, atheism and other antireligious aspects of liberal rationalism, the relaxation of traditional sex morality—especially in the larger urban communities and in "bohemian" circles—political and economic radicalism, and the like. The compulsive adherents of emancipated values on the other hand tend to brand all traditional values as "stupid," reactionary, unenlightened, and thus a vicious circle of mounting antagonism readily gets started. This polarization in fact corresponds roughly to structured differentiations of the society, with latent or more or less actual conflicts of interest as between rural and urban elements, capital and labor, upper and lower class groups, and the like, which feed fuel to the flames.

[12] Cf. Parsons, Talcott, Some Sociological Aspects of the Fascist Movements, *Social Forces*, Nov. 1942. Also: The Sociology of Modern Anti-Semitism in *Jews in a Gentile World*, Graeber & Britt [ed.]; N. Y., Macmillan, 1942.

It is above all important that the values about which the funda-mentalist pattern of reaction tends to cluster are those particularly important in the constitution and symbolization of informal group solidarities—those of families, social class, socio-religious groups, ethnic groups, and nations. Many of these solidarities are seriously in conflict with the explicit values of the Western world which largely stem from the rationalistic traditions of the enlightenment.[13] They are hence particularly difficult to defend against rationalistic attack. Since, however, they are of fundamental emotional impor-tance, the consequence more frequently than not is their "defensive" assertion rather than their abandonment. This very difficulty of rational defense when rational values are in fact accepted favors this context as a field for the mobilization of repressed aggression, since it is in a state of bafflement that people are most likely to react with "unreasonable" aggression.

These circumstances seem to go far toward explaining the strik-ing fact that aggression in the Western world tends to focus so much on antagonisms between solidary groups. Some of these groups are, to be sure, those growing out of the formal and utili-tarian structure of modern society, like the conflict of business and the labor unions. Probably more important, however, are the lines of conflict which cut across these groups, particularly those between religious and ethnic groups within nations and, above all, the con-flict of nationalisms. Group conflict seems to be particularly signifi-cant because on the one hand solidarity with an informal group, the appeal of which is to "infra-rational" sentiments, is a peculiarly potent measure for allaying the neurotic types of anxiety which are so common; on the other hand an antagonistic group is a peculiarly appropriate symbolic object on which to displace the emotional re-actions which cannot be openly expressed within one's own group lest they threaten its solidarity. In this whole context, it is peculiarly appropriate that groups be available in regard to which the ambiv-alent structure of emotions in relation to the two dominant themes discussed above can be expressed. The "outgroup" should, that is,

[13] Cf. Gunnar Myrdal's discussion of "The American Creed" in *An American Dilemma;* N. Y., Harpers, 1944 (2 vols.).

be a group in relation to which one's own group can feel a comfortably self-righteous sense of superiority and at the same time a group which can be plausibly accused of arrogating to itself an illegitimate superiority of its own. Correspondingly it should be a group with strong claims to a position of high ethical standing of its own which, however, can plausibly be made out to be essentially specious and to conceal a subtle deception. The Jews have in both these connections furnished almost the ideal scapegoat throughout the Western world.

Latent aggression has thus been channeled into internal group conflicts of various sorts throughout the Western world: anti-semitism and anti-laborism, and anti-negro, anti-Catholic, and anti-foreigner feeling are found in this country. There are, however, potent reasons why nationalism should be the most important and serious focus of these tendencies. The first is the realistic basis of it. The organization of our civilization into nation-states which are the dominant power units has been a crucial realistic fact of the situation. Above all, in the chronic tendency to resort to war in crisis situations the loyalty to one's government has had to be in one sense the ultimate residual loyalty, the one which could claim any sacrifice no matter how great if need be.

At the same time it is highly significant that as between the fundamentalist and the emancipated poles of modern attitude structure, nationalistic loyalty as such is largely neutral. It is, however, a particularly suitable focus for fundamentalist sentiments in accusing their opponents of a specious sincerity since it does tend to be an ultimate test of altruism and sincerity. The "foreigner" is, moreover, outside the principal immediate system of law and order; hence aggression toward him does not carry the same opprobrium or immediate danger of reprisal that it does toward one's "fellow-citizen." Hostility to the foreigner has thus furnished a means of transcending the principal, immediately threatening group conflicts, of achieving "unity"—but at the expense of a less immediate but in fact more dangerous threat to security, since national states now command such destructive weapons that war between them is approaching suicidal significance.

Thus the immense reservoir of aggression in Western society is sharply inhibited from direct expression within the smaller groups in which it is primarily generated. The structure of the society in which it is produced contains a strong predisposition for it to be channeled into group antagonisms. The significance of the nation-state is, however, such that there is a strong pressure to internal unity within each such unit and therefore a tendency to focus aggression on the potential conflicts between nation-state units. In addition to the existence of a plurality of such units, each a potential target of the focussed aggression from all the others, the situation is particularly unstable because of the endemic tendency to define their relations in the manner least calculated to build an effectively solidary international order. Each state is, namely, highly ambivalent about the superiority-inferiority question. Each tends to have a deep-seated presumption of its own superiority and a corresponding resentment against any other's corresponding presumption. Each at the same time tends to feel that it has been unfairly treated in the past and is ready on the slightest provocation to assume that the others are ready to plot new outrages in the immediate future. Each tends to be easily convinced of the righteousness of its own policy while at the same time it is overready to suspect the motives of all others. In short, the "jungle philosophy" —which corresponds to a larger element in the real sentiments of all of us than can readily be admitted, even to ourselves—tends to be projected onto the relations of nation-states at precisely the point where, under the technological and organizational situation of the modern world, it can do the most harm.

CONCLUSION

In conclusion, to forestall misunderstanding, it is well to call explicit attention to some of the limitations of the analysis just developed. That it is specifically limited to analyzing sources of aggression and their channeling has already been stated. It needs, however, to be repeated that the more positive sides are deliberately omitted. It is thus not in any sense a complete or balanced picture of the dynamic psychological balance of Western society, even so far as such a picture could be drawn in the light of present knowledge and on a comparable level of generality and abstraction. Above all, it should not by itself be taken as an adequate basis for any suggestions of remedial action. By omitting consideration of the positive aspects, it has precisely neglected the principal assets on which any such program would have to rely. It is confined to a specifically limited diagnostic function. Its results must be combined with those of other studies before they have any practical value beyond this.

This analysis has also been couched in terms of a very high level of "ideal-typical" abstraction. It has presumed to deal with the social structure and psychological dynamics of the Western world as a whole, in full consciousness of the fact that there are and have been innumerable ranges of variation within this enormously complicated socio-cultural system, many of which are of prime significance to any practical purpose.

In the first place, within any one national society this analysis applies unequally to different elements of its population. In fact, it applies most completely and directly to the urban, middle-class elements, those which have been most heavily involved in the consequences of the industrial revolution. Substantial modifications need to be made in dealing with rural populations. The same is true of the highest élite groups, particularly those whose position was firmly institutionalized before the major social changes of the industrial era took place. This is especially true of the older European hereditary aristocracies. It is even necessary to make substantial modifications for the case of social groups which have so low a status that their being in the major competition for places on the general scale of prestige cannot be realistically supposed, thus for large parts, at least, of the "proletarian" elements. These are only among the most conspicuous of the qualifications, each of which would have important consequences for the psychological reaction patterns of the relevant groups.

Similarly, most of the "secondary" complications of the system of dynamic relationships under consideration have perforce been neglected. It is a fact of the first importance that, for instance, in American adult culture there is a fundamentally important institutionalization of "adolescent" values which is in continual competition with the main system.

Finally, it is quite clear that there are extremely important national variations in the relevant patterns. To a considerable degree the analysis has been focussed on American conditions. Their greater familiarity favors this. But it is not necessarily a source of serious bias, since in certain respects the United States represents a closer approach to the "ideal type" of structure which is of prime strategic significance for the whole Western world—significant because the fundamental patterns of industrial society here have been less modified by powerful institutional complexes which were present in the pre-existing society.

France, for instance, has developed less far along these lines than most Western countries, and has integrated more of the older society with the new tendencies. There seems, for instance, to have been far less isolation of the immediate conjugal family there than in this country.

Certain of the consequences most important to the practical situation have appeared most highly developed in Germany and greatly accentuated under the Nazi regime.[14] The peculiarly virulent nationalistic aggressiveness of Nazi Germany certainly cannot be adequately explained in terms of the factors analyzed in the present paper. It depended on other elements which were either peculiar to Germany, or relatively far more important there than for instance in this country. This is true of the strongly authoritarian character of the father-son relationship, and of the much more sharply subordinated position of women in Germany. There was also a much more rigidly formalistic and hierarchical occupational system there, and conditions were much more favorable to the development of a strongly militaristic variety of nationalism.

[14] Cf. Parsons, Democracy and Social Structure in Pre-Nazi Germany, *J. Legal and Political Sociology*, Nov. 1942, and The Problem of Controlled Institutional Change, PSYCHIATRY (1945) 8:79-101. See also Erikson, Erik Homburger, Hitler's Imagery and the Dream of German Youth, PSYCHIATRY (1942) 5:475-493.

Nevertheless, differences of this sort do not invalidate the analysis presented here. They are, however extremely deviant, variations on the same fundamental themes. Much of the general foundation of the situation has been in fact common to all the major nations of the Western world where the process of industrialization and rationalization has taken strong hold. It is a question, not of a right and a wrong analysis, but of the appropriate adaptation of one which is in the nature of the case general and abstract, to the concretely variable circumstances of different particular situations. This adaptation is achieved, not by substituting a new "correct" for an incorrect explanation, but by introducing an analysis of the effect of specific modifications of the generalized structure presented here, and by taking account of additional factors which the generality of this analysis has not permitted to be treated.

CONTINUITIES AND DISCONTINUITIES IN CULTURAL CONDITIONING

Ruth Benedict

ALL CULTURES must deal in one way or another with the cycle of growth from infancy to adulthood. Nature has posed the situation dramatically: on the one hand, the new born baby, physiologically vulnerable, unable to fend for itself, or to participate of its own initiative in the life of the group, and, on the other, the adult man or woman. Every man who rounds out his human potentialities must have been a son first and a father later and the two roles are physiologically in great contrast; he must first have been dependent upon others for his very existence and later he must provide such security for others. This discontinuity in the life cycle is a fact of nature and is inescapable. Facts of nature, however, in any discussion of human problems, are ordinarily read off not at their bare minimal but surrounded by all the local accretions of behavior to which the student of human affairs has become accustomed in his own culture. For that reason it is illuminating to examine comparative material from other societies in order to get a wider perspective on our own special accretions. The anthropologist's role is not to question the facts of nature, but to insist upon the interposition of a middle term between "nature" and "human behavior"; his role is to analyse that term, to document local man-made doctorings of nature and to insist that these doctorings should not be read off in any one culture as nature itself. Although it is a fact of nature that the child becomes a man, the way in which this transition is effected varies from one society to another, and no one of these particular cultural bridges should be regarded as the "natural" path to maturity.

From a comparative point of view our culture goes to great extremes in emphasizing contrasts between the child and the adult. The child is sexless, the adult estimates his virility by his sexual activities; the child must be protected from the ugly facts of life, the adult must meet them without psychic catastrophe; the child must obey, the adult must command this obedience. These are all dogmas of our culture, dogmas which, in spite of the facts of nature; other cultures commonly do not share. In spite of the physiological contrasts between child and adult these are cultural accretions.

It will make the point clearer if we consider one habit in our own culture in regard to which there is not this discontinuity of conditioning. With the greatest clarity of purpose and economy of training, we achieve our goal of conditioning everyone to eat three meals a day. The baby's training in regular food periods begins at birth and no crying of the child and no inconvenience to the mother is allowed to interfere. We gauge the child's physiological make-up and at first allow it food oftener than adults, but, because our goal is firmly set and our training consistent, before the child is two years old it has achieved the adult schedule. From the point of view of other cultures this is as startling as the fact of three-year-old babies perfectly at home in deep water is to us. Modesty is another sphere in which our child training is consistent and economical; we waste no time in clothing the baby and, in contrast to many societies where the child runs naked till it is ceremonially given its skirt or its pubic sheath at adolescence, the child's training fits it precisely for adult conventions.

In neither of these aspects of behavior is there need for an individual in our culture to embark before puberty, at puberty or at some later date upon a course of action which all his previous training has tabued. He is spared the unsureness inevitable in such a transition.

The illustration I have chosen may appear trivial, but in larger and more important aspects of behavior, our methods are obviously different. Because of the great variety of child training in different families in our society, I might illustrate continuity of conditioning from individual life histories in our culture, but even these, from a comparative point of view, stop far short of consistency and I shall therefore confine myself to describing arrangements in other cultures in which training, which with us is idiosyncratic, is accepted and traditional and does not therefore involve the same possibility of conflict. I shall choose childhood rather than infant and nursing situations not because the latter do not vary strikingly in different cultures but because they are nevertheless more circumscribed by the baby's physiological needs than is its later training. Childhood situations provide an excellent field in which to illustrate the range of cultural adjustments which are possible within a universally given, but not so drastic, set of physiological facts.

The major discontinuity in the life cycle is of course that the child who is at one point a son must later be a father. These roles in our society are strongly differentiated; a good son is tractable, and does not assume adult responsibilities; a good father provides for his children and should not allow his authority to be flouted. In addition the child must be sexless so far as his family is concerned, whereas the father's sexual role is primary in the family. The individual in one role must revise his behavior from almost all points of view when he assumes the second role.

I shall select for discussion three such contrasts that occur in our culture between the individual's role as child and as father: 1. responsible—non-responsible status role, 2. dominance—submission, 3. contrasted sexual role. It is largely upon our cultural commitments to these three contrasts that the discontinuity in the life cycle of an individual in our culture depends.

1. RESPONSIBLE—NON-RESPONSIBLE STATUS ROLE.

The techniques adopted by societies which achieve continuity during the life cycle in this sphere in no way differ from those we employ in our uniform conditioning to three meals a day. They are merely applied to other areas of life. We think of the child as wanting to play and the adult as having to work, but in many societies the mother takes the baby daily in her shawl or carrying net to the garden or to gather roots, and adult labor is seen even in infancy from the pleasant security of its position in close contact with its mother. When the child can run about it accompanies its parents still, doing tasks which are essential and yet suited to its powers, and this dichotomy between work and play is not different from that [which] its parents recognize, namely, the distinction between the busy day and the free evening. The tasks it is asked to perform are graded to its powers and its elders wait quietly by, not offering to do the task in the child's place. Everyone who is familiar with such societies has been struck by the contrast with our child training. Dr. Ruth Underhill tells me of sitting with a group of Papago elders in Arizona when the man of the house turned to his little three-year old granddaughter and asked her to close the door. The door was heavy and hard to shut. The child tried, but it did not move. Several times the grandfather repeated, "Yes, close the door." No one jumped to the child's assistance. No one took the responsibility away from her. On the other hand there was no impatience, for after all the child was small. They sat gravely waiting till the child succeeded and her grandfather gravely thanked her. It was assumed that the task would not be asked of her unless she could perform it, and having been asked the responsibility was hers alone just as if she were a grown woman.

The essential point of such child training is that the child is from infancy continuously conditioned to responsible social participation while at the same time the tasks that are expected of it are adapted to its capacity. The contrast with our society is very great. A child does not make any labor contribution to our industrial society except as it competes with an adult; its work is not measured against its own strength and skill but against high-geared industrial requirements. Even when we praise a child's achievement in the home we are outraged if such praise is interpreted as being of the same order as praise of adults. The child is praised because the parent feels well disposed, regardless of whether the task is well done by adult standards, and the child acquires no sensible standard by which to measure its achievement. The gravity of a Cheyenne Indian family ceremoniously making a feast out of the little boy's first snowbird is at the furthest remove from our behavior. At birth the little boy was presented with a toy bow, and from the time he could run about serviceable bows suited to his stature were specially made for him by the man of the family. Animals and birds were taught him in a graded series beginning with those most easily taken, and as he brought in his first of each species his family duly made a feast of it, accepting his contribution as gravely as the buffalo his father brought. When he finally killed a buffalo, it was only the final step of his childhood conditioning, not a new adult role with which his childhood experience had been at variance.

The Canadian Ojibwa show clearly what results can be achieved. This tribe gains its livelihood by winter trapping and the small family of father, mother and children live during the long winter alone on their great frozen hunting grounds. The boy accompanies his father and brings in his catch to his sister as his father does to his mother; the girl prepares the meat and skins for him just as his mother does for her husband. By the time the boy is 12, he may have set his own line of traps on a hunting territory of his own and return to his parent's house only once in several months—still bringing the meat and skins to his sister. The young child is taught consistently that it has only itself to rely upon in life, and this is as true in the dealings it will have with the supernatural as in the business of getting a livelihood. This attitude he will accept as a successful adult just as he accepted it as a child.[1]

2. DOMINANCE—SUBMISSION

Dominance-submission is the most striking of those categories of behavior where like does not respond to like but where one type of behavior stimulates the opposite response. It is one of the most prominent ways in which behavior is patterned in our culture. When it obtains between classes, it may be nourished by continuous experience; the difficulty in its use between children and adults lies in the fact that an individual conditioned to one set of behavior in childhood must adopt the opposite as an adult. Its opposite is

[1] Landes, Ruth, *The Ojibwa Woman*, Part 1, Youth—Columbia University Contributions to Anthropology, Volume XXXI.

a pattern of approximately identical reciprocal behavior, and societies which rely upon continuous conditioning characteristically
invoke this pattern. In some primitive cultures the very terminology
of address between father and son, and more commonly, between
grandchild and grandson or uncle and nephew, reflects this attitude.
In such kinship terminologies one reciprocal expresses each of these
relationships so that son and father, for instance, exchange the same
term with one another, just as we exchange the same term with a
cousin. The child later will exchange it with his son. "Father—
son," therefore, is a continuous relationship he enjoys throughout
life. The same continuity, backed up by verbal reciprocity, occurs
far oftener in the grandchild-grandson relationship or that of
mother's brother-sister's son. When these are "joking" relationships,
as they often are, travellers report wonderingly upon the liberties
and pretensions of tiny toddlers in their dealings with these family
elders. In place of our dogma of respect to elders such societies
employ in these cases a reciprocity as nearly identical as may be.
The teasing and practical joking the grandfather visits upon his
grandchild, the grandchild returns in like coin; he would be led to
believe that he failed in propriety if he did not give like for like.
If the sister's son has right of access without leave to his mother's
brother's possessions, the mother's brother has such rights also to
the child's possessions. They share reciprocal privileges and obligations which in our society can develop only between age mates.

From the point of view of our present discussion, such kinship
conventions allow the child to put in practice from infancy the
same forms of behavior which it will rely upon as an adult; behavior
is not polarized into a general requirement of submission for the
child and dominance for the adult.

It is clear from the techniques described above by which the
child is conditioned to a responsible status role that these depend
chiefly upon arousing in the child the desire to share responsibility
in adult life. To achieve this little stress is laid upon obedience but
much stress upon approval and praise. Punishment is very commonly regarded as quite outside the realm of possibility, and natives
in many parts of the world have drawn the conclusion from our

usual disciplinary methods that white parents do not love their children. If the child is not required to be submissive, however, many occasions for punishment melt away; a variety of situations which call for it do not occur. Many American Indian tribes are especially explicit in rejecting the ideal of a child's submissive or obedient behavior. Prince Maximilian von Wied who visited the Crow Indians over a hundred years ago describes a father's boasting about his young son's intractibility even when it was the father himself who was flouted; "He will be a man," his father said. He would have been baffled at the idea that his child should show behavior which would obviously make him appear a poor creature in the eyes of his fellows if he used it as an adult. Dr. George Devereaux tells me of a special case of such an attitude among the Mohave at the present time. The child's mother was white and protested to its father that he must take action when the child disobeyed and struck him. "But why?" the father said, "he is little. He cannot possibly injure me." He did not know of any dichotomy according to which an adult expects obedience and a child must accord it. If his child had been docile he would simply have judged that it would become a docile adult—an eventuality of which he would not have approved.

Child training which brings about the same result is common also in other areas of life than that of reciprocal kinship obligations between child and adult. There is a tendency in our culture to regard every situation as having in it the seeds of a dominance-submission relationship. Even where dominance-submission is patently irrelevant we read in the dichotomy, assuming that in every situation there must be one person dominating another. On the other hand some cultures, even when the situation calls for leadership, do not see it in terms of dominance-submission. To do justice to this attitude it would be necessary to describe their political and especially their economic arrangements, for such an attitude to persist must certainly be supported by economic mechanisms that are congruent with it. But it must also be supported by—or what comes to the same thing, express itself in—child training and familial situations.

3. Contrasted Sexual Role

Continuity of conditioning in training the child to assume responsibility and to behave no more submissively than adults is quite possible in terms of the child's physiological endowment if his participation is suited to his strength. Because of the late development of the child's reproductive organs continuity of conditioning in sex experience presents a difficult problem. So far as their belief that the child is anything but a sexless being is concerned, they are probably more nearly right than we are with an opposite dogma. But the great break is presented by the universally sterile unions before puberty and the presumably fertile ones after maturation. This physiological fact no amount of cultural manipulation can minimize or alter, and societies therefore which stress continuous conditioning most strongly sometimes do not expect children to be interested in sex experience until they have matured physically. This is striking among American Indian tribes like the Dakota; adults observe great privacy in sex acts and in no way stimulate children's sexual activity. There need be no discontinuity, in the sense in which I have used the term, in such a program if the child is taught nothing it does not have to unlearn later. In such cultures adults view children's experimentation as in no way wicked or dangerous but merely as innocuous play which can have no serious consequences. In some societies such play is minimal and the children manifest little interest in it. But the same attitude may be taken by adults in societies where such play is encouraged and forms a major activity among small children. This is true among most of the Melanesian cultures of Southeast New Guinea; adults go as far as to laugh off sexual affairs within the prohibited class if the children are not mature, saying that since they cannot marry there can be no harm done.

It is this physiological fact of the difference between children's sterile unions and adults' presumably fertile sex relations which must be kept in mind in order to understand the different mores which almost always govern sex expression in children and in adults in the same culture. A great many cultures with preadolescent sexual license require marital fidelity and a great many which value pre-marital virginity in either male or female arrange their marital life with great license. Continuity in sex experience is complicated by factors which it was unnecessary to consider in the problems previously discussed. The essential problem is not whether or not the child's sexuality is consistently exploited—for even where such exploitation is favored in the majority of cases the child must seriously modify his behavior at puberty or at marriage. Continuity in sex expression means rather that the child is taught nothing it must unlearn later. If the cultural emphasis is upon sexual pleasure the child who is continuously conditioned will be encouraged to experiment freely and pleasurably, as among the Marquesans; [2] if emphasis is upon reproduction, as among the Zuni of New Mexico, childish sex proclivities will not be exploited, for the only important use which sex is thought to serve in his culture is not yet possible to him. The important contrast with our child training is that although a Zuni child is impressed with the wickedness of premature sex experimentation he does not run the risk as in our culture of associating this wickedness with sex itself rather than with sex at his age. The adult in our culture has often failed to unlearn the wickedness or the dangerousness of sex, a lesson which was impressed upon him strongly in his most formative years.

DISCONTINUITY IN CONDITIONING

Even from this very summary statement of continuous conditioning the economy of such mores is evident. In spite of the obvious advantages, however, there are difficulties in its way. Many primitive societies expect as different behavior from an individual as child and as adult as we do, and such discontinuity involves a presumption of strain.

Many societies of this type however minimize strain by the techniques they employ, and some techniques are more successful than others in ensuring the individual's functioning without conflict. It is from this point of view that age-grade societies reveal their fundamental significance. Age-graded cultures characteristically demand

[2] Ralph Linton, class notes on the Marquesans.

different behavior of the individual at different times of his life and persons of a like age-grade are grouped into a society whose activities are all oriented toward the behavior desired at that age. Individuals "graduate" publicly and with honor from one of these groups to another. Where age society members are enjoined to loyalty and mutual support, and are drawn not only from the local group but from the whole tribe as among the Arapaho, or even from other tribes as among the Wagawaga of Southeast New Guinea, such an institution has many advantages in eliminating conflicts among local groups and fostering intra-tribal peace. This seems to be also a factor in the tribal military solidarity of the similarly organized Masai of East Africa. The point that is of chief interest for our present discussion, however, is that by this means an individual who at any time takes on a new set of duties and virtues is supported not only by a solid phalanx of age mates but by the traditional prestige of the organized "secret" society into which he has now graduated. Fortified in this way, individuals in such cultures often swing between remarkable extremes of opposite behavior without apparent psychic threat. For example, the great majority exhibit prideful and non-conflicted behavior at each stage in the life cycle even when a prime of life devoted to passionate and aggressive head hunting must be followed by a later life dedicated to ritual and to mild and peaceable civic virtues.[3]

Our chief interest here, however, is in discontinuity which primarily affects the child. In many primitive societies such discontinuity has been fostered not because of economic or political necessity or because such discontinuity provides for a socially valuable division of labor, but because of some conceptual dogma. The most striking of these are the Australian and Papuan cultures where the ceremony of the "Making of Man" flourishes. In such societies it is believed that men and women have opposite and conflicting powers, and male children, who are of undefined status, must be initiated into the male role. In Central Australia the boy child is of the woman's side and women are tabu in the final adult stages of tribal ritual. The elaborate and protracted initiation ceremonies of

[3] Henry Elkin, manuscript on the Arapaho.

the Arunta therefore snatch the boy from the mother, dramatize his gradual repudiation of her. In a final ceremony he is reborn as a man out of the men's ceremonial "baby pouch." The men's ceremonies are ritual statements of a masculine solidarity, carried out by fondling one another's *churingas,* the material symbol of each man's life, and by letting out over one another blood drawn from their veins. After this warm bond among men has been established through the ceremonies, the boy joins the men in the men's house and participates in tribal rites.[4] The enjoined discontinuity has been tribally bridged.

West of the Fly River in southern New Guinea there is a striking development of this Making of Men cult which involves a childhood period of passive homosexuality. Among the Keraki [5] it is thought that no boy can grow to full stature without playing the role for some years. Men slightly older take the active role, and the older man is a jealous partner. The life cycle of the Keraki Indians includes, therefore, in succession, passive homosexuality, active homosexuality and heterosexuality. The Keraki believe that pregnancy will result from post-pubertal passive homosexuality and see evidences of such practices in any fat man whom, even as an old man, they may kill or drive out of the tribe because of their fear. The ceremony that is of interest in connection with the present discussion takes place at the end of the period of passive homosexuality. This ceremony consists in burning out the possibility of pregnancy from the boy by pouring lye down his throat, after which he has no further protection if he gives way to the practice. There is no technique for ending active homosexuality, but this is not explicitly tabu for older men; heterosexuality and children however are highly valued. Unlike the neighboring Marindanim who share their homosexual practices, Keraki husband and wife share the same house and work together in the gardens.

I have chosen illustrations of discontinuous conditioning where

[4] Spencer, B., and Gillen, F. J., *The Arunta;* N. Y., Macmillan, 1927 (2 vols.). Róheim, Géza, Psycho-Analysis of Primitive Cultural Types. *Internat. J. Psychoanal.* (1932) 13:1-224—in particular, Chapter III, on the Aranda, The Children of the Desert.

[5] Williams, Francis E., *Papuans of the Trans-Fly;* Oxford, 1936.

it is not too much to say that the cultural institutions furnish adequate support to the individual as he progresses from role to role or interdicts the previous behavior in a summary fashion. The contrast with arrangements in our culture is very striking, and against this background of social arrangements in other cultures the adolescent period of *Sturm und Drang* with which we are so familiar becomes intelligible in terms of our discontinuous cultural institutions and dogmas rather than in terms of physiological necessity. It is even more pertinent to consider these comparative facts in relation to maladjusted persons in our culture who are said to be fixated at one or another pre-adult level. It is clear that, if we were to look at our social arrangements as an outsider, we should infer directly from our family institutions and habits of child training that many individuals would not "put off childish things"; we should have to say that our adult activity demands traits that are interdicted in children, and that far from redoubling efforts to help children bridge this gap, adults in our culture put all the blame on the child when he fails to manifest spontaneously the new behavior or, overstepping the mark, manifests it with untoward belligerence. It is not surprising that in such a society many individuals fear to use behavior which has up to that time been under a ban and trust instead, though at great psychic cost, to attitudes that have been exercised with approval during their formative years. Insofar as we invoke a physiological scheme to account for these neurotic adjustments we are led to overlook the possibility of developing social institutions which would lessen the social cost we now pay; instead we elaborate a set of dogmas which prove inapplicable under other social conditions.

PERSON, PERSONALITY, GROUP, CULTURE *

Harold D. Lasswell

THE four terms which figure in the title of this article are among the cardinal terms in the science of interpersonal relations. The purpose of this discussion is to clarify the method by which the meaning of these terms may be made explicit. The terminology owes something to the Cambridge logical school, and especially Whitehead.[1] The debt is evident in the use of such expressions as "event," and "event manifold."

Perhaps it is not beside the point to remind ourselves of the interest in the study of meaning which has been so acute among social scientists and psychologists in recent years. A great impetus was given to "word consciousness" by the publication of *The Meaning of Meaning* by Ogden and Richards, with a valuable appendix by Malinowski.[2] It is significant that this book was a collaboration of specialists on different aspects of psychology and culture. Ogden was a psychologist, Richards was a literary critic and humanist,

* This is part of a larger memorandum which dealt with personality, culture, and education, and which was prepared for the use of a seminar on educational measurement organized under the auspices of the General Education Board. Used by permission.

[1] See especially Whitehead, Alfred North, *An Enquiry Concerning the Principles of Natural Knowledge;* Cambridge, Cambridge University Press, 1919 (xii and 200 pp.); *The Concept of Nature;* Cambridge, Cambridge University Press, 1920 (viii and 202 pp.); *Process and Reality, an Essay in Cosmology,* New York, Macmillan, 1929 (xii and 547 pp.).

[2] Ogden, Charles K., and Richards, I. A., *The Meaning of Meaning: A Study of the Influence of Language Upon Thought and of the Science of Symbolism;* New York, Harcourt, Brace and Co., 1927 (xxxi and 544 pp.).

and Malinowski was a social anthropologist. This is typical of the many quarters from which interesting contributions have been made to the understanding of words and their meaning. Specialists on general linguistics like Sapir, clinical psychologists like Freud, child psychologists and educators like Piaget and Thorndike, have had something to offer.

It was no accident that the *Meaning of Meaning* came from England and that it was profoundly influenced by the "Cambridge Logical School." Since the migration of Whitehead to Harvard there has been a growing body of scientific speech in the United States which makes use of the "event" categories which were so profoundly shaped by Whitehead. Developments similar to those in England and the United States were taking place at the same time in the other intellectual centers of Western European civilization. Perhaps the group of most interest to Americans was the logical positivists of Vienna. (Probably the names best known in this country are Carnap and Reichenbach.) A Polish philosopher, Korzybski, long resident in the United States, has attracted a great deal of popular and some scientific attention by his systematic treatise, *Science and Sanity*.[3] Arthur Bentley, an American social psychologist, has also published in the newer idiom.

One result of this discussion among logicians has been to clarify three dimensions of word analysis. The relationship of words to words may be called logic—syntactics; the relationship of words to their events of reference may be called semantics; and the relationship of words to practical causes and practical results may be called pragmatics. Distinctions of this kind have been clearly made by Charles W. Morris in the *International Encyclopaedia of Unified Science*.[4]

Among historians and students of comparative history, word-

[3] Korzybski, Alfred, *Science and Sanity: An Introduction to non-Aristotelian Systems and General Semantics,* Lancaster, Pa., Science Press, 1933 (xx and 798 pp.).

[4] The *Encyclopedia* is in process of publication at the University of Chicago Press under the general editorship of Otto Neurath, with the assistance of Rudolph Carnap and Charles W. Morris. Professor Morris has developed the "Foundations of the Theory of Signs" in the second number.

consciousness has been of growing importance for at least one hundred years. The study of words and their place in society has been closely connected with the revolutionary movements of the nineteenth and twentieth centuries. The group which centered modern attention upon the symbol was largely made up of critics of the dogmas with which Western European civilization entered the nineteenth century. The students of comparative religion developed secular interpretations of religious ritual and belief. Students of comparative economics and politics challenged the "ideology" of modern capitalism. One of the great names in connection with the analysis of the religious tradition of Western Europe is Feuerbach. Marx made use of some of the categories of Feuerbach in analyzing other forms of accepted language in our society. It was Marx and Engels who were chiefly responsible for the controversies which have centered around the term "ideology."

The word "ideology" was used by them to refer to all of the words, and supporting subjective states, which contributed to the survival of capitalism.

As the number of specialists on social science increased, more attention was given to the examination of ideology. One result was to generalize the concept of myth—Sorel. In recent usage the term "myth" is impartially employed to refer to any words in the name of which social groups undertake to advance or defend their position in society. The mythology of the established order is ideology and, following the terminology of Karl Mannheim, the mythology of those who attack an established order is called Utopia.

The analysis of the myth has gone forward simultaneously in every center of European life. In recent times France has contributed Durkheim; Italy has been represented by Mosca and Pareto. The most important name in the history of English thought in this connection is Jeremy Bentham, with his *Theory of Fictions*.[5]

The growth of word consciousness has another interesting aspect. The study of words has encouraged the study of the word user. Indeed, one distinguishing mark of the intellectuals of our time is

[5] Bentham, Jeremy, *The Theory of Fictions* [with an Introduction by Charles K. Ogden]; London, Kegan Paul, Trench, and Trubner, 1932 (161 pp.).

the growth of that special form of tool consciousness which is word consciousness. As the intellectuals have become more aware of their distinctive tools, they have become more aware of themselves. Hence, intellectuals have been taking themselves as objects of scientific investigation. They are a segment of the skill specialists of modern society. Their distinctive skill is the manipulation of symbols.

The problem of the intellectual was sharply posed in the writings of Marx and Engels, who gave attention to the alleged parasitism of the intellectual. They thought of the intellectuals as dependent upon the dominant economic classes.

As systematic reflection on the problem of the intellectual in society has increased, new hypotheses have been advanced. One of the most interesting was that of the Polish-Russian revolutionist who wrote under the name of Wolski, and whose ideas have been made available in the West by Max Nomad. Instead of dismissing the intellectuals as a subordinate social formation, Wolski spoke of the intellectuals and the semi-intellectuals as constituting a new social class which was in process of rising to power. The "capital" of the intellectual is his knowledge, and the intellectual is rising at the expense of aristocracy and plutocracy. As a means of rising, the intellectuals have allied the manual workers with them by means of an inclusive symbol—by speaking in the name of the proletariat. Thus the rising intellectuals got the jobs in a state like Russia, benefiting from the revolutionary energy of the workers. In the nineteenth century the rising intellectual class created the orators and bureaucrats and journalists of the socialist political parties, the trade unions, and the consumer cooperatives; and in the twentieth century they take the jobs in the Russian bureaucratic state and in the Fascist movement or Fascist states outside Russia.

Another contribution to the theory of the intellectual was made by a vivacious literary critic, Benda—author of *The Treason of the Intellectuals*.[6] His point was that intellectuals in modern society are grasping for power by talking to the masses rather than by

[6] Benda, Julien, *The Treason of the Intellectuals;* New York, William Morrow, 1928 (xii and 244 pp.).

talking to themselves and adhering to the austere pursuit of truth as judged by scholarly standards. This, says Benda, has brought about a steady disintegration of the integrity of the intellectual and has contributed to the barbarization of our time.

The problem of the intellectual and his place in history is commonly spoken of as an aspect of the "sociology of knowledge" to which Max Weber was an influential contributor.[7]

Culture Trait and Personality Trait

As a result of modern concern with the analysis of words and word users, the key terms of our present discussion—personality, culture, education—have received new connotations. More important, we have become aware of methods by which meanings could be fixed for an observer who occupies a specified position in relation to a field of events of potential reference. The observer and his words are events among events. The term "field" refers to the event at the observer's focus of attention. In the manifold of events, observers may take different positions, standpoints. Observations may be calibrated from standpoint to standpoint by comparing observations with regard to what is taken to be the same field.

Suppose we begin by referring to the position of an observer in a strange community who has just noticed that the one who addressed him made a certain gesture.

Suppose the observer writes in his notebook, "At eleven A.M. X, a child, came to see me and rubbed his right ear with his right hand when we greeted one another. I don't know whether this was a gesture of politeness, or whether it shows that X is embarrassed." The observer has two possible relations in mind with reference to the act of ear rubbing. He wants to place it in terms of culture and personality.

In order to determine whether the act is a culture trait, the observer collects *testimony* and notes *occurrences*.

---

[7] For a convenient summary see Parsons, Talcott, *The Structure of Social Action: A Study in Social Theory with Special Reference to a Group of Recent European Writers;* New York, McGraw-Hill, 1937 (xiii and 817 pp.).

Suppose that he asks a group of those who participate in the culture whether they expect to have this particular gesture made when two persons meet. The answer may be unanimous, "We expect this gesture to be made when a younger person meets an older person who is in authority over him." Suppose also that the observer follows a series of situations in which younger persons meet older persons in authority over them and the gesture always appears.

We will not complicate the discussion at this point by raising questions of the reliability, adequacy and validity of the samples.

Some of the acts noted by the observer may not be easy to describe. Suppose the observer is told that the knee should be bent at the same time that the ear is rubbed whenever a younger person meets an older relative of his mother. Assume that all testimony is unanimous on this point. Yet the observer finds that the act of bending the knee fails to occur in five out of ten situations which correspond to these specifications. Or suppose that the observer faces still another complication: a disagreement among those whom he asks to testify. Assume that seven out of ten say that they expect a given gesture under specified conditions. Is the gesture a culture trait? The observer must set rather arbitrary limits for what he is going to call a trait. The frequencies which he selects are of no direct interest to us here. Assume that the observer decides to use the expression "trait of this culture" when six, or more, of ten testifiers agree that it is expected, and when the expected act occurs in no less than six of ten possible situations.

We ought to stop at this point to say that the working social scientist very seldom finds it possible to keep his records as carefully as our hypothetical observer. The working observer of a primitive community only approximates these strict requirements. Even the published monographs which describe our own culture do not in practice meet these standards. When the Lynds describe Middletown, they make no effort to specify the frame of reference of their words as carefully as our hypothetical observer.[8] Our remarks do

[8] Lynd, Robert S., and Helen M., *Middletown; A Study in American Culture;* New York, Harcourt, Brace, 1929 (x and 550 pp.); *Middletown in Transition; A Study in Cultural Conflicts;* Harcourt, Brace, 1937 (xviii and 604 pp.).

not imply that it is always advisable to operate within the framework of super-strict requirements. The aim is only to make entirely clear what is necessary for very refined observation and communication.

We have carried our observer to this point: he has standardized his terminology so that he (and perhaps others) can understand what he is talking about. He uses the expression, *"trait of a specified culture" to refer to an act which is expected to appear and which does occur with at least a specified minimum frequency in a given field of observation.* Our observer may use the word "conduct" to refer to an act which conforms to a culture trait and the word "behavior" to refer to an act which does not conform. We may note that an act which is behavior in one community may be conduct in another community, but it is also possible that an act may conform to no pattern anywhere. The latter act would be behavior in all observed communities.

Our observer has succeeded in placing the act of ear rubbing in one dimension of the context in which it is found. He is also interested in placing the act in proper relationship to another dimension of this manifold of events. The act is one of the acts which compose the career line of the actor. Some of the acts are representative of the person under specified conditions. If our observer watches the future acts of the same person, or records the past acts of the person, under the same conditions, the results may be as follows: "The politeness gesture was made on ten of the ten occasions when there was an opportunity to make it." Or, "The politeness gesture was made on seven of the ten occasions when there was an opportunity." *The frequency of occurrence of an act on comparable occasions in the career-line of a person is a trait of the personality.*

Personality traits are thus described in relation to acts which are related to culture. But all events which enter into the act are not necessarily defined in the culture. Our observer may borrow Chester W. Darrow's portable psychogalvanometer and induce the subject to wear it. As a result he may learn that ear rubbing is preceded by a sharp drop in skin conductance. Our observer can be quite sure that the participants in the culture do not entertain any expectations whatever about the electrical reactions of the skin.

The reason the observer bothers to describe skin conductance at all is that he expects to make use of these data in examining the personality-culture manifold. For purposes of concreteness we may consider the following possibility: the observer may find the same individual differs markedly in skin conductance reactions when addressing people whom he loves or hates, and when addressing persons to whom he is indifferent. He may find that measuring skin conductance reactions of subjects who are exposed to pictures of different individuals is an economical way of discovering the emotionally active, or the emotionally indifferent, relationships of élite or non-élite groups in the culture. Tests of the presence or absence of the "startle pattern"—as defined by Carney Landis and associates— may be devised for different personality-culture manifolds.[9] This indicates how "physiological" events may be used in the examination of personality and culture.

As a matter of convenience our observer may use the following terms: "response" for the acts, including parts of acts, which are the objects of expectation in a culture; "reaction" for the acts, including parts of acts, which are not objects of expectation in the culture: Ear rubbing is thus a response in the context in which our hypothetical observer has been at work. Skin conductance is a reaction.

Now all of the acts which are expected in a culture are not necessarily approved by the participants in the culture. Politeness expressed in ear rubbing may be expected. But the occurrence of violations may also be expected. That is, while it is agreed that morality and propriety dictate this gesture, it is recognized that some immoral and improper breaches are likely to take place among those who belong to the culture. Contrast this with the expectations which prevail regarding incest with a small daughter. The very idea that such a thing could occur may be alien to those who share a given culture. They may be shocked to have the possi-

[9] Landis, Carney, and Hunt, William A., and Strauss, Hans, *The Startle Pattern;* New York, Farrar and Rinehart, 1939 (xiii and 158 pp.).

bility mentioned and they may know of no examples of it. Intimate observers of the culture may agree that this simply doesn't happen. We know from general study of culture that when events of this kind do take place the participants in the culture refuse to recognize that anyone capable of sharing their culture would perform such an act. They do not regard it as compatible with human nature. The shocking and outrageous event is treated as subhuman.

The distinctions which we have just made can be fixed in our terminology by setting up the following conventions: *mores traits* of a culture are recognized to be obligatory by the bearers of the culture, and this is signified by the indignation with which violations are met. *Counter-mores traits* of a culture are acts which violate the *mores* and are recognized to occur, regrettable as they are. Acts which fall completely outside culture traits are not conduct at all. They are, as mentioned above, behavior. The term *mores* came into the language of modern social science by way of Sumner.[10] The expression *counter-mores* has been proposed to emphasize a neglected though tacitly recognized aspect of cultural analysis. To round out the terminology: for cultural traits which are not *mores* or *counter-mores,* we may use the expression "folk-ways," or "expediencies."

Personality and Culture as Wholes

Although we have defined culture trait and personality trait, we have not defined culture or personality. These terms refer to wholes, and as wholes they include not only the traits of which they are composed, but the inter-relationships of these traits. When we describe ear rubbing as a trait, we have not located it with reference to the culture or personality until we show how it is inter-connected with the other traits of which personality or culture is composed.

An observer knows that the number of traits which can be isolated for purposes of description is legion. The length of trait lists

[10] Sumner, William Graham, *Folkways; A Study of the Sociological Importance of Usages, Manners, Customs, Mores, and Morals;* Boston, Ginn and Co., 1906 (vii and 692 pp.).

is largely a function of the imaginative subtlety of the one who makes them. Hence our observer seeks to avoid sinking in the never-ending task of enumerating traits. There is no event so inconspicuous in the field of observation that it cannot be subdivided, since every whole of reference may be referred to as composed of parts, and each part can be taken as a whole, which in turn is composed of parts, and so on without end. The description of a trait as ear-rubbing-with-the-right-hand may be useful for some purposes, but there are questions which call for splitting this trait into two traits. There is ear-rubbing-of-the-lobe-of-the-ear-with-the-right-hand, and there is ear-rubbing-of-the-entire-ear-with-the-right-hand; and there may be very meticulous workers, who, for purposes best known to themselves, count the fingers of the right hand involved in ear rubbing, describe slight inclinations of the head, indicate whether palm is in or out, and so forth.

Since the trait list is unlimited, our observer undertakes to orient himself with reference to the whole context of personality and culture by using a limited list of words to refer to the principal features of each context.

What are some of the words which may prove serviceable in referring to the whole of personality or culture?

As students of human relations we are—by definition—concerned with interpersonal relations. Parenthetically, the felicitous phrase "interpersonal relations," first launched and emphasized by Harry Stack Sullivan, has established itself rapidly. J. L. Moreno and the "sociometry school" have been among those to incorporate it into their terminological system.[11] The significant feature in the environment of any personality is another personality, and the significant feature in the environment of any culture is another culture.

Interpersonal relationships are *indulgent* or *deprivational*—or indifferent. Hence the interpersonal environment of any personality or culture is indulgent or deprivational—or indifferent. Through any period, the interpersonal environment is indulgent when the

[11] Sullivan, Harry Stack, "Psychiatry," *Encyclopaedia of the Social Sciences* (1935) 12:578-580; and Moreno, J. L., *Who Shall Survive? A New Approach to the Problem of Human Interrelations,* Nervous and Mental Disease Monographs, Washington, D. C., 1934 (440 pp.).

value position of a personality or a culture is improved, and de-privational when it is impaired. For many research purposes, an indulgent environment may be indexed by *increase—*or *promised increase,* or *avoided loss—*in deference, income, and safety. A de-privational environment may be indexed by *decrease—*or *threat of decrease,* or *lost gain—*in these values.

It is evident that the acts of a personality or a culture in relation to its interpersonal environment are also indulgent or deprivational —indulgent when they increase the deference, income, and safety of the other personality or culture, and deprivational when they diminish deference, income, and safety.

We have now selected a frame of reference for our inquiries—"interpersonal relationships of indulgence and deprivation." *"Personality" is the term used to refer to the way a person acts toward other persons. "Culture" is the term used to refer to the way that the members of a group act in relation to one another and to other groups. A "group" is composed of persons. A "person" is an individual who identifies himself with others.* Our observer may find it difficult at first to determine whether individuals identify themselves with one another sufficiently to constitute a group—or, to say the same thing another way, it may not be easy to decide whether individuals who are persons in some relationships are sufficiently identified with others in certain situations to be called persons in the latter.

Observers have reported that some primitive people for whom we have names share no symbol of identification. Margaret Mead found that the mountain Arapesh have no name for themselves, nor have their neighbors any name for them.[12] They use names to distinguish small locality groups varying from 150 to 250 people. Although there is no shared symbol, investigation would probably reveal that those who live in certain villages believe that they are more like those who live in mountain villages than they are like the villagers of the plains or beach. Under such conditions, the ob-

[12] Mead, Margaret (ed.), *Cooperation and Competition among Primitive Peoples;* New York, McGraw-Hill, 1937 (xii and 531 pp.).

server must do more than make a simple inquiry for the name of the tribe.

A group may be distinguished from an aggregate of individuals by the degree to which they share symbols of mutual identification. The individuals who live near the fortieth parallel, north latitude, are not a *group,* but they constitute an *aggregate.* They have no name for themselves—like "forty parallelers"—and they have no sense of being more like one another than they are like thirtieth parallelers. If our observer studies these people at a time when "parallel-consciousness" is a rising social trend, he may find that one in a million has attained "parallel-consciousness" up to the present time. He will need to select the critical frequencies which will enable him to separate a group from an aggregate. He may decide that three out of every four persons living near the fortieth parallel must identify with an inclusive symbol before the term group is applied to them.

So far in this memorandum the term "culture" has been used as if it were a synonym for the collective practices of any group. However, there is no advantage in using the word culture as a synonym for all group customs, no matter how trivial. There has been a tendency in recent social science to use the term indiscriminately. We often speak of culture patterns when we are talking about the customs which prevail in Muncie, Indiana, or in the Middle West as a whole, or in the United States, or in all countries sharing Western European civilization. *There is no advantage in having such a term as culture unless it is reserved for the most representative and distinctive group practices found in the world of today and of yesterday.* It would be desirable to classify the group practices which prevail over the face of the world today, and which have prevailed in the known past of mankind, and to lay down criteria of importance and distinctiveness. This task has not been performed by the students of comparative culture in a way which gives general satisfaction. In the interim, therefore, we are perhaps justified in retaining the terms culture and culture pattern when we refer to the practices of a group.

When our observer uses the expression "a personality" or "a culture," the terms are very poor in meaning until they are exhaustively elaborated. The process of elaboration is the study of traits and their interrelationships. We need to know how the traits vary in relation to one another when the environment changes. Our observer must relate the gesture of politeness to the other traits of the culture or the personality under various environmental conditions.

The crucial relationships of a person or a culture are to other persons or to other cultures. Each person and each culture is part of a context of interrelationships which is—in varying degrees—indulgent or deprivational.

The immediate environment of the person making the gesture of politeness which we have been discussing is an older person in authority. By proper means of investigation our observer can find out what mutual expectations prevail in this situation. The person in authority expects to be indulged by this gesture. It is probable that the subordinate expects the superordinate to act in a certain indulgent way toward him. On the basis of these expectations, we can classify the degree of "indulgence" and "deprivation." When a subordinate uses an abrupt or sketchy gesture, his act is less indulgent than when he makes a full gesture. When the superordinate is less attentive than expected, a deprivation has been inflicted upon the subordinate. The following combinations are possible in the situation:

ENVIRONMENT	INDULGENT	—POLITE GESTURE
ACTIVITY	INDULGENT	—POLITE GESTURE
ENVIRONMENT	INDULGENT	—POLITE GESTURE
ACTIVITY	DEPRIVATIONAL	—IMPOLITE GESTURE
ENVIRONMENT	DEPRIVATIONAL	—IMPOLITE GESTURE
ACTIVITY	INDULGENT	—POLITE GESTURE
ENVIRONMENT	DEPRIVATIONAL	—IMPOLITE GESTURE
ACTIVITY	DEPRIVATIONAL	—IMPOLITE GESTURE

The situation may be read as indulgent or deprivational in several ways. The subordinate's gesture of politeness may be met by politeness, and hence the subordinate's gesture may be termed "successful" in eliciting a gain (indulgence) from the environment. If the subordinate's gesture is met by impoliteness, it is a "failure." If the authority enters the situation with an impolite gesture, the subordinate then makes a polite gesture, and the authority comes through with a polite gesture, the subordinate's gesture may be called "successful," in the obviation of threatened loss. If the superordinate is very polite at the start, the subordinate is polite, and then the superordinate is less polite, the gesture by the subordinate may be judged a "failure," a loss of promised gain. In general, indulgence is gain, promise of gain, and obviation of threatened loss; deprivation is loss, threat of loss, and obstructed gain.

The environmental events E and the activity events A are treated as concurrent.

It is not enough to connect A with E, and to explain the variation of A as a function of E. A is also a function of certain previous events which we call predispositions, P. The frame of reference of the term P may be arbitrarily defined to suit the convenience of the observer who operates with reference to a given field. The P may be defined to mean the "ten preceding comparable situations in which the person was observed."

Our observer has now arranged his data in time order. If he is fortunate, these dated data may disclose—after proper analysis—the functional interrelationships of varying magnitudes of A as a function of EP.

But the probability is that his data will soon prove to be inadequate. The data about the politeness gesture may describe very completely how the authoritative person conducted himself in the presence of the subordinate. And it may summarize a great many situations in which the subordinate and the superordinate interacted upon one another. Yet the data may not suffice for the purpose of displaying the significant interrelationships of the trait in question with other traits of the personality. Expectations founded upon the data may be of little use in predicting how the person will act in the next series of situations which involve authority. Our observer may be prepared to see the subject respond politely to an authoritative person who initiates the situation with a very polite gesture.

But, no! The next few occasions may show a wholly unpredicted series of acts by our subject. He may snub authority, as he has never done in the past which we have recorded. Always in the past we have seen him meet politeness with politeness.

Our data obviously left something to be desired. How could we improve our observer's efforts to locate the politeness gesture correctly in reference to the personality in question?

THE PERSONALITY AS A SYSTEM

Our observer may allow himself to be guided by the thought that the personality is a going concern which is constantly relating itself as a whole to the environment in which it is living.

To say that a personality is a going concern means that we expect it to act in such a way as to maintain a certain degree of internal consistency among its parts. We expect it to display the characteristics of a system—if one part of the whole is changed, substitutive changes occur among the other parts of the whole. This means that a person may be accustomed to receive a great deal of indulgence from authority, and to maintain this indulgence—if it diminishes—by withholding indulgence from authority until authority again becomes indulgent. It is quite thinkable to our observer that something like the following may account for the unexpected response of the subject to authority:

Our subject may have expected to receive a gift from his father on every occasion when his father is away from home. For the first time since he can remember his father was away from home and no gift came. He had an impulse to withdraw indulgence from his father, by pouting, for example. But father was out of reach. At this point the child goes to school and receives the polite greeting from another authority, the teacher. Our observer sees that the child responds by making a sketchy gesture that constitutes a deprivation of the teacher.

As we said, our observer did not see the hypothetical events to which these words refer. He is quite prepared to regard such a sequence as plausible because he is thinking of the personality as a system. If certain expectations are not fulfilled by the environment during a given period of time, he expects that the personality will exhibit substitutive reactions. The substitutive reactions, the observer predicts, will be in the direction of restoring the level of expectation which is usual for the person. We understand the personality if we are able to demonstrate, during any period of time, which changes occur in the personality if there is a change in any part of it. Our observer would have understood the child if he had known what change in its expectations of indulgence would be followed by what substitutive changes.

It is plain that our observer was not using the method of observing the child which provided him with the data which he most needed for understanding the personality of the child. Our observer saw the child in a single situation—one which involved certain subordinate and superordinate relations. He made a great many observations in situations in which the child participated. But he was not prepared for the sudden appearance of impoliteness in relation to the politeness of the teacher.

Our observer may alter his procedure. He may try to understand the personality as a system, not by stationing himself at one vantage point through a long period of time, but rather, by focussing his attention upon *all the activity* of his subject over shorter time periods.

For this scrutiny of the career line as a whole through a given cross-section, he may choose some recurring cycle, like days, or weeks, or menstrual periods. The events of each full cycle period, he may describe by means of a fixed list of terms, variables. Each term, variable, refers to some part of the whole pattern of events. The observer has achieved formal completeness when he can correctly state the changes in all the variables which occur upon a given change in the magnitude of any one of them. When he has found the pattern of intervariable relationship which is maintained, promptly re-approximated after interference, he has found the "dynamic equilibrium" of the system. What is sometimes called "static equilibrium" is a special case of dynamic equilibrium.

The technical problem of our observer is to discover the terms and the indices, measures, which will enable him to execute this program. Students of personality and of social science are still groping after satisfactory terms and procedures. The mathematical and statistical problems involved are already exemplified in several fields of science; but the sticking point among psychologists and social scientists has been the task of finding categories and procedures which are appropriate for the specific event manifolds with which they are concerned.

The Resistance to "Systemic" Analysis

To some extent, there has been resistance against this mode of conceiving the task of students of personality and culture. It may be worthwhile to say something about the methodological situation in this respect.

A sterling example of the successful use of the equilibrium pattern of thought in the sciences is furnished by the work of L. J. Henderson and associates upon the blood as a physico-chemical system.[13] Henderson has been an enthusiastic exponent of this methodological standpoint for the psychological and sociological sciences. He was deeply impressed by the sociological system of Vilfredo Pareto, and went out of his way to bring it to the attention of scientists and laymen in this country.[14] Henderson's influence on the study of personality is explicitly acknowledged by Henry A. Murray and associates at Harvard.[15]

The formal pattern of thought which is needed in equilibrium analysis is congenial to anyone trained in the calculus of variations. But it should be remembered that the dominant methodo-

[13] Henderson, Lawrence J., *Blood: A Study in General Physiology;* New Haven, Yale University Press, 1928 (xix and 397 pp.); and Pareto's *General Sociology: A Physiologist's Interpretation;* Cambridge, Harvard University Press, 1935.

[14] Pareto, Vilfredo, *The Mind and Society;* New York, Harcourt, Brace, 1935 (4, vols.).

[15] Murray, Henry A. (ed.), *Explorations in Personality: A Clinical and Experimental Study of Fifty Men of College Age;* New York, Oxford University Press, 1938 (xiv and 761 pp.).

logical tradition in social science has favored a different mode of thought. At the risk of seeming to stigmatize this mode of thought in advance, we may speak of it as the "one factor—one result" pattern of analysis. This pattern of thinking does not disregard the multiplicity of factors which operate in psychological and sociological relationships. But it specifies that the goal of analysis is the discovery of the necessary factor which determines a given outcome. John Stuart Mill's logic helped to standardize this mode of thought, especially when it was generalized for the field of sociology by Émile Durkheim.[16]

An interesting re-application of Durkheim is found in the work of the influential French sociologist, François Simiand.[17] Simiand was committed to the "one factor—one result" goal of sociological research. But he insists upon the importance of conducting research upon event series which are found in a given cultural setting. Simiand took the fluctuation of wages in France as his problem. He made a long list of factors which might conceivably affect this variable. He abstained from hypotheses—except insofar as the choice of a factor implied the expectation that it might be important. In abstaining from hypotheses he paralleled the logic of many other multiple-factor studies. Simiand then analyzed the wage data with reference to each variable in turn. Ultimately he arrived at what he considered to be the critical factor which accounted for wage fluctuations.

It is not wholly correct to say that resistance to the "systemic" approach among some social scientists is to be attributed to their lack of knowledge of the calculus. Many psychologists who are well equipped mathematically have gone ahead for years with a "non-systemic" approach. They have operated with variables, but they have not undertaken to select a list in terms of which they could describe the fluctuations of the whole personality in relation

[16] Durkheim, Émile, *The Rules of Sociological Method* [8th ed., translated by Sarah A. Solovay and John H. Mueller, and edited by George E. G. Catlin]; Chicago, University of Chicago Press, 1938 (lx and 146 pp.).

[17] Simiand, François, *Le salaire: l'évolution sociale et la monnaie; essai de théorie expérimentale du salaire, introduction et étude globale*, Paris, Felix Alcan, 1932 (3 vols.).

to the environment. The essential point about the "systemic" pattern of analysis is not that it uses variables, but that it chooses a list whose interrelations are studied with regard to fluctuations in the environment.

Biologists are the scientists who have found it most useful to think "systemically." L. J. Henderson derives from Claude Bernard, and a physiologist like Walter B. Cannon easily puts his researches into the "systemic" framework.[18]

In this respect biologists differ from physicists, who are able to carry on successful work with no selective conception of an "organic pattern" which maintains itself in an environment. Whatever may be the forms of thought which aid in the exploration of cosmic evolution, or which explore the "individuality" of certain subatomic forms, the prevalent physics is "non-organismic." These non-systemic traits of physics are particularly prominent in elementary physics, and elementary physics is often the only physics which enters at any time into the training of future social and psychological scientists. Physics seems to operate with a list of variables which can be treated as dependent or independent at the convenience of the experimenter. The picture of scientific method which is obtained by those who learn physics—chiefly elementary physics—is "non-organismic." When they undertake to apply quantitative procedures to psychological and social events, they expect to operate with much the same freedom in the handling of variables as the physicist.

In appraising the resistance which "systemic" patterns have often encountered, we should not overlook the sterility with which they have often been associated. Pareto was both pretentious and sententious. And if his sociological system made a clear programmatic statement of the advantages of an "equilibrium" approach, it should not be forgotten that it furnished a clear example of failure to achieve definitive results by its application. There has been no dearth of "systemic" proposals for a science of personality and of culture. The difficulty has been the inadequacy of the specific categories and modes of observation with which these proposals have

[18] Cannon, Walter B., *The Wisdom of the Body;* New York, Norton, 1932 (xv and 312 pp.).

been associated. Meanwhile, science seemed to be growing by the discovery and exploration of new standpoints, and by the discovery of inter-part relations independent of explicit modes of describing "wholeness."

The "organismic" vocabularies have encountered stout resistance in some quarters on political grounds. "Organic" metaphors were part of the language of the conservative movements that came in the wake of the French revolutionary epoch. Respect for the "organic" was supposed to defeat the claims of reason, and to disparage the "rationalism" of eighteenth century reformers and revolutionists. Organismic analogies have been abundant in the thinking of modern anti-individualists like Othmar Spann. It is characteristic of many Protestant thinkers that they are suspicious of "organic" phrases on account of the frequency with which these phrases have been used by Catholic theologians. It is not one of the least distinctive achievements of Whitehead that he has lifted the conception of the organic from the battle-scarred phraseology of preceding centuries.

If our period in history is one in which the individual is in at least temporary eclipse in the presence of collective demands, we may predict the further diffusion of "systemic" methods of thought. This diffusion may have nothing to do with technical superiority. It may be an answer to the *Zeitgeist;* that is, the popularity of categories of wholeness may be a means by which the harassed and insecure individual minimizes some of his insecurities by identifying with the whole. Preoccupation with the whole, familiarity with ideas of the whole—these are possible means of seeking to abate the anxieties bred of the instabilities of our epoch.

To call attention to these possibilities is not to stigmatize, nor to endorse, the use of systemic ideas. It is to suggest how our own intellectual processes can be related to the context in which they operate. If we obtain insight into the factors which dispose us to accept, or to reject, a certain pattern of thought on non-rational grounds, we may be better prepared to accept or reject the pattern on rational, technical, grounds.

OBSERVING THE WHOLE PERSONALITY

We left our observer confronting his task of personality analysis, intent upon finding the most economical ways of discovering the interrelationship of traits under various environmental conditions. We left him dissatisfied with the results of observing a trait in one recurring situation, because he saw that he had no means of exposing the systemic reactions of the personality as a whole. He was considering the study of all activities of the personality during a few selected periods.

The chief difficulty in this program of total observation is how to station the observer in relation to the whole gamut of events. Direct observation of the activity cycle is only possible with adults or adolescents when they are confined to very circumscribed situations—penitentiaries, hospitals, boarding schools—or when the participant observer is in a very intimate relationship to the subject —an inseparable companion. Indirect observation is possible if subjects are willing to make diary notes of how they spend their time.[19]

Each of these observational standpoints has distinctive possibilities and limitations. And one common limitation is that the subject who is being observed may not be exposed to a sufficiently wide range of environmental changes during the cycle of study to reveal many of the important facts of trait interrelationship. It is always possible, of course, that we happen to be observing somebody who loses his dearest friend and makes a suicidal attempt; or we may be on hand to see how a man takes a great political or business victory. But there is some "waste" in observing many persons who do not happen to be subjected to the shifts in the environment whose effects we want to study.

A solution of this difficulty readily springs to mind in this experimental age. Subject the personality to a gamut of environmental changes of the kind which we want to study! But there are

[19] One of the most recent uses of this method of indirect observation is by Pitirim Sorokin and Clarence Q. Berger, *Time-Budgets of Human Behavior*, Cambridge, Harvard University Press, 1939 (xi and 204 pp.).

practical limitations in the path of such a procedure. It is not feasible to arrange an accident in order to crush the leg of a subject, and to see how he responds to this form of deprivation. Nor is it feasible to arrange for the death of a loved one, for the sake of discovering how the person copes with another kind of deprivation. It is also difficult to arrange for the sudden advancement of a subject in order to study the response to such indulgence. The experimental approach is not entirely hopeless, of course, but it quickly tends to move over into a test situation. The test situation requires validation, while the experiment does not. The test is an economical change in the environment of a subject which is supposed to be the equivalent of changes in the natural environment to which that subject is exposed. This equivalence must be demonstrated by comparing test with non-test data.

An important example of what may be done experimentally is the Western Electric experiment under the auspices of Elton Mayo, T. N. Whitehead, and associates.[20] The work situation—which included many hours of the waking day of the subjects—was systematically varied. One of the ideal, though scarcely attainable, methods of validating a personality test would be to examine the responses of the same person as he passes through cycles of deprivation and indulgence.

THE CULTURE AS A SYSTEM

Our observer has been engaged in the task of placing the politeness trait with reference to personality. When he undertakes to locate the trait with reference to culture, his problem is similar, but the relevant context of events is larger. It is necessary to show the position of the culture as a whole with respect to other cultures in its environment.

Intercultural relations, like all interpersonal relations, are indulgent or deprivational, or indifferent. Suppose that our observer

[20] Whitehead, T. N., *The Industrial Worker: A Statistical Study of Human Relations in a Group of Manual Workers;* Cambridge, Harvard University Press, 1938 (2 vols.).

finds that the culture which he is studying is going through a period of humiliation at the hands of all surrounding cultures. Land previously regarded as belonging to culture A is now occupied by persons affiliated with cultures B, C, D. Convinced of their own weakness, the authorities of culture A do nothing to stop the appropriation of their tribal lands.

The observations made by our observer on politeness gestures between subordinate and superordinate now take on new relevance. Suppose that our observer found that politeness was declining during the period of his studies. Subordinates were becoming less respectful of authority, and authority, in turn, was growing suspicious of disloyalty and supersensitive to criticism. The provisional picture seen by our observer is something like this, then: culture A has been subjected to deprivation at the hands of other cultures, but the authorities of A, feeling weak, have done nothing about it; this has weakened the deference given to authority, and in turn diminished the indulgence shown by authority to subordinates. Broadly speaking, the culture has responded to deprivation, not by acting upon the outside environment, but by acting upon itself. In the situation referred to, the authority-subordinate relationships have been sharply reduced in number and in mutual indulgence. Study may show that more people spend more time out of contact with others (indulging in private fantasies stimulated by the increased use of opium, for example).

By studying the fluctuations of a given culture we may discover the interrelationship among its component traits. In our symbolic statement, we treat the A of the culture as a function of EP. We may choose cycles for investigation—from victory to victory, or from defeat to defeat in war, for instance. None of our cycles will be conditioned by the succession of biological phases, as are the cycles along the career line of the individual. It is a mistake to project the succession of biological phases from the individual to culture. Many efforts have been made to speak of young and old cultures, but no one has demonstrated a recurring series of patterns comparable with the recurring series along the career line of the individual from birth to death.[21] A culture appears and disappears; but the succession of patterns does not display the regularity and irreversibility of the phases through which the individual passes.

Without pursuing the subject much further, an additional remark may not be out of place in this connection. The idea that the career line of the individual is composed of an irreversible succession of patterns has been very helpful because of its "obviousness," an "obviousness" which has been conspicuously lacking in regard to culture histories. But "obviousness" is becoming less and less as the control of the environment is perfected. In experimental embryology we see that more and more processes are reversible. By reversibility is meant the capacity to resume a state congruent with a former state. Tissues may be permitted to differentiate in the direction of one pattern, then shifted toward another pattern, and ultimately brought back to the initial direction. There are limitations upon this procedure, to be sure; but these limitations are fewer and fewer. It is no longer a paradox to say that we have less "heredity" than we used to have.

From the comparative study of culture we expect to learn how different cultures interact with their cultural environments. And from the comparative study of personality we expect to find how different personalities meet their personal environments.

If we want to think "systemically" of culture or personality, how may we proceed? Suppose we explore the following line of thought: During any given period, any personality or culture tends to maintain a certain pattern of subjective events. This is the "dynamic equilibrium" of the whole, and it is evidenced by the tendency toward prompt restoration of the pattern when it is subjected to interference.

Consider the act which puzzled our observer, the sudden appearance of impoliteness. He tried to make it more intelligible by allowing for such possibilities as these: The impoliteness toward the teacher was a displacement of hostility which was originally

[21] The most elaborate treatment of the subject of cycles in history is found in some of the publications of Pitirim Sorokin. Sorokin, Pitirim, *Social and Cultural Dynamics;* Cincinnati, American Book Company, 1937. See volume 2.

directed toward the father, but which could not express itself against an absent father, who had neglected to send an anticipated gift.

Careful study of the child during daily—or other—cycles might reveal the following characteristic pattern: The child entertains high expectations from authority, and if these are not fulfilled, the child feels somewhat resentful and withholds some indulgence from authority. If, on the contrary, expectations are fulfilled, the child promptly evolves a new set of high expectations until authority fails to come through. Then the resentful-aloofness-pattern makes its appearance. Investigation may show that the person spends about the same time every day being a little injured and a little aloof from authority. It is the tenacity with which this pattern maintains itself, despite many changes in the environment, that shows that it is part of the pattern of dynamic equilibrium characteristic of this personality.

The pattern which we have been describing may involve everybody, whether authority objects, or colleagues or subordinates. In extreme instances the cycle may occur repeatedly with everyone: large expectations are evolved until they are unfulfilled, followed by resentfulness and aloofness. The preferred pattern is one of high expectation, light resentment and depression, and slight attack upon the personality of the other by aloofness.

The study of personality may be expected to disclose the presence of many different patterns. From general experience we are more or less acutely aware of some of the more extreme forms. There is the enthusiast, the person who maintains a state of incessant enthusiasm about the self and others, despite adverse environmental factors. These is also the cyclical personality, in which enthusiasm is followed by torpid depression. There is the detachment pattern, whose distinguishing mark is the restoration as promptly as possible of subjective states free of vivid love, enthusiasm or anger.

Ruth Benedict has classified cultures on the basis of the characteristic subjective event which they tend to maintain in the lives of those who are exposed to the culture. In her classification, the Pueblo Indians are Apollonian: they avoid intense subjective states.

The Plains Indians are Dionysian: they facilitate intense subjective states.

The formal ideal of research on the dynamic equilibrium of personality and culture remains the same: to explore the interrelations of equilibrium patterns. In the interest of brevity, this memorandum will not discuss the problems connected with the construction of dynamic patterns for short or for long periods of the career. Freud's bold speculation about the "life and death instincts" is an equilibrium pattern for the career line as a whole. The existing data are far too fragmentary to confirm or to disconfirm such inclusive ideas.

GENERAL CATEGORIES

What general categories are useful in personality study?

We may profitably distinguish between internalized and externalized acts. An act is externalized when it involves the environment as it runs to completion. When the environment is not implicated, the act is internalized. Through a given period, the acts of a person or a culture involve measurable degrees of internalization and externalization.

The person who sits alone and thinks is internalized during that period. The person who is greeting other persons is externalizing. Those who bear a given culture may withdraw from contact with neighboring cultures by physical migration or non-intercourse. In contrast with war or trade, which are externalized, flight or non-intercourse are internalizations. Acts are collectively externalized within a culture when individuals act in concert upon other individuals—in a business enterprise, a political party, for example. When individuals act in concert upon themselves, acts are collectively internalized within the culture—in a sect which devotes itself to secret rites.

We have already had occasion to speak of acts as destructive when they endanger the wholeness of a personality or a culture. Suicide is the extreme form of internalized destructiveness. But there are self-destructive acts short of suicide, such as drug addiction. Many bodily diseases are "functional" in origin and belong to the self-destructive reactions.[22] Other destructive internalizations are moods and fantasies irrelevant to reality, autistic reactions. Collective autism occurs when there is collective participation in the encouragement of fantasy, as in some forms of the Peyote cult. The ceremonies of the cult consist in chewing a plant, thus stimulating visions which are later communicated.[23] A more extreme example of collective autism is the observance of a lifetime vow of silence by Trappist monks.

The categories of indulgence and deprivation have already been introduced.

Studies of culture from the standpoint outlined here have begun, and many existing studies are partially relevant. The most explicit published research is that of Philleo Nash on revivalism among the Klamath Indians.[24] Revivalistic movements were studied in three groups, and the distinguishing characteristics of the different movements were accounted for by referring to the degrees of deprivations and indulgences to which the groups had been exposed, and the antecedent state of cultural predisposition. The sequence of events was established from historical records and from living informants.

A comparative study of three modern nationalistic movements has been made from this point of view, but the findings are not yet available in English. Dinko Tomasic studied nationalistic movements during the same period in Serbia, Croatia and Slovenia. He was able to account for the distinguishing marks of each movement by referring to the deprivations and indulgences to which they were exposed, and to antecedent cultural predispositions.

[22] A convenient handbook of the experimental work on mind-body relations is that of Dunbar, H. Flanders, *Emotions and Bodily Changes. A Survey of Literature on Psychosomatic Interrelationships, 1910–1933* (Second Edition with Supplementary Introduction and Additional Bibliography); New York, Columbia University Press, 1938 (601 pp.).

[23] La Barre, Weston, *The Peyote Cult;* New Haven, Yale University Press, 1938 (188 pp.).

[24] Nash, Philleo, The Place of Religious Revivalism in the Formation of the Intercultural Community on Klamath Reservation. Eggan, Fred (ed.), *Social Anthropology of North American Tribes;* Chicago, University of Chicago Press, 1937 (xvii and 456 pp.).

A general theory of response to economic indulgence—prosperity —and deprivation—depression—was stated by the present writer in Chapter VII of his *World Politics and Personal Insecurity*.[25] Douglas Waples has considered the bearing upon these hypotheses of data about reading habits in *People and Print*.[26] This book also presented some preliminary formulations relevant to the rise and fall of élites. The élites of a state are indulged or deprived by other élites beyond the frontiers of the state, and by counter-élites within the boundaries of the state.

These allusions are intended only to indicate that a body of specialists are finding it convenient to work with similar categories for the statement of their problems and the communication of results. Terminological parallelism is—as we have repeatedly had occasion to say—far less important than inclusiveness of formulation from any specified standpoint. We have deliberately used terms to refer to the whole observational field of the observer, and equivalent terms are usually in the vocabulary of an observer who is accustomed to think of his field "as a whole." The "part reference words" are more readily understood when they are arranged with explicit relationship to "whole reference words."

There has been an increasing tendency to use a language of wholeness in many fields. Quite often the change comes by the redefinition of a vocabulary that was once restricted to part-ness as distinguished from wholeness. To choose but a single example, the language of stimulus-response has been thoroughly overhauled by Clark Hull and his collaborators at the Yale Institute of Human Relations.[27]

Another example is the spread among psychologists and social psychologists of categories connected with topological and "Gestalt" psychology. It came as a distinct revelation to many psychological and sociological workers that there could be "non-

[25] Lasswell, Harold D., *World Politics and Personal Insecurity;* New York, Whittlesey House, 1935 (vii and 307 pp.).

[26] Waples, Douglas, *People and Print;* Chicago, University of Chicago Press, 1938 (xvi and 228 pp.).

[27] Dollard, John, and others, *Frustration and Aggression;* New Haven, Yale University Press, 1939 (viii and 209 pp.).

quantitative" categories employed in the name of the most rigorous of all the traditional sciences—mathematics. This is one of the factors in the extraordinary release of creative insight which has frequently accompanied the discovery of topology. Some experimenters who were unaccustomed to allow themselves to think freely about total contexts were genuinely emancipated. Formerly they studied only what they could be very precise about. They used words whose frames of reference they defined very carefully: there were exact measures specified for the limited aspects of the environment of the animal that were called "stimuli," and of the limited aspects of the animal that were called "responses." Topology supplied these experimenters with language—properly sanctioned as mathematical—for thinking about the relevant wholes—the context—in which they were making observations. It was now possible to use words like "field" and "barrier"—and to draw diagrammatical representations—without bothering too much about precision. New experimental insights have arisen as a result of this new freedom in using words of reference to a whole—the whole that was formerly treated as the vague sum of all the parts, if you ever got around to adding them all up. Quite apart from any other advantages or disadvantages, Kurt Lewin has performed this valuable function by his topological emphasis.[28] For many special students of perception, the equivalent release came through the earlier *Gestalt* psychology.

A CLASSIFICATION OF OBSERVATIONAL STANDPOINTS

"A distinction may be drawn between observational standpoints which are relatively *intensive* and those which are relatively *extensive*. There are two distinguishing marks of the intensive standpoint: it is *prolonged* and *complex*. The observer concentrates his attention upon the career line of a particular person for a protracted period of time, and uses complex ways of exposing the structure of what he sees. When the standpoint is extensive, the relationship to the career line of the individual is *cursory* and *simple*. The psychoanalytical interview is an example of the intensive stand-

[28] Lewin, Kurt, *Principles of Topological Psychology;* New York, McGraw-Hill, 1936 (xv and 231 pp.).

point: the psychoanalyst may see the analysand for an hour a day for many months, and he utilizes the technique of free fantasy—free association—as a complex means of exposing the detailed structure of the personality. The interviews which are undertaken as a means of polling opinion during an election are extensive methods of observation: the contact with each individual is brief, and nothing more may be elicited than 'Yes' or 'No' in response to questions.

"Other useful distinctions may be made between the *direct* and *indirect, guided* and *unguided, subject aware* and *subject unaware* relationships. When we listen to what the individual is saying, we are in direct relationship to the event in question—the saying. When we listen to words which refer to a past act, we are in an indirect relationship to the act of reference. When we ask a subject to fill out the blanks on a test form, we are guiding the course of what we observe. When we unobtrusively note the conduct of a person during a regular committee meeting, over which we have no control, the observation is unguided. When we explicitly solicit the co-operation of persons in the preparation of a life history document, our subject is made aware of the fact that he is being studied for scientific purposes. When we look through an observational aperture and record the conduct of children on a nursery playground, the subjects may be unaware. It is evident that our intensive or extensive procedures may be direct or indirect, guided or unguided, with subject aware or subject unaware.

"Four general types of observer-observed relationship may be distinguished: the observer as *participant, spectator, interviewer, collector.* The participant observer engages in activities with the subjects which are part of the ordinary pattern of the life of his subjects. The participant picks up many references to events which he cannot directly observe, since he is in a favorable position to listen to gossip, myth and legend. The participant may guide activities: he may agree with a confederate to engage in controversies in situations where they are bound to be joined by others who act in good faith. The participant observer seeks to avoid or to mitigate the awareness on the part of his subjects that they are under investigation.

"The spectator relationship is one in which the observer is out of the focus of attention in relation to ongoing activities. The extreme case is that of the spectator who is concealed from his subjects. The spectator shades into the participant by imperceptible degrees when he is lost from the center of attention in a general activity—when, for example, he is an unobtrusive onlooker in a vast crowd witnessing a sport competition. The audience at the sport is in one of the ordinary activities of the culture, and this fills the minimum requirement for participation. But the degree of participation is so attenuated in relation to the situations in which the observer is at the center of general attention that we may classify the observer in the crowd as a spectator. The spectator may give experimental guidance to the situation in which he is interested, as when he determines the composition of play groups which he desires to study, without allowing the fact to come to the knowledge of the children.

"The interviewer relationship is always characterized by awareness on the part of all concerned that the subject is being studied. The participant and the spectator may record conversations, but these are not interviews unless the subject knows that he is being studied. It is possible to guide the interview according to a rigid interrogatory, questionnaire, or to let it develop with a minimum of direction.

"In the collector relationship the observer makes use of records which he has not himself made. The records may be prepared by specialists who use the same methods, or by persons who use different methods for different purposes. Among the intentionally created records are public autobiographies, histories, biographies, and some of the inscriptions left on steles, obelisks, triumphal arches, and public edifices. The unintentional records of past events include documents not meant for the eyes of others, like a very private diary, and most of the material remains of past cultures.

"The records which are prepared by participant, spectator and interviewer merge into the records assembled by the collector when the observer relies upon certain aids. The interviewer may use the transcript of an interview which is made by a stenographer from shorthand notes, or from the rolls or discs of a recording apparatus. The interviewer may attach the subject to instruments which show how the blood pressure, pulse rate, or respiration vary, and he may take moving pictures of the behavior of his subject. The same devices may be utilized by the participant and the spectator. The participant, for example, may obtain instrumental tracings of blood pressure by introducing the procedure as a game, and not as a serious scientific experiment." [29]

It would be possible to discuss the division of the world of events into *movement events* and *meaning events,* and the fundamental procedures involved in measurement. This would carry us too far afield, no doubt, from the present range of topics. It may be said, too cryptically it is feared, that meaning events refer; movement events do not. The measurement of both kinds of events calls for a consensus of observers with respect to the terms and procedures to be used. Since a consensus is a meaning event, the measurement of movement events as well as meaning events depends upon events of meaning. Indices of movements and of meanings are needed for cultural and personality study. A notational system for words and gestures is proposed by the present writer in *A Provisional Classification of Symbol Data.*[30]

How to Observe Changing Developments

We are in an earthbound universe of interpersonal events. Like the students of wind and ocean, we need a network of observation stations over the face of the earth. Like the student of vulcanism, and of the emergence and subsidence of continental blocs, we need large scale organizations equipped to gather inclusive data. Like the student of the morphology of landscape, the physiographer, we need observers and mappers of on-going processes. Like the student of plant and animal ecology, we need to spot the distribution and succession of many forms of life in time and space.

[29] Lasswell, Harold D., Intensive and Extensive Methods of Observing the Personality-Culture Manifold. *Yenching J. Social Studies* (1938) 1:74-76.

[30] Lasswell, Harold D., A Provisional Classification of Symbol Data. *Psychiatry* (1938) 1:197-204.

The planned observation of the emerging future is one of the tasks of science. Important data are irrevocably lost unless they are collected by contemporary observers of events. Wise planning is needed if well-equipped observers are to be stationed around the world to make proper use of the latest and best tools of scientific observation. When the observation of the emerging future is provided for, we may expect to follow world developments with greater insight and to obtain data which confirm or disconfirm our basic theories. Although most of the data will be non-experimental, we can arrange in advance for the experimental control of at least a few situations.

As students of personality and culture, we are professionally concerned with the changing interrelationships of personality and culture through time. This calls for systematic worldwide observation. Already mankind is partially organized for systematic self-observation. Every modern state has extensive census agencies for the gathering of social facts, and one of our special functions as social scientists is to contribute to the steady improvement of official and unofficial observation and analysis.

At the present time the gap between what we need for scientific purposes and what we have is enormous. Whenever the social scientist looks into any standard yearbook, like the *Statesman's Yearbook,* he is reminded of the great discrepancy between what he needs to know and what is readily available. Most of the yearbooks have not yet begun to make use of many of the modern devices for the meaningful presentation of data. Even atlas-makers have stayed close to conservative ways—with the ever-stimulating exception of Otto Neurath.[31]

In exploring culture and personality, we can divide culture into *situations,* and we can study the way *persons* are related to these situations. *Personality* is revealed when we study all of the situations in which specific persons are placed during given cross-

[31] Neurath, Otto, *Gesellschaft und Wirtschaft, bildstatistisches elementarwerk; das Gesellschafts und wirtschaftsmuseum in Wien zeigt in 100 farbigen bildtafeln produktionsformen, gesellschaftsordnungen, kulturstufen, lebenshaltungen;* Leipsic, Bibliographisches Institut, 1930 (130 pp.).

sections of their career-lines. We can describe *culture* only when the data are in about the component situations of the culture, and about the surrounding cultural environment. Some of our observations on persons may relate the persons to a number of situations, and yet provide us with inadequate information about personality. We may inventory all of the school, home, street and other situations to which persons of a given age are exposed, and still know next to nothing about personality patterns. It is necessary to follow the same person through his whole gamut of exposure to situations before we have described personality.

It is evident that there are several different though interrelated starting points for exploring the manifold of events which comprise personality and culture. We may enumerate the patterns found in specific situations. We may start with persons who share a common characteristic, like age or sex, and enumerate all of the situations in which such persons are found. We may begin with specific persons, and examine all of the situations in which they function. Each set of observations is potentially related to those which are made from any other starting point. Observers who study the sixth grade situation are providing us with some of the data for studying, for example, the situations in which all of the twelve year-olds of a given culture are found. And some of the data can be related to the context of personal relationships which involve particular persons, and thus reveal their personalities. By relating the sixth grade situations to the other situations of the culture, and of the environment of the culture, we contribute to the understanding of the culture as a whole. No matter what our point of departure, we may illuminate the entire manifold of events, if we bring all of our data into the proper interrelationship.

Any cross-section which it is convenient to use in observing culture and personality is somewhat protracted. The Lynds were in direct contact with Middletown for several months and most of the studies which have been made of primitive societies have required months or years. When the time interval is rather long, it is possible to discover *developmental profiles* within the period.

Assume that our observer chooses a two year period for observational purposes. During this period many profiles will have altered. The *situation profile* of the sixth grade, for example, may change in at least a few respects. Sixth graders may pay more attention during the second year to contemporary events, and they may be less submissive to their teachers. By comparing the two sixth grade profiles, we arrive at the *developmental profile of the situation.*

During the same two year interval, the *person to situation* profiles may have changed. There may be a smaller proportion of the community's twelve year old youngsters in the sixth grade during the second year than the first. By examining the contrast in the total range of situations in which the twelve year old group operates, we have the *developmental profile of the person to situation* relationship. If data are collected for the same individuals, and their personality profiles described, we have the *developmental profile of personality.* By viewing the totality of relationships which constitute culture, and the environing cultures, we have the *developmental profile of the culture.*

The data not only establish developmental relationships; they also have an important bearing on all our theories about the relationship of activity *A*, to environment *E*, and to predisposition *P*. It may be possible to relate the change in self-confidence and aggressiveness which is noted in the second year of the study to the presence of a more indulgent environment, and to the growth of self-confidence and aggressiveness during the first year of the study. The growth during the first year is called a "predisposition" with respect to the environment during the second year. The data gathered by our observers have a double relevance therefore: they bear upon developmental patterns and upon equilibrium patterns of relationship.

We may undertake to expose one of the most complicated profiles of development, namely, that which concerns *personal position.* We saw how sixth graders—or twelve year olds—in the first half of the two-year period differed from the sixth graders—or twelve year olds—of the second half of the period. Can we determine at the beginning of the sixth grade period *which* person will probably occupy *which* position in the distribution of personal traits at the end of the sixth grade? For example, can we examine the least aggressive tenth at the start of the sixth grade and determine what their relative position will be at the end of the sixth grade, assuming a specified environment during the sixth grade? The same question can be asked for *personality position* among the personal positions.

For several purposes it is convenient to arrange data in sequences in which the groups which follow one another in time are composed of different persons:

First Year	Second Year
SEVENTH GRADE	SEVENTH GRADE
SIXTH GRADE	SIXTH GRADE
FIFTH GRADE	FIFTH GRADE

For other purposes it is convenient to arrange the data in sequences in which the groups which succeed one another are composed of the same persons:

First Year	Second Year
SIXTH GRADE	SEVENTH GRADE
FIFTH GRADE	SIXTH GRADE
FOURTH GRADE	FIFTH GRADE

The second plan of arrangement may be called the *interlapping method* to distinguish it from certain overlapping methods of arranging data which do not follow precisely this selective principle.[32] If we plan our observations so that they fall readily into the interlapping method, we can summarize longer profiles of development than when we use the first plan.

THE INTERLAPPING METHOD OF OBSERVATION

The interlapping method of observation is by no means restricted to the study of school situations or of age groupings. Suppose the civil service of the community is divided into fifteen classifications. We can apply the method of interlapping observation to the study

[32] Lasswell, Harold D., The Method of Interlapping Observations in the Study of Personality in Culture. *J. Abnormal and Social Psychol.* (1937) 32:240-243.

of the interrelationships which are found within, and among, these several classifications. As students of interpersonal relations, we should like to be able to say which persons who enter class 1, or who act in certain ways during their period of service in class 1, will act in a predictable way in class 2. The same questions, of course, can be raised all along the line. What can be said of conduct in class 3 from observations made in class 2, and in class 15 from observations made during service in class 14? The entire profile of development can be summarized by the interlapping method during a two year cycle of observation. Observers can follow persons during the first year who are in rank 1, and who pass to rank 2, at the same time that another group is being observed which passes through ranks 2 and 3. Since the change from one civil service classification to another does not always follow a regular chronological sequence, many of the data gathered in a two year cycle of observation would not bear directly on the developmental problem to which we have referred. Many persons may stay in the first rank for five years, in the second rank for six years, and so on. The same problem is well known in the study of school grades, since some children remain in the same grade for more than one year. In order to get most satisfactory results in the study of the civil service, we may need to work with a basic cycle that is longer than two years. But if the two year cycle is chosen, the data will illuminate at least some developmental sequences. Thus we are interested in following the changes of experience from year to year in each classification of the service. There is a widespread impression that originality and zeal diminish with experience, and these relationships can be explored to advantage by means of the method of interlapping observation. Inside the schools, it may be valuable for many purposes to make use of shorter cycles than the two years which we have been using for convenience of illustration. Passage from one part of a grade to another part of the grade usually takes place at mid-year; hence the year cycle may be utilized for interlapping studies.

In general, we may say that the events which are suitable for the use of the method of interlapping observation are those which pass through easily identifiable and regular phases—and all phases are always exemplified by many examples.

There are many organized activities in society which answer to these general requirements. The civil services of government are in some ways less amenable to study by the method of interlapping observation than the armed forces. Well-defined hierarchies are found in nearly all churches and in many business institutions.

Family situations are suitable for study by the method of interlapping observation. Children are passing from the status of the only child to the eldest child of two, to the eldest child of three . . . and so on. Children are passing from the status of being the child of two parents to the status of having one surviving parent or no surviving parent. Mothers are passing from the status of having one child to the status of having two children, three children, and so forth. Parents are passing from the status of providing a home and support for children to the status of providing a home and support for more children, or fewer children . . . and so on through an infinity of possibilities which are potentially relevant to the study of culture and personality.

Persons are constantly changing their income classification in society. Many persons are rising or falling in deference—passing from one social class to another. Persons are rising or falling in safety—passing from peaceful civilian life to civilian life in a beleagured city, or *vice versa*.

States are constantly rising or falling in influence in the world balance of influence. Power is influence calculated in terms of fighting effectiveness. Other institutions—churches, businesses, colleges, hospitals—are passing up and down in the scale of influence. These changes are less amenable to fruitful study by the method of interlapping observation because the change in influence does not follow prearranged phases.

For the same reason communities lend themselves less readily to interlapping studies. Yet villages are always passing from a few hundred to a few thousand people, while towns are dropping from a few thousand to a few hundred. Brunner and Lorge have made observations on a large number of rural communities in America over intervals of about 10 years.[33] Some of the data are no doubt amenable to treatment by an interlapping procedure over twenty year cycles. The categories could be set up, not simply in terms of population, but of more or less prosperity, more or less cultural homogeneity in the population, and the like. The Lynds have made two observations on a middle-sized western manufacturing community. If similar investigations were conducted simultaneously in other urban areas, we would greatly enhance the value of each inquiry. For the future we might select a number of towns and cities in all the continents, and follow them at five or ten year cross-sections. Serial data are already at hand for some communities. Peking, China, for instance, was surveyed by the Sociology Department of Yenching University.[34]

It is abundantly evident from the foregoing that the time-interval of culture and personality studies is subject to much expansion or contraction to fit the emerging expediencies of the problems in hand. The method of interlapping observation, while not universally applicable, can be adapted to the study of many more problems than those to which it has been applied in the past.

It is plain that by extending the cross-sectional period backward or forward we can deepen our insight into development and add to the data needed to confirm or to disaffirm our equilibrium propositions.

If we try to extend our observations backward in time there are kinds of data which forever elude us. We cannot hope to psychoanalyze Napoleon, nor to watch the psychogalvanic reactions of Brutus to Julius Caesar. Some data require contemporary observation of events; and we must carefully plan in advance if we are to have competent observers on the spot.

What are the cross-sections which lend themselves to the study of different problems of culture and personality? We spoke of extending our cross-sections forward and backward in time. But the sheer

[33] Brunner, Edmund de S., and Lorge, Irving, *Rural Trends in Depression Years: A Survey of Village Centered Agricultural Communities, 1930–36;* New York, Columbia University Press, 1937 (xvi and 387 pp.).

[34] Published in Series C of the publications in Sociology and Social Work of Yenching University.

magnitude of the potential field of personality and cultural events is overwhelming. Some data can be obtained by total enumeration through time, like bank clearings. But other data are less amenable to total enumeration and serialization.

The World Survey of Influence

There is still a great deal of uncertainty about the sampling procedure which is best adapted to the study of world changes in influence to which we have attached so much importance in this memorandum. Some important indices of influence are abundant for modern states. Income stratifications are fairly well known, since the modern state collects income data for tax gathering purposes. But stratification by deference, or stratification by personality form, are inadequately known. The modern state has not concerned itself with such data, and facts must be laboriously assembled by private research, or inferences drawn from highly fragmentary material.

Comprehensive data about influence and the influential are of varying degrees of adequacy and reliability. Under these circumstances it seems wise to set up some provisional goals of comparative research. The present writer has suggested that we undertake to build up the best possible picture of the distribution of influence throughout the world at five-year intervals. Several scholars have voluntarily agreed to adopt this procedure wherever convenient.

Our knowledge of the main sequences of influence throughout the world is rapidly being improved by modern research. Karl A. Wittvogel has recently completed an elaborate investigation of the social origins of the Chinese bureaucracy during several centuries. Preliminary contributions are published in the *Zeitschrift für Sozialforschung* from time to time. There were many valuable studies of social and economic stratification in pre-National Socialist Germany by Emil Lederer, Theodor Geiger, and many other economists, sociologists and political scientists. Among all nations, however, the most exhaustive work appears to have been done by Scandinavian scholars on Scandinavian sources. A mine of information about the distribution of influence in the past is found in Gaetano Mosca's classical work on *The Ruling Class*.[35] Abundant material is in the encyclopaedic contributions of Vilfredo Pareto, Pitirim Sorokin, and William G. Sumner.

We may consider world politics with reference to the rise and fall of skill groups, but the "sociology of the professions" and of other skill groups is of relatively recent origin. The existing state of knowledge may be conveniently appraised by examining the work of A. M. Carr-Saunders.[36] There is a growing body of data upon the social origins, the economic position, the prestige and the activities of the teaching profession itself. Some other exploratory studies have been made of the social attitudes of boards of education, and of the social origins and affiliations of these boards in different communities.[37] Outside pressures of organized groups upon the schools have been treated in several monographs.[38] As a general criticism it may be said that most of these researches, valuable as they are, fall short of placing the school firmly in the framework of the chief stratifications of the community. There are many questions connected with the effects of upper and lower class teachers upon upper and lower class pupils which have yet to be subjected to methodical study. The term class in this connection means both "economic" and "social."

The study of the changing influence of skill is newer than the study of class changes. The powerful effect of Marxist sociology is everywhere discernible in this sphere, since it was Marx who first set up, and made influential, political analysis in terms of class successions. Because of the prominence given to class, and to the world

[35] Mosca, Gaetano, *The Ruling Class (Elementi di Scienza Politica)*; New York, McGraw-Hill Book Co., 1939 (xli and 514 pp.).

[36] Carr-Saunders, A. M., and Wilson, P. A., *The Professions*; Oxford, Clarendon Press, 1933 (vii and 536 pp.).

[37] A representative monograph on the activities of the teachers themselves is Selle, Erwin, *The Organization and Activities of the National Education Association: A Case Study in Educational Sociology*; New York, Teachers' College, Columbia University Press, 1932 (vii and 180 pp.).

[38] Notably, Beale, Howard, *Are American Teachers Free? An Analysis of Restraints upon the Freedom of Teaching in American Schools*; New York, Scribner's Sons, 1936 (xxiv and 855 pp.).

revolutionary sequence, it may not be amiss to give a little more attention to these potentialities.

"The analysis of world politics . . . implies the consideration of the shape and composition of the value patterns of mankind as a whole. This necessitates the comparison of world élites in terms of social origins, special skills, personality traits, subjective attitudes, and sustaining assets, such as symbols, goods, and violence. Attention is particularly aroused by any fundamental change in the characteristics and methods of élites. A *revolution* is rapid and extensive change in the composition and the vocabulary of the ruling few; *world revolutions* are those which inaugurate new principles of élite recruitment and new reigning ideologies in the political life of humanity.

"No doubt the French and Russian revolutions were major innovations in the world history of rulers and ruling symbols, although we may entertain some reservations on our judgment when we remember the extent to which we are saturated in the details of European history, and the meagreness of our information about oriental, 'primitive,' and ancient peoples.

"If the significant political changes of the past were signalized by revolutionary patterns which rose and spread until they were blocked or superseded by new revolutionary innovations, the future may follow the same course of development. Hence our 'present' would be transition between the latest and the impending world revolutionary emergent.

"Correct self-orientation would therefore consist in discerning the principle of élite recruitment and the predominant symbols to appear in the next phases of world political change. Sound political analysis is nothing less than correct orientation in the continuum which embraces the past, present, and future. Unless the salient features of the all-inclusive whole are discerned, details will be incorrectly located. Without the symbol of the total context the symbols of detail cannot be data." [39]

"A great question mark in world politics, then, is this: Will the Third International succeed in universalizing the Soviet Union?

[39] Reference footnote 25; pp. 3-4.

Regardless of local failures or concessions, will the trend of history be toward world union in the name of Communism?

"We are not wholly at a loss for objective ways of approaching this question. From one point of view it is a problem of diffusion and restriction, and such processes have been studied by several specialists in the social sciences. The most vigorous discussion of the technical issues involved is in the literature of students of comparative history and of primitive society. Some of their methods may profitably be applied to the understanding of the political events with which we are concerned.[40]

"Russia may be taken as the world center from which a revolutionary pattern is spreading. Beyond the boundaries of the Soviet Union the Third International rises and falls in influence. Its geographical dispersion at any given time is the net result of the factors which affect the total process of diffusion and restriction. Our problem is to discover the relative strength of these factors, and in the light of the total world picture to evaluate the possibility of development toward inclusiveness.

"World revolutionary waves are not unique in the history of modern civilization. Those who seized control in France at the end of the eighteenth century spoke in the name of all mankind, prophesied the age of reason, and demanded active support for the realization of the rights of man.

"The world revolutionary waves of the past have come short of universality. The élite which seized power at the world revolutionary center was restricted by the play of the balance of power.

"Our judgment of the world-unifying potentialities of the Communist revolution depends upon the analysis of the relative strength of factors making for diffusion and restriction of world revolutionary initiatives.

"Among the possibilities we may distinguish the following:

[40] An important theoretical statement by Edward Sapir is Time Perspective in Aboriginal American Culture, A Study in Method. *Geol. Survey of Canada, Memoir 70, Anthropological Series 13,* 1916 (30 and following pp.). Useful discussions are found in the publications of Roland Dixon, Leslie Spier, Alfred Kroeber, Paul Radin, Bronislav Malinowski, Ralph Linton, Wilson Wallis.

"*Total diffusion.* The world beyond the boundaries of the Soviet Union may eventually adhere to the new order, and the new order may retain its revolutionary characteristics.

"*World unity with restrictions from within.* The world adheres to the Soviet Union, but in the meantime the revolutionary characteristics of the center are modified by the reactivation of older social patterns.

"*Restriction of the scope of the world revolutionary* center from without by the reactivation of older social patterns. One well-established pattern is loyalty to local regions (national territory); and nationalistic sentiment may be utilized to block the spread of control from Russia. This may be called restriction by geographical differentiation. Old feudal practices may be reinstated as means of emphasizing local distinctiveness.

"*Restriction by partial incorporation.* The restriction of the élite in control at the center may proceed by incorporating some of the distinctive characteristics of the revolutionary pattern. Some incorporation may be limited to symbols: 'Socialist revolution,' 'soldiers' and workingmen's councils.' Some may include practices: the monopolization of legality by a single political party, the governmentalization of organized social life.

"*Restriction by functional differentiation.* The restriction of the élite at the center may involve the rejection of the claim of the élite to bear the true revolutionary burden, and a call for a new revolutionary initiative.

"The understanding of the diffusion-restriction process calls for case studies of communities of different characteristics at varying distances from the center of the world revolutionary wave." [41]

"It may be that world revolutionary waves themselves are one of the permanent as well as basic features of the western European pattern of civilization. Before the Russian upheaval was the French upheaval; both of them were marked by the cataclysmic emergence at a circumscribed center of an élite which invoked new symbols

---

[41] Lasswell, Harold D., and Blumenstock, Dorothy, *World Revolutionary Propaganda; A Chicago Study;* New York, Knopf, 1939 (xii and 393 and xii pp.); pp. 13-15.

to justify its control and new practices for the benefit of hitherto 'underprivileged' class formations. The élite in France spoke for the 'rights of man' and predominantly benefited the bourgeoisie; the élite in Russia spoke for the 'proletariat' and predominantly benefited the 'skill groups,' a part of the 'lesser bourgeoisie,' which in its turn is a layer of the 'bourgeoisie.'

"If we decide to extrapolate the past into the future, we may add to our description of the world revolutionary waves as permanent features of western European civilization the following statement: the élite which seizes power at the eruptive center of a new revolutionary movement does not succeed in unifying the world. Another conspicuous feature of the western European pattern of civilization is the multiple state system, which is sustained by such symbolic formations as the demand for 'sovereignty' and the expectation of violence. Most potent of all, the multiple state system is supported by nationalistic sentiment. . . . Thus it seems highly improbable that world unity will occur by the incorporation of all states within the U. S. S. R.

"To predict that the scope of the élite which seizes power at a world center will fall short of the world does not imply that all elements of what was called before 'the world revolutionary pattern' will fall short of universal diffusion. We must distinguish the *original* world revolutionary *pattern* of the revolutionary *center* from the world revolutionary *pattern of the epoch*. The first—the original center pattern—is no doubt destined to be restricted; the second—the epoch pattern—is moving toward universality among the major powers.

"If we look back at the French case, we plainly see in the perspective of subsequent happenings that many of the innovations in symbol and practice which took place within the borders of France also appeared beyond France, without formal affiliation of the other states with the eruptive center. That is, practices concerning the relationship of governments to economic processes which favored the rise of the bourgeoisie at the expense of the aristocracy became more and more universal during the nineteenth century, although the world remained separated into independent states.

The same may be said for a series of other practices—universal suffrage, supremacy of legislatures over executives—as well as for certain symbols [such as] 'rights of man.' In all of these cases the connection between them and the élite of the eruptive center of revolution in France was severed. It is evident, too, that the most extreme features of the original revolutionary pattern did not persist, even in France.

"What are the features of the Russian center of world revolution which are also components of the world revolutionary pattern of our entire epoch? Perhaps one may attribute a predominant place to the *moderation of income differences* by the abolition of private ownership in the instrumentalities of production, unaccompanied by reinstatement of differences of the same magnitude within governmentally controlled enterprises. Possibly another pattern is the increasing *governmentalization of organized social life*. Another is the *predominance of a party with a privileged status*." [42]

"No doubt the tendency to abolish unemployment—at least symbolically—will prove to be as universal as the tendency to moderate income differences." [43]

In the light of such constructions, we come to attach a new importance to certain questions about educational processes in different nations. In the United States, for example, do we find that educational processes, in-school and out-of-school, coincide more and more—or less and less—with the world revolutionary pattern of the epoch? And are the young people who are exposed to these educational environments left with attitudes which will foster the adoption, or the restriction, of this pattern? To what extent do attitudes now—or ultimately—favor the approximation of the epoch pattern by affiliation with the Russian center, or by affiliation with vehement nationalistic anti-revolutionary movements of the German and Italian type?

We can bring into the purview of our world studies the data from areas of primitive culture. Already some of the students of social anthropology have organized research in a way which fits

[42] Reference footnote 41; pp. 354-356.
[43] Reference footnote 41; p. viii.

neatly into the program of world observation which is here out-lined. Robert Redfield is studying a series of communities which it is planned to re-survey from time to time in the future.[44] Rough studies were made of the distribution of primitive traits in Lower Mexico and Guatemala. Communities were chosen which bore the following relation to the areas as a whole: a community at the center of the area in which primitive traits are best represented; a community removed from the center and in closer contact with other centers of cultural diffusion; and a community on the margin of the area, whose traits were heavily intermixed with outside traits.

Although most of the primitive cultures which lie dispersed over the face of the earth are of minor political importance in contemporary world politics, since they are under the domination of the superior technology of Western civilization, they should not be completely underestimated. The native Indians of Central and South America, and the native African tribes of that huge continent, are not entirely "passive" factors even at the present time. And studies of the diffusion of the dominant symbols and practices of the Great Powers can not by any means ignore the primitive cultures. I encountered an Indian in a New Mexico pueblo who dreamed of going to Mexico where the "Indians really amounted to something," so that some day he could join in introducing soviets all over the American continent.

The students of primitive culture have gone far enough in the study of the "remnant Cultures" for us to include them in the general program of world observation which is here proposed. By bringing the world picture to the focus of attention of anthropologists, new questions will occur to them; and new data—and even new hypotheses—may come to the social scientists who specialize upon the study of the Great Powers. Some of the primitive groups are still almost wholly isolated from the rest of mankind. But there is evidence that no primitive group is wholly without outside connections. This is the sense—no matter how tenuous—in which it is

[44] Redfield, Robert, *Chan Kom, a Maya Village;* Washington, D. C., Carnegie Institution, 1934 (viii and 387 pp.); *Tepoztlan, a Mexican Village; A Study of Folk Life;* Chicago, University of Chicago Press, 1930 (xi and 247 pp.).

no romantic exaggeration to say that the present history of man is a common enterprise.

In connection with the contact of Western civilization and other cultures, there are many opportunities for study within the boundaries of the United States. There are still remnants of the Indian cultures which were vanquished in the struggle for the control of this continent, and in some cases it is not too late to gather data of unusual importance for the understanding of personality and culture. The schools which are operated by the Department of the Interior are excellent vantage points for the pursuit of these investigations, and the Commissioner for Indian Affairs is warmly cooperative at the present time. How can the world-view of our Western civilization—and its accompanying techniques—be communicated to the carriers of the surviving cultures in a way that simplifies, rather than complicates, the problem of transition? Some of these cultures provide children with a view of the world that is strongly reminiscent of the dominant outlook which prevailed in Europe until the Enlightenment. The boundary between "being alive" and "being dead" is not nearly as sharp as modern scientific knowledge has tended to make it. The supernatural influences are less remote than in our modern world-view. There is a more active sense of kinship with many forms of life. We know from the gory history of Europe the difficulties which arise as the new scientific method of thought, coupled with technology, comes in contact with pre-scientific views of the world. It seems probable that more work is being done on the problem of managing these transitions in the Soviet Union than anywhere else in the world. But many opportunities survive, notably in Alaska and in the Southwest, for fundamental research on culture and personality.

SOCIAL AREAS

We may think of the different kinds of data we need in terms of different geographical distributions. There are different kinds of *psychological (symbolic) areas*. The *attention area* is occupied by the persons who share a common focus of attention. The attention area of New York is composed of all people who have New York brought to their attention with at least a specified frequency—one reference a month, for example.[45]

The study of the attention groups with which young people are connected is a matter of very special significance. What is the relationship between the attention areas which include the children of a given grade in school, and their parents? teachers? colleagues of like age who are out of school? The milieu of a person is defined by what he thinks and muses about, and the attention area is defined by those who share a common object of reference, with or without knowledge of the similar preoccupation of the other person. The study of the daily cycle of activity of representative young people may provide more and more of the relevant information. To what extent is the daily cycle of attention distributed among newspapers, magazines, radio programs, motion picture films, books, lectures, conversations; and how are the specific objects of attention—direct and in imagination—to be classified? Because of our special interest in the subjective-expressive cycle which constitutes personality, we are especially interested in references to the *self* in relation to *others;* and, among *others,* to members of the immediate and the remote environment classified according to the social structure of the community. Thus the very low class person in the deference pyramid may pay a great deal of attention, direct and in fantasy, to persons of the same class; persons of the middle classes may focus upon the upper classes; and persons of the upper classes may focus upon one another. The preoccupation with the self may be greatest among the middle classes. If more class distinctions appear on the basis of the criteria which are selected, distinctive attention patterns may be demonstrated. Subjective events may also be classified as *pro* or *anti,* hence pro- or anti-self, and pro- or anti-

[45] The reading areas of metropolitan newspapers in 1920 and 1929 are summarized in *Recent Social Trends,* New York, Whittlesey House, 1934, Chapter IX. Some of the book reading areas of the United States are outlined in Wilson, Louis R., *The Geography of Reading: A Study of the Distribution and Status of Libraries in the United States;* Chicago, American Library Association and the University of Chicago Press, 1938 (xxiv and 481 pp.). Radio listening areas are described in publications put out by the radio industry.

other. Moods with no symbol of reference may be classified "eu-phoric" or "dysphoric," agreeable, disagreeable. Anxiety is a sub-jective event which shows acute dysphoria, and stress toward action. On the basis of these fundamental distinctions, the sub-jective cycle of the person may be explored, and the degree to which he shares a common focus of attention with other persons may be discovered.

The relation of the focusing events to the dynamic equilibrium of personality is very important in this connection. If we are deal-ing with personalities which, at a given period, re-instate light fear states, these fear states may be procured on exposure to radio or motion picture; and if not forthcoming from these media, the indi-vidual may provide his own nightmare, or act provocatively toward someone in the environment.

Several indices of attention areas have been used, notably the zones of newspaper circulation, of radio listening, of reading. Most of these studies have not analyzed the symbols to which the reader or the listener was exposed; hence their relationship to true atten-tion areas is incomplete.

The *public* is a psychological area which is made up of those who make debatable demands for action. The public is smaller than the attention area, since it is composed of those who occupy a sufficiently direct relationship to certain activities to expect to in-fluence them. The New York attention area is vast; but the New York public is comparatively circumscribed.

Another psychological area is the *sentiment* area, and is consti-tuted by those who share common sentiments. Racial, nationalistic, regional, and many other groups share common sentiments, and determine the area.

Besides psychological areas we may speak of *activity* and *or-ganization* areas. An organization area has an explicit hierarchy; an activity area does not. The organization areas include legislative districts, administrative districts, judicial districts; activity areas in-clude zones of trade, travel, and fighting. Official school districts are, of course, organization areas; but there may be very different degrees of participation in school activities within the districts.

Modern social science has accumulated a huge amount of information about all kinds of social areas. Under the name of "ecology" many distributions have been charted. The analysis of spatial distributions, particularly in urban sociology, received a vigorous impetus from Robert E. Park.[46] Many rural sociologists and economists have worked out the relationship between small population nuclei, like villages, and areas defined by those who came in to trade, to attend church, to go to lodge, to go to school and the like. In the field of world politics, the study of boundaries and of the zones of conflict, has developed a huge literature. The "human geography" of France has stimulated much scientific interest in regional phenomena. In the United States this interest is conspicuously served by sociologists like Howard W. Odum, and by many other social scientists besides professional geographers.[47]

The charting of data in space and time is an excellent exercise in social reality, but it leads nowhere in particular unless it is given significance by means of developmental constructions, or equilibrium analyses. We have had, as yet, comparatively few studies of the interrelationship among areas. Hence we have had few investigations which pivot around problems like these: If the psychological areas are modified in a given way, how will the activity and organization areas be modified? If the activity and organization areas are modified, how will the psychological areas be changed? Alfred Weber's theory of industrial localization remains one of the few elaborate systematic works in this field.[48] Students of administration, notably educational administration, have undertaken to find the criteria for the optimum size of school districts. The data which are called for in such investi-

[46] Park, Robert E., Human Ecology. *Amer. J. Sociol.* (1936) 42:1-15. For a selected and annotated bibliography see Caldwell, Morris Gilmore, The Sociological Tract: The Spatial Distribution of Social Data. *Psychiatry* (1938) 1:379-385.

[47] Odum, Howard W., *Southern Regions of the United States;* Chapel Hill, University of North Carolina Press, 1936 (xi and 664 pp.).

[48] Weber, Alfred, *Alfred Weber's Theory of the Location of Industries;* Chicago, University of Chicago Press, 1929 (xxxiii and 256 pp.). For an admirable discussion of the problems connected with culture area studies, consult Kluckhohn, Clyde, On Certain Recent Applications of Association Coefficients to Ethnological Data, *Amer. Anthropol.* (1939) 41:345-377.

gations are of very general importance for social science, as well as practical administration.[49] It is no doubt relevant to this plexus of problems to raise certain questions about the relationship between schools and the community as a whole. To what extent can schools protect their influence in the community by undertaking to concentrate activities in the school building? Under what conditions does it strengthen the school to provide meeting places, and even headquarters, for adult groups, like lodges, women's societies, farmer's associations, political parties? When do such activities weaken the school? Where the community is homogeneous, and where the facilities of other agencies are meagre, the school can doubtless become the center of more and more activity areas. Can we locate any more clearly the degree of heterogeneity which is compatible with these policies?

Can we discover the situations in which certain school policies increase community conflict? Does the centralization of school administration in larger and larger units of government diminish, or does it increase, the extent to which schools contribute to community conflict? No doubt the most promising hypothesis here is that when the enlarged area most deviates from the local area in social structure, the probability of conflict is greatest.

It is important to pursue that relationship of the school to conflict somewhat further. It may be that an enlarged school area does not precipitate local conflict over the school, but intensifies the struggle among local factions to gain control of the remaining vestiges of local authority. This might be expected to occur when struggle over the school was obviated by the social homogeneity of the larger area, and when tax burdens were expected to diminish.

The enlarged area of school administration may have significant effects upon the vitality of democratic processes. Is there a slumping off of participation in public affairs on the part of the local community when school control is gone? Or is there a quickening of interest in participating in the life of the enlarged unit? Is there a shift of politi-

[49] The area problem is given attention at many points in White, Leonard D., *Introduction to the Study of Public Administration* [revised edition]; New York, Macmillan, 1939 (xiii and 611 pp.).

cal expression from geographical units to functional units, as when the person becomes less active in local elections, but more eager to act in the wider administrative area through the Grange or the union to which he belongs? It may be that the homogeneity of the larger area tends to diminish the intensity of political participation, but that heterogeneity provokes even more political activity. This may happen, for example, when a local Protestant group strives to keep itself from being "dominated" by the Catholic group in the larger area.

Within any culture area it is evident that much of the process of education goes forward outside of school. It is possible to examine in detail the structure of the local area with the aim of discovering where significant educational activities take place. Wherever young people congregate there are important implications for attitude and skill, and from this point of view the ecology of the school in relation to congregating facilities is of particular interest. Pupils may be expected to develop somewhat differently in areas where there are many restaurants, motion picture houses, and job-giving agencies, than in areas where the route from school to home is through a familiar residential neighborhood. The degree of these differences in "sophistication" may be worth noticing, since the relative balance of *mores* and counter-*mores* patterns in the community is affected by these factors.

The interrelationships of home, employer, companion and school are always worthy of careful study. Changes in the organization of authority in the home, or on the job, may be generalized to the school, or compensated against in the school. If the authority of the father, relative to the mother, is declining in the homes of a community, do the pupils act more assertively toward male teachers? Or do they, on the contrary, show special submissiveness, as if to restore an early demand to respect a male authority? [50]

In bringing this memorandum to a close, it is perhaps pertinent to

[50] For a valuable study of changing authority in European homes one of the studies of the Institute for Social Research, directed by Max Horkheimer, may be examined. Studien über Authorität und Familie. Horkheimer, Max (ed.), *Sozialpsychologischer Teil;* Paris, Felix Alcan, 1936 (xv and 949 pp.).

repeat that useful work in the field of interpersonal relations does not depend upon the achievement of a uniform vocabulary. After all, the field of the social and psychological studies has expanded with phenomenal rapidity in the last hundred years. Observers are always taking up new standpoints as social scientists become more numerous and their activities more diversified.

The rapid exploration of any continent imposes certain limitations upon the explorers. They grow a little apart from one another. Each new band of pioneers is rather completely taken up with the occupation of a new river valley, a new plateau, or a new peninsula. Local loyalties grow up and strange differences in dialect appear.

If each body of specialists upon the life of man displays some of the less congenial characteristics of isolated men, we must not forget that a degree of isolation is necessary to complete the general map of human knowledge. If these hardy adventurers speak a dialect very much their own and not always simple to understand, we may take solace in the reflection that these scientific vernaculars have not only grown up in isolation, but that they bear some relationship to the task of conquering the jungles and swamps of the local region where they are found.

For many reasons we find dialectical differences among specialists less irritating than we did a few short years ago. We are learning the technique of understanding and translating speech. A new optimism has begun to pervade the world of scientific work—an optimism born of confidence in the degree to which barriers of language can be overcome. Partly, this is a matter of new technique. New ways of understanding words have come to us from modern logic. From logic we learn how to translate from one set of scientific symbols into another and we learn to emphasize the standpoint of the particular observer in relation to the whole. From modern psychological and sociological research we have gained new insight into the attitudes which tend to color our conduct in the presence of alien speech. Why is it so common to hate the strange, and especially the strange word? Among the many relevant factors in this problem some are both suggestive and liberating. Words were once the property of the adults who surrounded us when we were children. With words, adults could live in a private world beyond our grasp. Commanding the tools of speech they screened themselves from us, and dictated our destiny. In many of us the childish feeling of weakness in the presence of words has not been entirely left behind. When we meet a strange word we draw back in alarm and frown in resentment.

Today, we do not disregard the advantages of common speech, but we are learning to deal with differences of speech without annoyance. This new detachment has led us to inspect our own language. We find that the same word in the mouths of two persons may betray us. The word seems to refer to the same event, but often it does not. Thus the word-awareness with which we greet the scientific stranger is turned toward the scientific colleague—and then toward the self.

When we try to state what we ourselves see, we find it wise to recognize the limitations imposed upon us by professional terms, by the traits of our own personality, and by the cultural surroundings to which we have been exposed. We take it for granted that we always speak more or less for ourselves—but at the same time we seldom speak exclusively for ourselves. And as the work of verification proceeds among social scientists and psychologists, we hope to widen the area of stable communication.

MENTAL HYGIENE
AND THE CLASS
STRUCTURE

Kingsley Davis

MENTAL hygiene constitutes for the sociologist a two-fold interest, first as a social movement (preparing now to celebrate its twenty-ninth anniversary), and second as an applied science (drawing upon several pure sciences of which sociology is one). Both sides of this interest fit with our present subject—the relation of mental hygiene to the vertical dimension of society—because any phenomenon which is at once a social movement and an applied human science cannot escape on two counts having some connection, however obscure it may seem, with the invidious, discriminatory aspect of social life.

We should like to define mental hygiene in terms of its chief aim, but the general goal as usually stated—improvement of mental health in the community, promotion of personal efficiency, or provision for personality expression and happiness—is ambiguous. It is difficult to determine whether mental hygiene practises are really conducive to such a goal, or whether the practises of any well-intentioned movement are not equally conducive to it. Our conception of mental hygiene, then, will embrace simply the movement and the point of view called by that name. The diffuseness of its main goal and the proliferation of subsidiary ends [1] will be viewed as symptomatic of its social role and function.

[1] "The ultimate in mental hygiene means mental poise, calm judgment, and an understanding of leadership and fellowship—in other words, cooperation, with an attitude that tempers justice with mercy and humility."—Dr. M. J. Rosenau, "Mental Hygiene and Public Health," *Mental Hygiene*, xix (Jan.

Now let us turn briefly to the vertical dimension in society. Its essence is the relative inferiority and superiority of persons in one another's eyes. It is manifest on the one hand in a *crystallized hierarchy* of positions (offices and statuses) which is supported by a correlative system of sentiments and a constraining set of legal and moral sanctions; and on the other hand in *interpersonal relations* where (in rough accord with the crystallized attitudes) every act, word and thought of the person is unremittingly subjected to the praising and condemning scrutiny of others. The vertical dimension is thus not limited to the wider or smaller circles; it is coextensive with the social.

Persons occupying similar positions in the hierarchy constitute a social class, in most cases a statistical rather than a real group. Class implies the division of persons into broad strata according to their final score in the summation of estimable tallies—the precipitate of all the countless criteria of invidious distinction. The strata may be so organized with reference to one another that movement up or down the scale is facilitated or blocked. The first type we call a sys-

---

1935):9. Bromberg attributes to a prominent spokesman of the movement the following statement: "Mental hygiene . . . presents many wider aspects. Industrial unrest to a large degree means bad mental hygiene, and is to be corrected by good mental hygiene. The various antisocial attitudes that lead to crime are problems for the mental hygienist. Dependency, insofar as it is social parasitism not due to mental or physical defect, belongs to mental hygiene. But mental hygiene has a message also for those who consider themselves quite normal, for, by its aims, the man who is fifty per cent efficient can make himself seventy per cent efficient. . . ."—W. Bromberg, *The Mind of Man*, New York, 1937, p. 217. So many similar statements can be found in mental hygiene texts, articles, and credos, that these quotations are typical.

Mental hygiene thus possesses a characteristic that is essential to any social movement—namely, that its proponents regard it as a panacea. Since mental health is obviously connected with the social environment, to promote such health is to treat not only particular minds but also the customs and institutions in which the minds function. To cure so much is to cure all.

A sane way to discuss mental hygiene is to assume that the purpose of mental hygiene is the prevention of positive mental disorder, and that it is therefore a branch of the public health movement, which intends not so much to make everybody bouncingly robust as to prevent the onset and spread of definite diseases. But since mental hygienists dub this limited goal as old fashioned, our realistic treatment cannot make the assumption.

tem of mobile classes, the second a system of immobile castes. Each type possesses its appropriate world philosophy common to its members, absolutistic in expression, and conceived as an order of justice. Its principles penetrate to every phase and aspect of life, taking hold of the person in the dynamic maze of communicative, especially interpersonal and primary, contacts.

Our interest lies in our own mobile class system and its accompanying world philosophy. The latter, which may conveniently be called the Protestant ethic, and which receives its severest expression in Puritanism, is: (1) *Democratic* in the sense of favoring equal opportunity to rise socially by merit rather than by birth. (2) *Worldly* in emphasizing earthly values such as the pursuit of a calling, accumulation of wealth, and achievement of status. (3) But at the same time *ascetic* in stressing physical abstinence and stern sobriety, thrift, industry, and prudence. (4) *Individualistic* in placing responsibility upon the individual himself for his economic, political, and religious destiny, and in stressing personal ambition, self-reliance, private enterprise, and entrepreneurial ability.[2] (5) *Rationalistic* and *empirical* in assuming a world order discoverable through sensory observation of nature.[3] (6) *Utilitarian* in pursuing practical ends with the best available means, and conceiving human welfare in secularized terms as attainable by human knowledge and action.

It can be demonstrated, we think, that this ethic is functionally related to an open-class society. Not only are the two historically con-

[2] The individualistic and worldly-ascetic qualities were delineated by Max Weber. See his *General Economic History*, trans. by F. H. Knight, Part IV; and *The Protestant Ethic and the Spirit of Capitalism*, trans. by Talcott Parsons, London, 1930.

[3] R. K. Merton, "Puritanism, Pietism, and Science," *Sociological Review*, xxviii (Jan. 1936): 1-30. Max Weber, *op. cit.*, also points out the rationalistic character of Protestantism, as does W. Sombart in his *Quintessence of Capitalism*, trans. by M. Epstein, London, 1915, in his article on "Capitalism" in *Ency. Soc. Sciences*, 1930, and in his *Jews and Modern Capitalism*, London, 1913. Sombart, in the article cited, sums up the capitalist spirit in the concepts: acquisition, competition, and rationality. Following this lead we could regard capitalism as the competition for social status in terms of the acquisition of goods by rational manipulative processes.

nected, but it seems that an open-class society could scarcely work without such a philosophy.[4]

But what has this Protestant ethic, plus the underlying system of mobile classes, to do with mental hygiene? Our discussion of this point, suggestive rather than conclusive, will embrace the following propositions: first, that mental hygiene, being a social movement and a source of advice concerning personal conduct, has inevitably taken over the Protestant ethic inherent in our society, not simply as the basis for conscious preachment but also as the unconscious system of premises upon which its "scientific" analysis and its conception of mental health itself are based. Second, that this unconscious incorporation of the open-class ethic has made mental hygiene doubly susceptible to the psychologistic approach to human conduct, though the latter has represented, in part, a contradictory feature. Third, that the unconscious assumption of the dominant ethic, together with the psychologistic interpretation, has served to obscure the social determinants of mental disease, and especially the effects of invidious or emulative relationships. And finally, that mental hygiene will probably fail as a preventive movement because it cannot overcome its defects, the free analysis and manipulation of invidious social elements never being permitted in an integrated society.

The relation between mental hygiene and the open-class ethic is an unconscious one. Tacitly the textbooks for teachers and practitioners of the subject assume the existence of a mobile class structure and teach by implication the congruent moral norms. Frequently they

[4] The Protestant ethic was perhaps most characteristic of early capitalism, and it has doubtless fallen into some desuetude with subsequent social changes, but it still tends to form the unconscious premises of our thinking about conduct, even when in practice we do not follow its precepts. Veblen was particularly impressed with the archaic character of our present 18th century moral philosophy. (See his *Vested Interests and the Common Man*, N. Y., 1920). The Protestant ethic is still the living message of our departed moral authorities—Jefferson, Franklin, Lincoln, and Emerson—and is woven into poetry, song, and precept.

interpret these norms as somehow given in the individual, and in the last analysis always define mental health itself in terms of them.[5]

Vertical mobility, for example, is taken for granted, and social advancement accepted as a natural goal. Democracy, in the form of equal opportunity to advance, is regarded as desirable. Lack of ambition is felt to represent a definite symptom of maladjustment, to be eliminated if possible. The normal person is considered to be one who chooses a calling and tries to distinguish himself in it, while the mentally sick person is one who needs occupational therapy.[6]

[5] Our generalizations are based upon a systematic study of selected literature in the field, chosen from a list sent out by the National Committee for Mental Hygiene, Inc. In addition, a few other standard works were read with a view to sampling. All told, thirteen volumes were gone through, with the aid of a fixed questionnaire designed to discover certain things about each book. The books systematically perused are as follows: V. V. Anderson, *Psychiatry in Education*, N. Y., 1932; W. J. Burnham, *The Wholesome Personality*, N. Y., 1932; E. R. Groves and P. Blanchard, *Introduction to Mental Hygiene*, N. Y., 1930; Howard and Patry, *Mental Health*, N. Y., 1935; D. W. La Rue, *Mental Hygiene*, N. Y., 1927; J. J. B. Morgan, *Keeping a Sound Mind*, N. Y., 1934; W. V. Richmond, *Personality: Its Study and Hygiene*, N. Y., 1937; L. F. Shaffer, *The Psychology of Adjustment*, Boston, 1936; G. S. Stevenson and G. Smith, *Child Guidance Clinics*, N. Y., 1934; D. A. Thom, *Everyday Problems of the Everday Child*, N. Y., 1928; J. E. W. Wallin, *Personality Maladjustments and Mental Hygiene*, N. Y., 1935; F. L. Wells, *Mental Adjustments*, N. Y., 1917; C. B. Zachry, *Personality Adjustments of School Children*, N. Y., 1929. Other literature, especially recent contributions in psychiatry dealing with the relation of mental disorder to social phenomena, was of course read.

[6] Burnham, p. 522: "The democratic ideal in its higher form is based, not on an abstract myth of human equality, made concrete in an equal share of human necessities and social privileges, but based rather on the psychological fact of profound individual differences." "The ideal democratic group today is one where each member of the group has the opportunity to become superior in something according to his special ability."

Howard and Patry consider mobility on the whole a desirable condition, since it offers a goal for effort. But they criticize the mad scramble for money and "material" things. In other words, they condemn some of the particular goals of vertical movement, but they do not condemn (or indeed consciously treat) mobility itself.

La Rue says that we must learn to adapt ourselves to any surroundings. "But that is no reason why we should rest satisfied with all these things, or make no effort to improve our condition."—p. 280. Ambition is assumed all

Likewise *competition* is assumed, life being regarded as a battle or a game in which victory goes to him who uses wit and strength to best advantage.[7] Since the morality of the competitive system requires that we not violate the rules of the game, and that we not envy the other fellow his accomplishments or gloat over his failures, this morality is incorporated into the mental hygiene teaching—the prevention of mental illness becoming at the same time the prevention of delinquency and the encouragement of good sportsmanship.[8] The healthy person is regarded as achieving victory against others only within the rules, by empirico-rational ingenuity and ascetic self-discipline. The maladjusted person must learn to face reality, i.e., the competitive facts.[9] He must not achieve victories in fancy only, or flee the memory of his failures. Parents must not coddle their child and thus make him unfit for the competition of adult life. Yet since to face reality means not only to grasp the fact of competition, but also to estimate correctly one's chances, and since one's chances depend upon capacity and circumstances as well as effort, a safety

---

through the book. Self-confidence, a necessary entrepreneurial virtue, is extolled and Emerson is quoted as saying that "Self-trust is the secret of success."

Wells assumes that the aim of life is to get ahead, and that ambition is a prerequisite to a well-functioning mind. P. 11: "The free imagination of wished-for things results well for the mind through painting in more glowing colors the excellence of what is wished for, and firing the ambition to strive for it the more intensely." The success vs. failure motif is apparent.

[7] Morgan, p. 166: "Your birth means that you have been selected as a player in the greatest game ever devised. . . ."

Wells, p. 7: "Yet the worth of existence depends on success in a game infinitely more complicated than that of chess, in which no mistake is ever overlooked and no move ever taken back, and where knowledge from one's own experience often comes too late for use."

[8] Morgan, p. 38: "The fight of the mature adult is thus transformed from the childish attempt to resist all conditions which produce physical discomfort to the battle against any infraction against his self-imposed standards of behavior."

[9] Shaffer states, p. 152, that one symptom of bad adjustment found in the inferiority complex is "a poor reaction to competition."

A literal translation of the phrase "personal efficiency," found so frequently in the literature, would be "competitive ability."

valve for the competitive drive is provided by the advice that one should not aspire beyond one's ability.[10]

Because competition has for its goal a worldly prize, but a prize not to be won by self-indulgence, the implied existence of competition as a sane way of life is buttressed by the tacit preachment of *worldly asceticism*. Mental hygiene does not frown upon enjoyment for itself, but it does insist that recreation shall be "wholesome." In other words, one should not choose a type of recreation that makes one unfit for the serious business of life,[11] or which violates the canons of Protestant morality. One's behavior should manifest prudence, rationality, and foresight, and material possessions should not be dissipated by whimsical extravagance.[12]

Individualism is tacitly assumed in three ways. (1) The person is held responsible for his own destiny. In case of neurosis his will is the object of treatment. In short he is the entrepreneur.[13] (2) Individual happiness is the ultimate good. Mental health is interpreted

[10] One of the five goals of "progressive" education, as listed by Zachry, p. 271, is: "The cultivation of ambitions which can be attained."

Morgan, p. 151: "Ambition must not be excessive." P. 22: "Facing life squarely is the first principle of mental health."

[11] Groves and Blanchard, p. 302: "The devotion of some leisure time to recreational pursuits is of positive value outside of the enjoyment which it affords, for it enables the individual to return reinvigorated to the more serious routine of study or work."

Another of the five goals of "progressive" education which Zachry lists is "healthful recreation."

[12] Wells, p. 276: "In life, the lubricating function of money to the social machinery is well known. It plays an equally essential part in the smooth operation of one's mental trends."

Shaffer, p. 539: The individual should "employ the scientific method for the solution of his personal problems." P. 382: It is assumed that rationality and insight are possible and desirable.

[13] Shaffer, p. 539: "The chief requirements for hygienic work are freedom and success. Each person must be free to select the kind of task that is most suitable and most satisfying to him. He must have freedom to plan it and to carry it to completion in his own way."

Another of Zachry's five goals of "progressive" education is "personal independence—intellectual and emotional."

as the satisfaction of individual needs.[14] (3) Human behavior is assumed to be understandable in terms of individuals abstracted from their society. Needs, desires, and mental processes are frequently discussed as if inherent in the organism.[15]

Specialization is implicitly taken for granted in the emphasis upon the value of a particular kind of work adapted to one's talents and identified with one's own personality.

Utilitarianism is obviously assumed in the action philosophy of mental hygiene. To function, to grow, to do is regarded as the purpose of life. Tangible ends and Progress are regarded as the goals. Human welfare is seen as attainable by the application of rational science.[16]

If the thesis is true that mental hygiene unconsciously incorporates the open-class ethic, it should be further indicated by a study of the movement's personnel. Such a study, constituting a type of circumstantial evidence,[17] was made, and it shows that the persons prominently connected with the movement are of the type one would expect to uphold the Protestant principles. They are mostly upper middle class professionals, predominantly of British ancestry, identified with

[14] La Rue, pp. 11-12: "Happiness is, in general, the sign of mental health."
Stevenson and Smith, p. 1: "The child guidance clinic is an attempt to marshal the resources of the community in behalf of children who are in distress because of unsatisfied inner needs. . . ."

[15] Shaffer assumes that individuals possess four types of motives which then come into conflict with the environment.—p. 86.
Zachry says that the child's "instinctive tendencies often conflict with one another. . . ."—p. 45.

[16] Shaffer, p. 539: The individual should "employ the scientific method for the solution of his personal problems." P. 382: Assumes that rationality and insight are possible and desirable.
Another of Zachry's five goals is "purposeful and rational activity."
Morgan, p. 1: Life is ever-changing and demands continuous readjustment. It is "a game with a continual challenge which you must meet if you are to keep alive. Stagnation and death come when you cease to rise to the challenge."

[17] The survey includes data on the lives of 51 persons, leaders of the mental hygiene movement. With no funds for detailed historical or questionnaire research, we could not secure as many facts as we wished. Our conclusions are therefore tentative, but on the information we do have, taken from available bibliographical sources in obituaries, *Who's Who,* etc., they seem quite justified.

a Protestant church, and frequently reared and educated in New England. Many of them apparently had well-to-do parents who themselves had risen in life through effort and initiative. Some of them are self-made men of undistinguished parentage in our own or in the old country. In general they seem to have taken to heart the necessity of a calling and have worked, abstained, and striven sufficiently to succeed. It follows from their background and is exemplified in their writings, that they believe in empirical science and have taken the American humanitarian religion seriously enough to apply scientific results zealously to the mental welfare of society. They are (without cavil) idealistic, respectable, and capable, and their sentiments lean on the side of humanitarian individualism.

Aside from the personnel of the movement, there exists for our main thesis still another (and more direct) evidence,—derived from examining a central and recurrent concept in the mental hygiene literature, namely, "mental health." This concept is usually defined as the "integration," the "balance," the "successful" or "happy functioning" of the personality; [18] but these words are as vague as the initial phrase. Furthermore, no adequate criteria for establishing the presence of this "integration" or "balance" are provided. The only consistent criterion, and in the last analysis the substance of every definition,

[18] Howard and Patry, p. 24: "We have seen that the prime condition of mental health is the integration of the psychophysical and psychosocial organism through the development of stable major circuits of energy or good patterns of behavior." La Rue, p. 13: "Happiness is, in general, the sign of mental health. But it should be lasting happiness; for of course one can be happy for the moment, like the maniac or the drunkard, without having a mind that is really healthy." Richmond: The healthy personality is one which "functions more or less perfectly in its cultural milieu."—p. 248. Shaffer, p. 138: "For a person to satisfy all his motives with regard for their functioning as an interrelated system, is good adjustment. To achieve this requires unified and integrated behavior." Thom, p. 135: "The well-adjusted personality, which characterizes a happy and efficient man or woman, is a harmonious blending of these varied emotions and character traits, resulting in self-control and habits of conformity." Wallin, p. 32: "That individual may be considered to be mentally sound and efficient who is able to react to his physical and social environment in an effective, consistent, and integrated manner. That is, an individual's mental soundness can be judged by the appropriateness and rationality of his behavior patterns on the psychological and social levels."

is normal behavior. Consequently we shall examine what the mental hygiene literature means by "the normal."

Does "normal" refer to the statistical average of actual behavior, or to ideal behavior? It seems that mental hygienists have not seen the issue. In practice they employ the concept in both senses, though ultimately the normative sense prevails. There is in the literature much criticism of *selected* moral rules and attitudes. Sometimes the apparent basis of criticism is that the rules are unrealistic—i.e., that they are too far removed from the average actual behavior. Generally, however, the criticism springs (as it inevitably must) from value-judgments of the author. On the basis of his own conscious or unconscious values, the selected norm may be judged to be "irrational," "unenlightened," and detrimental to mental health. But whence come the author's values? Due to his position in society, and the nature of his work, they must come from the central valuational system of his culture.[19] He can and he will criticize particular norms, but he can-

[19] In the following passage quoted from Howard and Patry, pp. 146-148, we find an illustration of typical reasoning along this line:

"The moralists and theologians who were not able to give sex a rational explanation sought to stamp sex interest out of life. This only tended to dam up its force. [Condemnation of an old moral attitude on ground of its effects.] When psychoanalysis began to disclose it as a factor in mental conflicts, the so-called realists . . . began to play fast and loose with sex themes, with the result . . . a flood of sex liberalism. [Condemnation of current attitude.] . . . There is at present the need of a middle ground between the old attitude of avoidance and the present indiscriminate flaunting of sex themes. [Advocacy of a particular attitude.] Wholesome-minded people are not averse to frank consideration of sex under proper conditions and right motives, but they do not enjoy having it dragged into prominence on every possible pretext and occasion. Dignity and decency are the marks of successful sex adjustment. [Bolstering the proposed attitude with words and phrases of praise and redundant identification of it with health and the right people.] In our approach to the problems and in procedures for the enlightenment of the young these qualities should be our guide and goal." [Assertion that everybody *should* accept the author's goal.] "In our attempts at sex education we have not yet learned to appeal to the highest motive—family formation. . . . Morality for its own sake no longer makes an appeal to young people. All moral codes should be tested by the degree to which they contribute vital values and call out deeper potentialities." [Justifying the proposed attitude on the basis of its connection with a fundamental institution and hence the central system of values in the culture.]

not impugn the basic institutions of his society, because it is in terms of these that conduct is ultimately judged to be satisfactory (i.e., adjusted) or unsatisfactory.[20]

The ethical meaning of "normal" is further borne out by the fact that when specific advice is given concerning life problems, the conduct prescribed is ordinarily such as would conform to our ideals, not to the statistical average. The mental hygienist tends to justify such advice, however, not on moral but on rational or "scientific" grounds. One can best secure mental health, best satisfy one's needs, by conforming. But since for certain selected norms he does not advise conformity, the hygienist violates his own contention. Furthermore, he never brings the question of conformity or non-conformity to a clear issue, because he does not define "individual needs" or "adjustment" apart from moral norms, and because he does not admit that the delinquent may escape detection and hence punishment.[21]

If we are to understand the logic by which mental hygiene identifies mental health with normality, and normality with an unconsciously assumed open-class ethic, we must turn our attention to a central factor in this logic, to what may be called the psychologistic conception of human nature. By the psychologistic approach is meant the explanation of human conduct in terms of traits originating within the individual, as over against traits originating within society. Any explanation is psychologistic, for example, which builds its analysis upon motives, drives, instincts, urges, prepotent reflexes, or what not, ignoring the social genesis of what is called by these names. In mental hygiene these elements are taken as given in the individual, existing prior to social forces and determining concrete actions. Since they are prior to the social, the only other alternative in accounting for them is that they are biologically given. The

[20] Here we see an illustration of the conflict between the humanitarian mores (by which certain established practices are criticized) and the organizational mores (the more basic and unconsciously accepted standards). See W. Waller, "Social Problems and the Mores," *Amer. Soc. Rev.*, i (Dec. 1936): 922-933.

[21] It is often difficult to get behind the emotionality and loquacity of mental hygiene literature to see the essential logic. This paragraph is meant to describe the general features of its main position after all the verbiage has been laboriously sifted.

psychologistic interpretation is individualistic, then, in the sense that it bases its explanation upon that which is purely individual, i.e., the biologically inherited constitution (the purely non-social part) of the person.

It is natural that mental hygienists have adopted this conception of human nature. Protestant individualism finds here a scientific rationalization. The philosophy of private initiative, personal responsibility, and individual achievement falls easily into an interpretation of human nature in individualistic terms. Furthermore, for those who are naive in the analysis of social relations and generally unaware of the sociological premises of their own thinking, it is extremely easy to read into the individual, as given in his nature, the characteristics that are really given in his society. By thus reading social traits into original nature a degree of permanence and certainty is given them which would disappear if they were realized to be merely socially acquired. In other words, psychologism is a means whereby an unconsciously held ethic may be advantageously propagated under the guise of "science." It protects the hygienist from a disconcerting fact—the relativity of moral judgments.

Yet, if applied with logical rigor to matters of conduct, the psychologistic approach would become an incompatible element in mental hygiene doctrine. Since mental hygiene constantly judges life-situations to be wholesome or hygienic according to whether or not they satisfy individual needs, the concept of "individual needs" calls for strict definition. If defined according to a logical application of the psychologistic approach, individual needs would reduce to those that are biologically inherited—namely, the organic. Applying this point of view to conduct, mental hygiene would urge us to satisfy our physiological needs independently of social standards and ideals, and to observe such standards and ideals only in so far as they can be proven to satisfy our needs. Of course, the hygienists do not do this. Instead they inculcate the dominant morality of a mobile society. They do not, then, apply the psychologistic approach with logical rigor, but misinterpret it by including as given in the individual many things which are in reality not genetically but socially determined, such as desires and standards. These social desires and standards construed as inherent in the individual are precisely the Protestant standards that the mental hygienist implicitly follows. It is no wonder, then, that the "scientific" hygiene yields results in striking conformity to the ethical configuration, seeing that the ethical configuration is intrinsically contained in the very definition of the goal to be achieved—namely, satisfaction of individual needs.[22]

We have shown thus far, by its preachments, its personnel, and its conception of mental health and normality, that mental hygiene tacitly assumes the Protestant open-class ethic. Let us now turn to the *results,* rather than the evidences, of the implicit assumptions. We shall argue that the ethical presuppositions, plus the psychologistic approach, necessarily vitiate the scientific validity of much mental hygiene work by limiting and biasing the study of mental disorder and consequently the working conceptions behind mental hygiene practice. Specifically, the presuppositions lead to neglect of the invidious element, and in fact social elements generally, as a determining factor in mental disorder.

An aspect of social relations possessing strong presumptive evidence of responsibility in mental disorders is precisely that which embraces invidious, discriminatory differences. If we suspect already that social forces are implicated, our suspicion becomes doubly certain for this particular branch of social phenomena. Sociological analysis of personality has long stressed the individual's conception of his role in the eyes of others. It has maintained that the self develops through

[22] Mental hygiene turns out to be not so much a science for the prevention of mental disorder, as a science for the prevention of moral delinquency. Thus an author may state that every individual has a need for some kind of useful work, then draw the conclusion that every individual *must* have useful work to be mentally adjusted, and finally declare that any social customs which do not permit this are irrational and unworthy. The conscious premise, that every individual has the alleged need, is a psychologistic fallacy. The other propositions, avowedly based on the initial premise, are in fact the product of countless unverbalized values which together represent an accepted ethical system. We are thus able to account for the extraordinary diffuseness of mental hygiene goals. Mental health being defined in terms of conformity to a basic ethic, the pursuit of mental hygiene must be carried on along many fronts. Also, since the fiction of science is maintained, the ethical character of the movement can never be consciously and deliberately stated—hence the goals must be nebulous and obscurantist in character.

the acquisition and internalization of the attitudes of others. It has shown that these attitudes, laden with approval or disapproval, not only become in time the foundation of the self but also assume tremendous emotional importance for the individual.[23] Since the attitudes of others are acquired only by symbolic communication, which is social in the strictest sense and necessarily connected with the cultural heritage, it can be seen that the key to the relation between organism and culture lies precisely in the dynamics of the social role. And since the social role is largely a matter of the communicated approval or disapproval of others, involving a constant comparison of one's own position with that of others, the invidious, emulative element is inevitably present. In so far as personality and mentality are socially determined, they are also emulatively determined.

As a slight test of this theory, an analysis of 70 hospitalized cases, reported in the psychiatric literature and mostly with functional disorders, was made.[24] All but four instances showed clear evidence of status involvements. Furthermore, the evidence would seem to bear out Campbell's contention that in the functional disorders the emotional problems are of sufficient intensity and consistency as to indicate a causal relationship.[25]

It follows that in the study of mental disorder, some attention should be devoted to the invidious elements in the social past of the patients. This holds true especially for the functional derangements —those, presumably, with which mental hygiene is most concerned.[26] But in mental hygiene at least, this phase of the subject has been neglected.[27] Much attention has perforce been devoted to guilt feel-

[23] The works of Cooley, Mead, Faris, and Dewey are here referred to.

[24] This study, though merely a straw in the wind, satisfied us that significant research could be carried on in this direction.

[25] C. M. Campbell, *Destiny and Disease in Mental Disorders*, N. Y., 1935.

[26] In so far as mental disorder results from definite disease processes, its prevention lies within the province of the ordinary public health program, the field of physical hygiene. Only when it is seen as somehow resulting from non-physical forces (Campbell's "personal" as opposed to impersonal factors) does it fall within the province of *mental* hygiene.

[27] Mental hygiene literature sadly neglects to analyze social processes, whether invidious or otherwise. Much is of course written about the importance of "environmental factors," but these so important "factors" are scarcely ever treated so as to discover their specific mode and intensity of operation.

ings, inferiority complexes, anxiety states, and emotional conflicts. Yet though these clearly reflect the power of invidious comparison, they are hardly seen to be social at all. The vertical element is merely assumed; it remains unanalyzed while attention is turned to "instincts," "reflexes," "habits," or other bio-individual determinants.

Now if we ask why this neglect, the answer seems obvious. It is a product of the implicit assumption of an open-class philosophy of life. Little attention is paid to the emulative, discriminatory social factors because to analyze them would bring to awareness the unconscious ethical premises. Such analysis would force recognition of the vertical dimension of our society and the axiological judgments associated with it, which have been assumed as premises. Hence it would destroy the myth of scientific objectivity and the myth of the universal individual—myths necessary to the self-confident optimism of the mental hygiene movement.

The logical device by which this blindness to invidious social determinants is made to appear satisfactory to the conscious minds of the mental hygienists, is the psychologistic approach. If human personality is understandable without reference to social reality, then

---

The same criticism applies, though in lesser degree, to psychiatry and abnormal psychology. In them too, even when a school is dealing avowedly with superiority and inferiority, there is a tendency to regard these as individual traits and not explore their social origins. This is true, for example, of Adler's so-called individual school of psychology. The limitation of his point of view has caused him to miss essential features of the very phenomenon he insists is important. Again we may mention the works of Dr. Macfie Campbell, who very skilfully points out the causal importance of what he calls personal factors, but disclaims any attempt to analyze these factors systematically. What he calls "personal" could equally well be called socio-genic, and studied sociologically.

Mental hygiene's neglect of social process springs partly from the fact that mental hygienists are for the most part trained psychologically to look for bio-genetic determinants, rather than sociologically to look for social determinants. But it also arises from the sociologists' own failure to clarify the role of social interaction in the etiology of mental derangement. At any rate mental hygiene seems to be limping along on one foot, because if there *are* social determinants, these are not being discovered and utilized in prevention.

Detailed proof and knowledge of determining social processes will not come until case histories are invented and utilized which give the *significant social past* of the patient. Such histories wait upon two achievements: first, the development of a conceptual scheme which, as a first approximation, indicates what facts in the social past are significant, hence guides the research

naturally social reality need not be analyzed. The latter can be accepted superficially as something to which the personality must adjust, something which represses or facilitates original wishes; but the more fundamental social forces are not reckoned with. If they are treated at all it is erroneously—the social elements being regarded as inherently given in the individual (i.e., as non-social).

To show that mental hygiene has neglected genuine factors, and to indicate further why it has done so, it is worth while to reflect upon some possible connections between the class structure and mental disorder.

Be the causes of mental disorder what they may, it is easy to show that the criteria are always social. Sanity lies in the observance of the normative system of the group. This allows wide latitude, of course, and we constantly make allowances for a person's rearing in the specialized culture of his particular groups. But sanity assumes acculturation in some group, and basically it is acculturation in the central mores of the widest society in which the person is an effective social unit. Furthermore, we do not judge by one lapse. We judge, rather, by systematized behavior and ideas in a direction con-

from the start; and second, the perfection and standardization, and the possible invention of new techniques of social investigation. The first achievement has perhaps been realized in sociological theory, but its application in the gathering of social data about specific patients lags far behind.

While much of our sociological work has not been sufficiently detailed to apply to the etiology of mental disorder, it does point in directions where further investigation may prove fruitful. This is true, for example, of the ecological and comparative approach to the distribution of functional disorders. In other words, though we cannot give an exact description of the operation of social determinants in particular psychoses, we have strong evidence, if not proof, *that* such determinants are there. The *how* need not escape us always. In the last analysis it seems that sociologists could be expected to produce the required knowledge, because they, of all those interested in the problem, are the only ones devoting themselves purely to social relations as such.

Of the two great systems of causation with reference to personality—one the biological (cellular interaction) and the other sociological (communicative interaction)—neither can be ignored by any science of mental disorder. Thus far, however, it seems that far more energy, thought, and money has gone into the investigation of the first. Problems are even stated in such a way as to preclude investigation of the second, and concepts are used which are stopgaps rather than invitations to a knowledge of it. And yet there exist countless evidences that sociological factors play a significant part in both normal and abnormal behavior.

trary to the accepted motivational complex. Thus a criminal is not regarded as insane because he does something contrary to mores and law. Stealing is an occurrence inherent in our social organization, and we all can see the logic of motives for stealing. But a man who steals because of a motivational complex contrary to the accepted one—say, a kleptomaniac—is judged to be mentally disordered: not because he steals, but because his reasons for stealing are removed from "reality." A man who forgets is not insane. We all forget. But a man who forgets the wrong things, such as his own name, his own city, or the excretory separation of the sexes, is definitely crazy.

In a class society the motivation of one class is understood by the members of other classes, because they each, in conforming to their class standards, are really conforming to the system of standards that constitutes the society. It may be that class ideologies, considered in themselves, vary in the degree of mental health they give their adherents; but this opinion assumes something that we do not possess —namely, a standard of reality by which all ideologies may be judged. In any culture the class ideologies are merely specialized parts of the central ideology, which is not identified simply with the outlook of the dominant class, but with that of all classes.[28] It is not necessarily true, therefore, that the more divergent the class ideology from the cultural standard, the greater the incidence of mental derangement in this class. It is a particular kind of divergence that counts, a divergence in the ultimate norms which unify the entire society and knit together its specialized groups.[29] In case of such divergence

[28] A class structure presupposes a hierarchy of values. Who possesses the highest values, or possesses these in the greatest degree, is of the highest class. It does not follow, as some would have us believe, that the system of values was instituted for the benefit of the upper class. Rather the system of values sets the framework and determines the goals of competition for position.

[29] This observation seems to be justified by the ecological studies of schizophrenia that have been made. Areas in which conduct violates the norms of the very society of which the persons are a part, are areas of high incidence. Cf. R. E. L. Faris, "Cultural Isolation and the Schizophrenic Personality," Amer. Jour. of Soc., xl (Sept. 1934): 155-164. Also, H. W. Dunham, "The Ecology of the Functional Psychoses in Chicago," Amer. Soc. Review, ii (Aug. 1937): 467-479.

other classes will focus attention upon the errant one and will seek to control its thinking and behavior through methods conforming to the sanctions of the society. But the important point is that a specialized part is not necessarily divergent in this latter sense. The ideological peculiarities of a particular class may be adequately provided for and incorporated in the central ideology.

This conclusion seems valid in a caste as well as an open-class organization, and is partially valid even where class struggle exists. So far as mental disorder is concerned, the significant question is not whether there is a caste or class system, for neither one is inherently destructive of sanity, but whether the system, whatever it is, is unified by a nucleus of common values. When the structure embraces conflicting principles of social organization based on incompatible values, psychic conflicts inevitably result. For example, ends may be presented to one group as possible and desirable, when in fact they are made impossible for that group by a conflicting mode of dominance. A clear illustration appears in the Southern part of the United States, where the avowed morality of equal opportunity to all is categorically denied in practice to Negroes.[30] The behavior of individuals caught in this situation manifests frequent attempts to escape an unbearable reality. Reality seems unbearable, however, only when another reality exists as a *conceivable* alternative; and another is conceivable only when it forms part of the social system and exists as a possibility within the cultural ideology. Mental conflict is engendered, then, not so much by the vertical structure itself as by inconsistency within the structure.

It might seem that a mobile class organization would have deleterious effects upon mental health because of the constant readjustments it requires of its circulating individuals. But the open-class system is protected against this adverse result by the fact that, as distinguished from a caste society, the limits of difference between the mores of different strata are narrow. If the differences were wide, vertical mobility, entailing a shift from one set of mores to a radically different

[30] See W. L. Warner, "American Caste and Class," *Amer. Jour. of Soc.*, xlii (Sept. 1936): 234-237. J. Dollard, *Caste and Class in Southerntown*, New Haven, 1937, especially pp. 72, 89, 182. Also K. Davis, "The American Caste System," unpublished manuscript in possession of the author.

set, would certainly have profound effects upon the person so shifting, and would end by prohibiting the change. But actually there
is a tendency in an open-class system for differences in class modes
of thinking to take the form of an infinite number of small gradations, and to reduce themselves to superficial externalities; so that
though vertical mobility places the strain of rapid change, responsibility, and adaptation upon the individual,[31] it compensates for this
by the pulverization and externalization of differences. The class
variations in mores become one of degree rather than kind. The same
fundamental wants and values pervade the whole hierarchy, the only
difference being that members of the various classes satisfy these
wants and attain these values in different amounts. The climber who
moves from the bottom to the top finds that he can still utilize practically all of his old habituations. No fundamental reorganization is
required. He merely satisfies the same old wants more readily and
in greater abundance. Thus does the mobile society safeguard the
sanity of the mobile person.[32] Basically its members, of whatever
class, all share a common set of values—the ethic of an open-class
world.

In all this, however, it should be remembered that social class is
but the roughest descriptive phrase for the invidious vertical aspect
of society. Actually it is not class differences alone that count, but
all differences describable in terms of inferiority and superiority. A

[31] Compare P. Sorokin, *Social Mobility*, New York, 1927, Ch. 21. Sorokin
concludes that since in a mobile system the individual must adapt himself to
changing milieus, mobility increases the incidence of mental disease. He admits increasing superficiality and externalization, however, but he interprets
them in terms of the individuals concerned and does not realize that they are
even more characteristic of the cultural differences between classes and therefore constitute a compensation for the mental strain. It is only in the initial
stages of becoming a mobile system that a class order may engender insanity.
But this is a period of social change, and the increased incidence is due to our
principle of conflicting values and not to the sheer fact of mobility itself.

[32] The open-class society is also protected by the fact that the class sieves
are never entirely open and hence most people move only a few rungs up or
down. For this additional reason the changes required of any individual are
usually not overwhelming. It should be remembered too that the open-class
ethic places a positive value upon upward movement, and that even in the
case of failure it always holds out hopes of recovery and progression. A person's mobility thus fulfills the values.

person's class position offers but the first (though necessary) index of the social determinants in his life. It may be important or unimportant in his particular case, but in either event an indispensable consideration is the sequence of his invidious experiences within limited circles of association—particularly within primary groups. Yet it is precisely these relations, as well as general class factors, that (as already pointed out) have been neglected by mental hygiene.[33]

Our speculations suggest that the vertical structure and mentality are intimately related, and that a neglect of social factors is a vital neglect for the mental hygienist. We have already said that there must be, and is, a reason for such neglect. It is obviously not our view that the mental hygienist is consciously enforcing alien class standards upon unwilling members of a lower stratum. Doubtless there is a tendency to spread the middle class Protestant ethic to classes which are not middle and hence not so mobile, but this could scarcely be interpreted as class "exploitation." We believe, rather, that the mental hygienist is really enforcing, in a secular way and under the guise of science, the standards of the entire society. This leads him beyond the goal of mental health, strictly defined, and to undertake such things as increasing the efficiency of the ordinary individual and readjusting some of our (more superficial) mores. Thus the diffuseness of the mental hygiene goal is integrally related to the hygienist's actual function. Mental hygiene can plunge into evaluation, into fields the social sciences would not touch, because it possesses an implicit ethical system which, since it is that of our society, enables it to pass value judgments, to get public support, and to enjoy an unalloyed optimism. Disguising its valuational system (by means of the psychologistic position) as rational advice based on science, it can conveniently praise and condemn under the aegis of the medico-authoritarian mantle.

Few will doubt that mental hygiene has thus far been less success-

[33] Psychiatry is waking up to the necessity of studying interpersonal relations. See H. S. Sullivan, "A Note on the Implications of Psychiatry, the Study of Interpersonal Relations, for Investigations in the Social Sciences," Amer. Jour. of Soc., xlii (May 1937): 848-861. Also, Karen Horney, The Neurotic Personality of Our Time, New York, 1937; and the works of Macfie Campbell.

ful in achieving the avowed goal of prevention than has the regular public health movement. Does this represent a lag which will shortly be overcome, or does it represent a circumstance inherent in the nature of the case? The latter view seems more tenable, for the following reasons.

Scientific knowledge of mental disorder requires knowledge of social determinants. But there is a social restriction upon the impersonal analysis of personal relations, and especially upon the use of knowledge thus gained. Such knowledge must be employed only for culturally prescribed ends and persons who believe in these ends. Unfortunately, if one serves and believes these cultural ends, one cannot analyze social relations objectively.[34] If this is true of an individual, it is even truer of a movement. The latter, dependent upon public enthusiasm, must inevitably adhere to ethical preconceptions.

[34] Psychiatry, as shown by Campbell, Horney, Sullivan, and others, has gradually come to realize the importance of social and cultural factors in the determination of mental derangement. Generally, however, there has been an overestimation of the power this places in the hands of the practitioner. As reported by a sociologist who has spent some time as an observer in a mental hospital, some doctors and psychiatrists assume that with further knowledge of social factors, these can be immediately changed so as to reduce the incidence of mental disorder. But for very profound reasons we cannot plan or alter our culture out of whole cloth. However, there is another type of optimism which is slightly more justified. This involves concentrating upon special or limited social environments as the field of social manipulation. Each of these has been studied in connection with the possible genesis of mental disease, and certain reforms advocated. But often, as in the case of the individual when he was first studied apart from his culture, the possibility of changing these particular social milieus is easily over-estimated. They are parts of our general culture, and resistances to changing them arise which were not at first apparent. Of course one particular individual's relation to one of his special social environments (say the court) can be helpfully altered, but this is casework and does not alter the situation so far as the general population is concerned. (For a detailed consideration of the problem of manipulating limited social milieus, see K. Davis, "The Application of Science to Personal Relations, A Critique of the Family Clinic Idea," *Amer. Sociological Review,* i (April 1936): 236-251.) Some features of society, moreover, are scarcely limited to any particular milieu. One of these is the class structure which, as a phase of the entire social organization, cuts across all special parts of that organization. When speaking of such factors it is difficult to advocate their immediate removal or change without becoming involved in ethical controversies and unseen consequences far transcending the immediate problem in hand.

Mental hygiene hides its adherence behind a scientific façade, but the ethical premises reveal themselves on every hand, partly through a blindness to scientifically relevant facts. It cannot combine the prestige of science with the prestige of the mores, for science and the mores unavoidably conflict at some point, and the point where they most readily conflict is precisely where "mental" (i.e., social) phenomena are concerned. We can say, in other words, that devotion to the mores entails an emotional faith in illusion. Devotion to science, on the other hand, when social illusion constitutes the subject matter of that science, entails the sceptical attitude of an investigator rather than of the believer toward the illusion. In so far as the mental hygienist retains his ethical system, he misses a complete scientific analysis of his subject and hence fails to use the best technological means to his applied-science goal. But if he forswears his ethical beliefs, he is alienated from the movement and suffers the strictures of an outraged society. Actually the mental hygienist will continue to ignore the dilemma. He will continue to be unconscious of his basic preconceptions at the same time that he keeps on professing objective knowledge. He will regard his lack of preventive success as an accident, a lag, and not as an intrinsic destiny. All because his social function is not that of a scientist but that of a practising moralist in a scientific, mobile world.

VARIETIES OF INSIGHT
IN HUMANS

Eliot Dole Hutchinson

THE PURPOSE of this paper is to offer for discussion some instances of the phenomenon that has recently been termed *insight*—especially instances on the human level. The animal psychologists have discovered so few undisputed illustrations that they have with difficulty been able to sketch the essential conditions for its appearance, and have even questioned its existence as a distinguishable phenomenon. And yet, from the standpoint of biography, insight constitutes one of the most experiential facts of creative life, substantiated by more evidence, though to be sure less commonly understood in process, than almost any other aspect of the productive mind. We shall, I believe, find the most instructive instances in connection with the solution of problems where the degree of difficulty and frustration is great, and the drive toward accomplishment persistently strong. We may even go so far as to call the phenomenon *creative insight* since it is usually in connection with constructive work that its most brilliant illustrations are to be found.

Let no one suppose that these experiences of insight are infrequent among creative thinkers, or that they are the vagaries of the untrained. They are not the playthings of obscurantists, nor the last resort of unscientific minds. In a questionnaire sent out by the American Chemical Society—a group naturally suspicious of anything undefined in methods of production—regarding the frequency of insight in scientific problems, 83 per cent of 232 directors of research laboratories and *American Men of Science*, chemists, mathematicians, physicists, biologists, men of standing generally, admitted assistance from this experience.[1]

That is a significant figure, and indicates in the scientific world, at least on its inventive side, the presence of a mode of thought that has received too little recognition. My own investigation into the problem with about the same number of artists, literateurs, musicians, and others, 253, seems to confirm the fact: *80* per cent. Though marked demonstrations of the phenomenon are rare, instructive evidences of it are common.

THE PHENOMENON IN SIMPLEST FORM

The scientist, the artist, the practical thinker—the profession makes little difference—has before him a problem involving some creative production or decision in life situations. For months or years, it may be, this problem has remained unsolved, this creative intention unfulfilled. Attempts at solution have ended only in bafflement. But suddenly, usually in a moment when the work has been temporarily abandoned, or when the attention is absorbed by irrelevant matters, comes an unpredicted *insight* into the solution, usually interpreted as a reorganization of the perceptual field, especially in regard to the relationship between means and end. As if "inspired," "given," arise ideas which constitute a real integration of previously accumulated experience—an answer, a brilliant hypothesis, a useful "hunch," forming, it seems, a short cut to artistic or scientific advance. Exhilaration marks such moments of insight, a glow or elation goes with them—so much so in fact that some psychologists refer to insight as the "aha! phenomenon." The content of these insights is either lost at once through inattention, or if caught and held by explicit statement in consciousness, takes full form only in a later period of verification and criticism. Owing to the suddenness and apparent revelation of new material, the experience is mistakenly looked upon by some as unrelated to past experience. Apparently the logical or explicitly statable alternatives of solution were too numerous to grasp.

[1] Platt, Washington, and Baker, R. A., The Relation of Scientific "Hunch" to Research. *J. Chem. Education* (1931) 8:1969-2002.

Elimination of them one by one would at least involve infinite labor. And yet here it is, prior to the exhaustion of such logical possibilities, what purports to be a solution, sometimes as accurate and useful as it is astonishing.

EXAMPLES

Let us consider several first-hand examples. No comment will be made upon them until the cumulative effect makes certain points clear.[2] Bertrand Russell writes:

In all the creative work that I have done, what has come first is a *problem, a puzzle involving discomfort*. Then comes concentrated voluntary application entailing great effort. After this a *period without conscious thought,* and finally a solution bringing with it the *complete plan of a book*. This last stage *is usually sudden,* and seems to be the important moment for subsequent achievement.

Sir James Flinders-Petrie, eminent British Egyptologist, writes:

I never try to settle a difficult matter offhand. I first assemble the ma. terial, state the problem as definitely as possible, and, *if no solution is evident, leave it alone*. From time to time I may look over it to refresh my memory, but never to force a solution. After *waiting days or years,* I suddenly feel a wish to go over it again, and then *everything runs smoothly and I can write without effort*. There is unconscious growth of mind without perceptible effort in the interval.

Dr. Banesh Hoffmann, Oxford mathematician and physical relativist, gives this account:

I had been attempting to work upon a problem *that had puzzled me for at least two years*. I made some sporadic, half-hearted calculations on odd bits of paper; but nothing came of them. In the evening *I had to go to a lecture upon an entirely different subject*. After the lecture, and an argument with a friend about the lecture, I went to my room and decided that I would read for the rest of the evening (a book by Trotsky on Lenin), and go to bed early. But somehow this idea of reading did not appeal to me. I picked up some scraps of paper, and straightway, *without realizing that there was any difficulty in the problem, I wrote out the*

[2] All italics are ours.

solution with hardly a pause. I knew somehow or other that something had solved itself at the back of my mind, but had no idea of the solution until my pencil *almost automatically wrote it out.* I can't remember my feeling during the hours in which I worked (amnesia), being, I suppose, too absorbed in production to notice actual surroundings. But after I had the solution down in front of me, *I remember that I was elated,* and though the hour was late, had no longer any desire to go to bed. I went over to the auditorium and practiced singing. There had been no conscious results until this moment.

A physicist writes:

For a couple of years I had been thinking about solid solutions or mixed crystals. There is a good bit known and some regularity has been discovered, summarized as Vegard's Law. (The law states that the crystal cell dimension is a linear function of the composition in molar percentages.) One morning on going to look up something in the *American Mineralogist,* I came across a paper which denied this law in regard to mixed crystals. Its denial was based upon the measurement of spacing, and not upon the cell dimension to which Vegard's Law is said to apply. This wrong application amazed and disgusted me. Being out of mood for further work, I went to meet a friend who was to take me to town. I returned to the laboratory for my hat and arrived at the car before my friend, at whose delay I was further annoyed. But suddenly, without warning, almost like a flash of light (note hallucinatory components) the idea burst upon me that I could start with Vegard's Law and *deduce* a law for the variation in spacing which those men had measured, and could use all their measurement data to check it.

The details of this science do not interest us here. The experience does! Two years of *preparation* involving all the technical methods applicable to the sciences; momentary abandonment of the problem with rising emotion and irritation; absorption in secondary interests, sudden insight . . . . what does it all mean? Is such insightful experience haphazard, or is there an underlying pattern?

Dr. John Yellot, Stevens Institute Research Engineer, gives this account:

I had been long working on a scientific problem in which the essential feature was a glass plate subjected to severe conditions of pressure by heat and steam. A similar apparatus had worked well at Hopkins. At Rochester there was repeated failure, the glass breaking several times without apparent cause. Plates were expensive, hard to procure, and delay was costly.

I had thought a great deal about the solution of the problem, but with no success. Moreover, I had come to the point where the breaking of glass had become a phobia, even causing nightmares. (I remember two in particular in which breaking glass was featured. Everything I heard of a similar sound was immediately feared.) There was actually a great deal of danger inasmuch as I had to look through the plate at a stream of high pressure steam.

My reputation as a scientist was built upon this apparatus; failure seemed imminent.

I had been in New York to deliver a paper on the subject of research. The paper was successful, but other personal matters were disturbing me. I was riding on a crowded bus, much absorbed in these matters so irrelevant to my scientific work, when suddenly the solution of the problem came to me.

In a flash, I *visualized* a drawing of the proper design of the apparatus, immediately drew out a notebook and, without consciousness of my surroundings, wrote down the answer. *I knew it was right. I felt much relieved about this major issue, and told my friends at once about it.*

Tremendous professional ambition, threatened failure, incipient neurotic symptoms (fear of glass, nightmares, etc.) during period of strain, incidental absorption in irrelevant matters, sudden insight under untoward circumstances, emotional release with arrival of success—it begins to look as if some community of experience, some technique of insightful thought could be discovered.

M. A. Rosanoff, long associated with Edison in his laboratory, had worked futilely for over a year in an endeavor to soften the wax of phonograph cylinders by altering its chemical constitution. Purposely withheld by Edison from knowledge of the previous work on the problem, Rosanoff found the solution to be more difficult than he had anticipated. He seemed unable to improve upon wax made earlier by a man named Aylsworth. After weeks of work the results showed nothing, theoretical as well as practical efforts failing. But with superhuman obstinacy he continued, trying even the most improbable methods of solution.

Then it came like a flash of lightning—not the Edison way (*i.e.*, by the progressive elimination of numerous hypotheses). On a Sunday evening

I lay on my couch with a headache, smoking cigarettes. I tried to keep my mind a blank, but after a year or more of being held down to my problem by Edison, I could no longer shut out the waxes, even in my sleep. And suddenly, through headache and daze, I saw the solution! True, the balanced chemical make-up of the Aylsworth wax must not be disturbed. But by a physico-chemical process which instantly quickened in my mind, I could modify the intimate physical structure of the wax almost at pleasure, and thus bring about any desired change in hardness. . . . A positive solution to my despicable problem.

I was restrained from rushing to the laboratory that evening. But the first thing next morning I was at my desk, and half an hour later I had a record in the softened wax cylinder . . . the acoustic reproduction was correspondingly excellent. . . . It was the solution! I had learned to think waxes, and the solution had *come without effort,* after a year of the Edisonian blind groping that had led nowhere.[3]

Still another scientist, Dr. Harold Alling, Head of the Department of Geology at the University of Rochester, gives this account:

I had long been working on rocks, especially feldspars, thinking of the lines of solubility. I knew from microscopic studies, that the concept of "line" was too definite, that truth lay in a less definite statement. Accordingly I was hunting for a zone of solubility, rather than a line. I was trying to express this for a paper that was to be read that evening. Intervening, however, was a dinner party to which Dr. X, whom I dislike, had been invited. I was annoyed, and reluctantly went upstairs to put on dress clothes. At dinner I was silent, enduring with difficulty the chatter of the table, others remarking upon my gloomy mood. As soon as possible after dinner I went to my study and there *quickly and easily solved the problem* that had been weighing upon me for so long. I worked it out in three-dimensional form, drawing it carefully, in color and on good paper. It proved so satisfactory that *I copied it for publication.* The idea had apparently come out of the blue. This happened eight years ago. I have not improved upon it since, because I can't.

Sir James Irvine, Principal of St. Andrews University, Scotland, says:

I can divide my ideas for scientific research into two groups. The best ideas are what I may call *inspired,* or insightful. Then come ideas which

[3] Rosanoff, M. A., Edison in his Laboratory. *Harpers Magazine* (1932) 165:402-417.

are logically and mathematically evolved. These give rise to sound scholarly productions which cannot be compared in quality with those which
are inspired. These latter appear at odd times and in unpredictable ways.

A physicist remarks:

Most clear-cut "hunches" come in mathematical problems or in the
mathematical formulation of physical and chemical problems. The mechanism is not clear in my mind. Nearly all important ideas come quick as
a flash, faster than they can be expressed in words; but always after long
gathering and analysis of data and usually after considerable unsuccessful
thought.

Mr. William F. Friedman, cryptoanalyst of the War Department
of Washington, working in a field where intuition, *i.e.*, insight, plays
perhaps a more important rôle than in any other, claims that his
most brilliant insights come in the most rigorous and baffling crypto-
graphic problems.

I believe that such an insight constitutes one extreme of a continuum which joins it with purely logical thought at the other extreme, *the degree of psychic frustration being the varying factor.*
Logical minds advance their problems deliberately, progressively
with a minimum of trial and error activity, and with full awareness
of the meaning of each step taken. But the person who relies on insight, having employed every known technical and dialectical device of the science involved *and being yet fundamentally baffled,* is
forced in sheer desperation and defense of emotional balance, to
relax his efforts for a time. The problem meanwhile is not forgotten,
but seems to sink back upon more profound levels of mind for ges-
tation (support this with whatever theory you will). When it reappears again as insight, or solution, it more fully represents the
whole range of mental experience, the entire intellectual and emotional background, than the less generalized products of the logical
method. It is really this enrichment which argues for its accumula-
tive latency. Hence the *resident richness,* the imaginative depth,
the power of polarizing like minds, so characteristic of genuine insight. Hence also its frequent extravagances which must be tem-
pered by later criticism. The method is no substitute for labor or

knowledge. In cost of psychic energy, owing to the frustration involved, it is the more exacting way. Nor is it a substitute for training. It has its pattern, in effective form founded upon the most rigorous and systematic effort, in part upon a renunciation of that effort, and again upon a resumption of it, looking toward elaboration. Certainly it is not some mysterious ladder by which men climb the back way to artistic and scientific eminence.

One could multiply examples indefinitely. Although scientific invention involves strictly logical effort in the preparatory phases of dealing with a problem, and again in the verification of the engendered hypotheses, it is nevertheless partly alogical and unpredictable in the original formulations of these hypotheses. It is at this point that science approaches art in its methodology.

Illustrations of insight from the literary and artistic world are equally common. A poet, Miss Lillian Whiting, of Boston and Florence, had for a long time been absorbed in a field of social history which suddenly reorganized itself in her mind in the following fashion:

I happened to be in New York in one of the large buildings. During the time that the elevator ascended with me to the office of my publishers, the outline of *an entirely undreamed-of book* to be called the "Florence of Landor," to picture Florence in its most brilliantly vivid period that closed with the death of Mrs Browning in 1861 and Landor in 1864, came into my mind, the entire *plan more perfect than I can give it today,* nineteen years after the book was written and published. I walked in and proposed it to my publishers, the Cassells, *as if I had been thinking of it for ten years.* They caught at it!

A well-known writer remarks:

For a long time I had been working upon a very difficult paper. Frankly I was stumped by part of it. I used every known device for getting on, but found my efforts fruitless. At last I resolved to forget it and turn to other pressing interests. I happened to be in Albany on the Fourth of July, but had made no plans for the day. The University Club furnished breakfast only, which fact annoyed me slightly. It being a glorious morning, I went for a walk in the park where I saw some youngsters playing. The sight of them made me homesick, and I became annoyed because I was not home with my own children. For lunch I went to a dairy restaurant, but could not stand the crowd. I purchased something to take back to my rooms to eat, and began to feel sorry for myself. On reaching my room I saw my manuscript which I had resolved to lay aside. It made me furious. I called it all kinds of names, idly turning the pages until I found an incomplete sentence which challenged me. Upon further reading, I became still more annoyed at the errors it contained. I had started that sentence two years before. Suddenly I realized that I could finish it then and there. I put it in the typewriter, and spent the afternoon and evening writing, finishing over twenty pages. When I "came to," it was 8.30 p. m. and my lunch was still untouched beside me. Incidentally, the authorities claim that this was the best part of the paper.

The initial frustration of an unsolved problem, the attempted repression, the mastery of mood resulting from that repression, seen in the self-depreciation and over-emotional reaction to petty annoyances, the involuntary recall of the work and the dissociated or isolated period of production—these need no further emphasis.

Historical Illustrations

Space will sparingly permit historical illustration. Biographies are filled with examples, especially in reference to decisions made in critical life situations. Several come readily to hand.

Rousseau's account of the sudden vision that came to him by the roadside on a hot summer day in 1794 in the course of a walk from Paris to Vincennes is typical. The insight had an importance in the movement of modern philosophic thought that is comparable to that of St. Paul on the road to Damascus for the future development of Christianity. Among the multitude of "truths" that flashed upon Rousseau in the sort of trance, or temporarily dissociated state, into which he fell at the moment was, to use his own words, "That man is naturally good, and that it is by our institutions alone that men have become wicked"—a complete reversal of the traditional doctrine of the church.

One day in Rome, Gibbon, according to his autobiography, sat musing on the ruins of the Capitol. Robed, barefoot friars were singing vespers in the Temple of Jupiter. Suddenly, as he also says, like a burst of light, the inspiration for a monumental work, *The Decline and Fall of the Roman Empire,* came to him—its outline vague, its content as yet unforeseen. But there it was, a central, expansive idea, a key-note or motif, that was to grow and gather accretions of material to itself, until it was finished some seven years later.

Metternich's mind worked in this fashion at times: "The necessary results mature rapidly," he said, "under apparent distraction. While eating, in ordinary conversation, or in riding, the clearest revelations and most important ideas come. As soon as the object has ripened quite lucidly within me, and my mind and spirit are saturated with it, I put it upon paper, unworried about order and sequence, which then arrange themselves of their own accord." His private physician, Dr. Jaeger, tells that Metternich had just returned from a wearisome night journey when he was met by a courier with an important dispatch. The courier asked what the answer was to be. Metternich replied, "I really do not know yet. Let me finish the novel in my travel bag. Perhaps the answer will come."

It was during a period of retirement into winter quarters that Descartes, while still in the army, had an insight which not only changed the course of his life from one of warfare to philosophic research, but changed the subsequent course of European thought. At Neuberg, on the Danube, at a time when Maximilian was raising troops to fight for the Catholic cause, Descartes secured for himself a warm, quiet room, uninterrupted by the revelry of the soldiers outside, and there devoted himself to serious study and meditation. For a long time the problem of his own future had been with him. Religious and political difficulties had stirred his mind. Suddenly, in a dream (note semi-dissociated state) recorded by him as of November 10, 1619, an illumination came advising him henceforth to combine mathematics and philosophy into a new discipline. The exhilaration of this experience seems to have lasted for some days. During the rest of the winter Descartes occupied himself with elaborating these plans and in fruitful writing.

Not only as regards productive thought, but also as regards *changes of character* and *education,* do these patterns of experience apply.

Henry Adams supposed that, except musicians, everyone thought Beethoven a bore, as everyone, except mathematicians, thought mathematics a bore. Sitting thus at his beer table, *mentally impassive,* he was one day surprised to find that his mind followed the movement of a "Sinphonie." He could not have been more astonished had he suddenly read a new language. Among the marvels of education this was the most marvelous. . . . Amid the fumes of coarse tobacco and poor beer, surrounded by the commonest of German *Hausfrauen,* a new appreciation burst into his life, so superior to his old senses, so bewildering, so astonished at its own existence, that he could not credit it, and watched it as something apart, accidental, not to be trusted. He slowly came to admit that Beethoven had become partly intelligible to him.[4]

A host of creative thinkers tell the same story. Kepler, "noting with exultation," on the 9th of July, 1595, his famous discovery; Darwin, strolling alone, as was his habit, in a South County lane; Wallace, ill with a fever on a southern island; Kelvin never quite attaining by logic his hypotheses; Yardley, after almost fruitless efforts, awaking at night to decipher the American Diplomatic Code; Spengler in his ponderous *Decline of the West,* saying that the original idea for that work came to him as a young man in such fashion; El Greco in Italy, suddenly abandoning the styles of Tintoretto and Veronese to embark upon the most audacious and individual manner any painter has ever affected; Goya, fiery participant in the crumbling violence of his time, the only "inspired" intellect in Spain; Hogarth poking into the odd places of London kaleidoscopic life for material, and then in a moment of reflection recreating it from memory in lasting cartoons; Gainsborough and Constable, Delacroix, Daumier, Van Gogh and Cézanne—such men are not visionaries voyaging through the airways of thought in a vehicle of their own contraption. They employ a technique well-nigh universal in creative minds.

GENERAL ANALYSIS OF THE EXPERIENCE

As analyzed from these illustrations, creative insight involves a pattern of behavior consisting of four essential stages.

[4] Adams, Henry, *The Education of Henry Adams;* Boston, Houghton Mifflin Co., 1927 (527 pp.); p. 80.

A *Period of Preparation*, entailing perhaps years of effort and a life-time's acquisition of technical habits, all centered upon some problem situation which defines itself as it is pursued, if it is not already explicit. Large reaches of past experience are requisitioned and a form of what is ordinarily called trial-and-error activity, false starts on the basis of inadequate hypotheses, or sheer blind random movement in the face of an apparently insoluble problem, are common. As these procedures fail, two things happen:—a fuller use of past experience is attempted; *i.e.*, deeper levels of hitherto unemployed knowledge and habit are called upon, and new habits in the form of tentative methods of solution are built up. As these two processes continue, *habit conflicts* are common, the specific revivals being dropped because of inadequacy, the newly formed ones being superseded by others supposedly more effective. Accordingly the course of adaptation is largely unpredictable, not only because the relevant elements of past experience cannot be isolated, but also because of the nature of the elements to which response is made— it being sometimes to a *specific* aspect of the situation, sometimes to a *relational* aspect, and sometimes to the *situation as a whole*. Solution is thus delayed, errors of various types especially of stereotypy creep in, defeat must be temporarily admitted. There is nothing trifling about the frustration; it is real, vivid, and undermining. We thus have: A *Period of Renunciation or Recession*, in which for a time the problem is given up in sheer defense of emotional balance, and other activities, usually avocational, are interpolated. This period, involving as it does, a large degree of frustration, is often characterized by rising emotional tone, restlessness, feelings of inferiority and in the last analysis temporary cessation of effort, in which all the traditional modes of emotional readjustment are likely to be observed—repression, regression, emotional excess, etc. Mild psychoneurotic symptoms are common. The necessary relaxation may be deliberately planned; usually is enforced. During the interval involuntary recall of the work is common. At any rate it is usually some sudden stimulus from the whole field of irrelevance, coming into periods of slight mental preoccupation, or active motor exercise (walking, etc.) and after periods of rest, which terminates the period of psychic tension and precipitates: *A Period (or Moment) of Insight,* usually unpredictable in time, though determined by circumstance. This insight consists of more than a simple reorganization of the perceptual field, a new alignment of possible hypotheses. It is often accompanied by a flood of ideas, alternative hypotheses appearing at the same time, many of which are difficult to make explicit owing to the crowded rapidity of their appearance. Noteworthy in this experience are the almost hallucinatory vividness of the ideas appearing in connection with any sense department—visual, auditory, kinaesthetic—the emotional release, feelings of exultation, adequacy, finality. The period is integrative, restorative, negating the symptoms of neurotic maladjustment engendered by the preceding period. The individual steps up to a new level of activity and a new possibility of reaction. Integration opens up new volitional possibilities: reactions, before impossible, now become commonplace. *A Period of Verification, Elaboration, or Evaluation,* in which all technical and explicit rules of practice are again summoned into use, and the possible exaggerations and overstatements of the *period of insight* are checked against external realities. The period is often characterized by secondary insights engendered during the course of labor which tend to swing the individual from an objectively critical attitude back again into productive activity. Without this evaluation the insight does not necessarily release anything of communicable or social value. It remains otherwise an uncoordinated experience.

The process of creative thinking is the cycle of these stages in multiple and everchanging emphasis.

The Occasion for Insight

The agent which sometimes occasions the insight is superficially an accident having its locus in the field of irrelevancy which occupies the thinker during his renunciation of the problem. This accident may have to do with the actual position of the observer in reference to the problem-situation, it may have to do with a change in the physical arrangement of items in that situation, or finally with a shift in mental attitude. At any rate, the accident is by no means an isolated phenomenon; it performs for [the] mind a special function. The real difficulty is not so much to explain the presence of seemingly brilliant ideas which constitute true insight, for their quality is a function of individual intelligence. It is rather to explain how the event that induces the insight can be so remotely and casually related to the creative purpose.

TWO TYPES OF ACCIDENT

Two types of the experience must be distinguished:

That in which the accidental event is consciously related to the creative undertaking, and is at once incorporated as part of the work.

That in which the accidental event is *not* used in the final product, but acts merely as a catalytic agent in the presence of which other ideas fuse into creative union. Look at examples of each type.

Mr. G. Elliot-Smith, English scientist, remarks:

As a rule, after collecting data for years, and thinking over their meaning, the explanation of the whole evidence flashed into mind in a complete and clear-cut form, as a rule when *accidentally reading the work of some stupid blunderer.*

Mr. Aldous Huxley writes:

Accidental events not only crystallize my ideas, but always bring something useful to the work in hand. (Naturally, for every event is examined with the work in mind.) *Je prends mon bien où je le trouve—* and I find it everywhere.

An old lady, singular and blundering, who entered a restaurant on the Rue de Clichy, Paris, was the immediate stimulus for Arnold Bennett's *The Old Wives' Tale.* An antique dealer who possessed a coveted lacquer cabinet, suggested to H. L. Vachell the origin of *Quinney's.* E. Phillips Oppenheim found the germ for *The Inevitable Millionaires* in two old men who came regularly to his restaurant.

It is needless to multiply cases. Music, art, science, all furnish endless examples. A cantata of Mozart's *Don Giovanni* came to him on seeing an orange, which recalled a popular Neapolitan air heard five years before. The sight of the Porter suggested to Leonardo da Vinci his *Guida*.

SECOND TYPE OF ACCIDENTAL STIMULUS

The second type of the experience, that in which the accidental event has little to do with the ideas which constitute the content of the insight, is, I believe, by far the more common. The first type may be thought of as a simple suggestion falling into a prepared and polarized field, and thus releasing the dynamic attitudes involved, much in the same manner as a sudden impressive stimulus will terminate the inhibitions of a trace reflex experiment. The second type of experience involves a degree of mental dissociation occasioned by the accident at the moment of insight. A chemist writes:

I remember distinctly, while head of the laboratory of the old U. M. C. Co. in Bridgeport, working on a problem that had bothered them for years (probably 15 or 20 years). We worked on it quite *intensively for several months* and after that only occasionally. One day while sitting at my desk *doing nothing*, thinking *about other matters* (certainly a state of mild dissociation) a thought flashed through my mind. I immediately left the office, went out into the plant by myself, made a few tests and solved the difficulty. I then went to the manager and told him about it. He would not believe it until I showed him several samples, as it seemed too simple (characteristic of many great generalizations). I have had the same thing happen since at different times.

Samuel Taylor Coleridge's mind frequently worked in such manner. Professor John Livingstone Lowes, in his masterly volume, *The Road to Xanadu*, again and again shows how ideas gathered by Coleridge from the most varied sources, and apparently long since forgotten, fused in the presence of some momentarily compelling and auxiliary idea, which, accidentally hit upon in the course of voluminous reading or conversation, was not itself employed in the final product, and in fact almost disappeared as a traceable factor in the experience.

For What Reason

In periods of incidental activity, unemployment, relaxation or slight mental dissociation, then, we find conditions most favorable to insight.

A parallel to the situation may be seen in psychoanalysis. The analysts have pointed to the integrative value of periods of free association punctuated by suggestive items linked to the unconscious thought systems of the individual. They have clinically demonstrated that anything which will momentarily remove inhibition will allow dynamic and expressive systems of thought to reach consciousness, and have applied the principle especially to the cure of neurosis. They produce a state of growing mental abstraction through suggestions directly given to the patient. Into this period of dissociation they inject a list of words or ideas (*accidental stimuli* as far as the patient is concerned) known to have relation to the as-yet unexpressed or unsolved complexes. Upon such stimulation random memories, forgotten incidents, long lost events, instinctive tendencies, all related to the repressed systems (whose converted physical symptoms have been causing the neurosis) become available to consciousness. There is, of course, reluctance and shame at the exposure of some of these thoughts; there is attendant emotion at others, which in turn projects itself upon the analyst in love or in hate. When the recovered materials are reassimilated and fortified by new habits of thinking and acting, the personality is again unified, and the neurosis tends to disappear. Any such technique can be used to secure integration of thought. The possible psychotherapeutic value of hypnosis, for example, is as well known as that of psychoanalysis, and the material it recovers is certainly secured in a period of dissociation, and re-integrated in a similar period of intermediate awareness.

Is there not something of this same psychology in the pattern of insightful thinking? Something of the same mechanism?

As we have seen, the intuitive thinker is often in a state of problem-generated "neurosis," or its lesser equivalent *tension*, owing to the block set to the immediate fulfillment of his creative desires.

The constructive purposes may be in a state of suppression, or even repression, intensified by the deliberate effort to turn away from them—a means of managing the tensions involved. What happens to them under such conditions we only vaguely know, but it is certain that they are augmented by a process of realignment and development, which upon their appearance again in consciousness, furnishes related concepts in great numbers. And as in psychoanalysis the pretext for their appearance is the stimulus word, or suggestion of the analyst (intentionally related to the repressed complex) so here the occasion for their appearance is the accidental idea, or event of which we have spoken, similarly related. This accidental idea may be hit upon while one is deliberately evaluating the relations inherent in the problem, and at such times appears in the form of a sudden assumption of new perceptual significance by some hitherto neglected or seemingly unimportant item; or it may be struck—and this I believe is more often the case —while one is consciously engaged in pursuits wholly irrelevant to the work in hand. At such times it acts as a catalyst merely, in the presence of which ideas coalesce in a state of intermediate awareness (*i.e.*, insight) which is but temporarily self-sustaining. As in psychoanalysis the neurosis is not really cured until the period of re-education has built a whole new system of acting and thinking, so here, the act of creation is not entirely accomplished until the ideas contained in the insight are secured for consciousness in some objectified form—written down, made explicit in memory and at length evaluated. And the attendant emotions attach themselves to the creative product or activity at first in attraction, sometimes later in repulsion.

The one great difference between insight and the psychoanalytic process lies, however, in the spontaneity. In the case of insight the process must wait upon purely chance factors, since there is no prediction as to just what element or what kind of experience will release the repressed system, the character of the creative complex being largely unknown; in the case of psychoanalysis, integration is deliberately fostered or set in motion, the general nature of the repressed system being known to the analyst. But I believe that if the proper circumstances are considered, and the proper regimen followed, insightful thought may be made more effective and brought more usefully under control, especially if periods of freedom (renunciation) are appropriately designed to furnish just such incidental stimulation. The timely combination of circumstances which brings release from inner tension can be sought, though its capture cannot be assured.

It is hardly necessary at such a place in our discussion to recall that intellectual discovery, though dependent upon certain casual factors at this point in its history, *is in no sense an accident* in its fundamental mechanism. It must have background and substructure from which to start, the result of continuous storing of the mind and growing polarization of interest. Focal points in that interest must have been established by hard, deliberate labor in technical preparation, abetted by an inveterate habit of ranging far afield in intervals of less serious effort. A blundering charwoman entering a restaurant in Paris does not make an *Old Wives' Tale;* a mistake of an apprentice does not give a scientist the needed coordination of scattered data, nor does an orange produce a *Don Giovanni* unless somehow materials versatile in their application, and capable of almost any organization are pressing to be written, the scientific interest already oriented, the musical theme tentatively scored in mind. Erudition, however, is not enough; unrelieved industry is not enough; accuracy in the use and presentation of facts is not enough; care in the use of inference and all the tools of art and science are not enough. There must be more; and that *more* has to do with the spontaneous reorganization of these acquired elements under the aegis of an event which is in reality not a mere addendum to, but rather an interpenetration of the levels of mental experience. And as a result one not only *creates something;* he *becomes something* as well.

THE PERIOD OF
FRUSTRATION IN
CREATIVE ENDEAVOR

Eliot Dole Hutchinson

IN A previous article entitled *Varieties of Insight in Humans*,[1] I pointed out that *insight*, or creative insight as it was called, usually develops in relation to the solution of problems connected with constructive work, and not infrequently involves a pattern of behavior consisting of a period of preparation, a period of renunciation or recession, a period or moment of insight, and a period of verification, elaboration, or evaluation.

The process of creative thinking is the cycle of these stages in multiple and ever-changing emphasis.

It is the purpose of the present paper to discuss in particular some of the implications of the period of renunciation or recession. Before proceeding with this let me review in outline each of the four essential stages.

The *Period of Preparation* may entail years of effort and a lifetime's acquisition of technical habits all centered upon some problem situation which defines itself as it is pursued, if it is not already explicit. Large reaches of past experience are requisitioned and a form of what is ordinarily called trial and error activity, that is, false starts on the basis of inadequate hypotheses, or sheer blind random effort in the face of apparently insoluble problems, are common. Solution is thus delayed, errors of various types, especially of stereotypy creep in, defeat must be temporarily admitted. There is nothing trifling about the frustration; it is real, vivid, and undermining.

[1] Hutchinson, Eliot Dole, Varieties of Insight in Humans. PSYCHIATRY (1939) 2:323-332. [Editor's Note: This paper is included in this volume.]

During the *Period of Renunciation or Recession* in which for a time the problem is given up in sheer defense of emotional balance, other activities, usually avocational, are interpolated. This period, involving as it does a large degree of frustration, is often characterized by rising emotional tone, restlessness, feelings of inferiority, and in the last analysis temporary cessation of effort. Mild psychoneurotic symptoms are common.

It is usually some sudden stimulus from this whole field of irrelevance, coming into periods of slight mental preoccupation after periods of rest, which terminates the period of psychic tension and precipitates a *Period (or Moment) of Insight,* usually unpredictable in time, though determined by circumstances. This insight consists often of a reorganization of the perceptual field, a new alignment of possible hypotheses. It is often accompanied by a flood of ideas, alternative hypotheses appearing at the same time, many of which are difficult to make verbally explicit. Noteworthy in the experience are the almost hallucinatory vividness of the ideas appearing in connection with any sense department, the emotional release, feelings of exultation, adequacy, finality. The period is integrative, restorative, negating the symptoms of neurotic maladjustment engendered by the preceding period. The individual steps up to a new level of activity and a new possibility of reaction. Integration opens up new volitional possibilities; reactions, before impossible, now become commonplace.

Finally there is a *Period of Verification, Elaboration, or Evaluation,* in which all technical and explicit rules of practice are again summoned into use, and the possible exaggerations and overstatements of the *period of insight* are checked against external realities. Without such evaluation the insight does not release anything of communicable or social value. It remains otherwise an uncoördinated experience.

As already stated it is the present purpose to concentrate attention on the second of these phases, the Period of Renunciation or Recession. In order to gain some idea of the bewildering variety of reaction of which the creative mind is capable when faced with a genuine frustration we must see the matter against the background of a whole science. And even here we must place our emphasis not upon the endless confusion of detail, but upon underlying patterns of reaction. The entire psychology of emotional conflict and its proper management, of complexes and their subtle determination of behavior, or borderline and even severe pathology, must be called into service. Unless the tensions generated by the problem situation are properly managed, that is, finally integrated into new behavior patterns, symptoms of strain inevitably appear. We are now ready to study these symptoms and to learn why frustration leads to a temporary renunciation of the creative effort. We shall ask, also, what relation the symptoms of frustration bear to severe mental disorder—and perhaps come to a better understanding of the relation of genius to such disorder.

PATTERN OF ADJUSTMENT

As we have seen, the intuitive thinker is often in a state of problem-generated "neurosis," or its lesser equivalent *tension,* owing to the *practical* block set to the immediate fulfillment of his creative desires. At bottom, therefore, we are dealing with situations involving conflict—conflict between the compulsive urge to push forward the creative enterprise and the agencies of delay. Such conflict occasions the same sort of personality readjustment as is seen in the thwarting of any common life-interest, except that it is likely to be more severe because it is more definite. In respect to the type of readjustment, creative life, though narrowed to particular problems and special disciplines, is in no way an exception. In more serious aspect these possible adaptations will involve tendencies toward repression of the creative problem, and dissociation of it from normal consciousness; regression; compensatory reactions; and emotional excess—over and above all the subtler processes of relief with which psychiatry and psychoanalysis are familiar. The choice of pattern will be made by the individual—as it is in life-situations—according to his constitutional and pre-established modes of response. The particular disorder—neurosis or possible psychosis—sometimes brought on by the effort of adjustment, in fact the whole range of nervous symptoms deriving immediately therefrom, provide a safety-mechanism for the release of energies which, otherwise entirely blocked, would develop dangerous psychic tension. But for the very reason that these symptoms relieve such tension, they reduce the intensity of the creative drive, forcing it into a state of temporary impotence. The productive process is thus thrown back, where in the last analysis it belongs, on the natural—physiological—capacity of integration operating in periods of relaxation, in this case gained by the enforced renunciation of the problem, unhampered by the immediate interference of consciousness.

We shall document these adjustment processes only briefly.

REPRESSION

Repression of the creative interest and consequent dissociation of the problem from normal consciouness, with sacrifice of the unity and integrity of the personality in order to find release from the insistent conflict, is perhaps the most common of them. Consider the following typical example. It will say in a few words by implication what it will take many to describe in detail.

Hector Berlioz, the famous French symphonist, struggled against the creative impulse and eventually killed it. He suffered from poverty while at the same time his wife's health was causing him anxiety. One night there came to him the inspiration for a symphony. It ran in his head, an allegro in 2-4 time, in A minor. He rose from his bed and began to write. But he thought:

"If I begin this bit, I shall have to write the whole symphony. It will be a big thing, and I shall have to spend three or four months over it. That means I shall write no more articles and earn no more money, and when the symphony is finished I shall not be able to resist the temptation to have it copied (which will mean an expense of a thousand or twelve hundred francs) and then of having it played. I shall have a concert and the receipts will barely cover the cost. I shall lose what I have not got. The poor invalid will lack necessities, and I shall be able to pay neither my personal expenses nor my son's fees when he goes on board ship. These thoughts made me shudder, and I threw down my pen, saying:

'Bah, tomorrow I shall have forgotten the symphony.' But the next night I heard the allegro clearly and seemed to see it written down (note hallucinatory characteristics of insight). I was filled with feverish agitation. I sang the theme. I was going to get up, but the reflections of the day before restrained me. I steeled myself against the temptation and clung to the thoughts of forgetting it. At last I went to sleep, and the next day upon waking all remembrance of it had indeed gone forever." [2]

The initial frustration by practical considerations of an unfinished purpose, the attempted repression, the involuntary recall of the work, the fatal adjustment to the multiple demands of inner necessity,—these are clear. Such artistic sacrifice, and the death of so pressing an idea not only ties down inspiration, it leaves the personality hobbled, unable later to vault the fences to creative freedom. Few can stand the strain and counterstrain which such a life entails.

The creative desire may not only be blocked, it may on that account be purposely repressed, relegated to some back-corner of the mind in such a way that the individual is no longer torn by the pain of conscious desire and conflict. His interest turns to some goal easier of attainment. He tries to forget his ambitions, to cut them off from awareness. But these dynamic groups of ideas, —forming a repressed "creative complex,"—still control his perceptions, determine his moods. The hidden enterprise bobs up in hydra-headed forms producing sometimes melancholy, anxiety, fatigue, sometimes inflation of the ego, sometimes over-idealization of purpose. Repression tends to inhibit all reactions which do not belong to the repressed behavior system itself, and these it amplifies in their undefined influence upon consciousness. In extreme cases even a 'conversion' of the affect—emotion—of the repressed system into bodily symptoms may take place. Mild hysterical or neurasthenic symptoms are common. These play up and down the whole gamut of symptomatology from possible disturbances of action, perception, and memory to the most serious functional disorders. It is impossible to detail or illustrate all these symptoms

[2] Rolland, Romain, *Musicians of Today* [translated from the 1908 French edition by Mary Blaiklock]; New York, Henry Holt, 1915 (ix-xii and 324 pp.); pp. 16-17. Also in Clark, Barrett Harper, *Great Short Biographies of the World;* New York, McBride, 1928 (xiii and 1407 pp.); p. 1385.

here, nor is it necessary to do so; it is sufficient to remember that a whole range of disorder is possible,—a range to which I believe the psychopathologists have given insufficient attention, since they have overlooked the importance of what are largely temporary symptoms,—if the creative endeavor later turns out satisfactorily,— in their search for permanent abnormalities.

DESTRUCTIVE EFFECT OF REPRESSION

There seems little question that prolonged, enforced repression of the creative desire may lead to actual breakdown of the personality. A number of the best known French, modernist painters will serve to illustrate the point. Without a public, shut out of academic circles, railed at, despised, forgotten, blocked at every turn, many of them found production fruitless if not impossible, gave up altogether, crushed their creative ambitions, and foundered to uncertain ends. Delacroix, a persistent and aristocratic applicant for admission to the *Institute* was kept out until late in his life, when the continued repression had made significant work no longer possible and when the honor turned to ashes in his hand. Courbet, likewise rejected by the *Salon,* unable to show his pictures without the aid of profit-devouring dealers, was accused of radical leanings, denounced for his painting of common women in the nude, financially ruined and exiled from the country, never to paint again. Manet, the most harassed of all, was indicted for indecency, prevented from showing his work, and perished a total nervous wreck. While their complete breakdown may not be attributable to this one cause alone, it was in part brought on by it. The stifling of creative interests is no incidental matter; it cuts at the very roots of satisfaction in living. If the burden is not too great, such men escape the fate of neurosis, or breakdown, through the expressive medium of their genius. Otherwise pathology is too often the price paid, and disintegration the result.

REGRESSION

Others may show symptoms of *regression,* return for solace to the inner world of fantasy, preserving the integrity of the person-

ality by breaking connections with the outer world. They drop
mature patterns of creative enterprise in favor of outgrown and
easier ones, perhaps for those of even infantile character. Part of
the childlikeness of genius has here its explanation. Such men make
a retreat toward introversion, becoming negativistic, stubborn, inaccessible. Friends and ordinary events cannot release their emotions, and in fact they seem to have none. Unwarranted bursts of
anger, irresponsible and compulsive movements, strange apathy,
sluggish thought, feelings of inferiority, negligence in personal
habits—such symptoms—present the typical picture of the highly
introverted. Loneliness haunts existence, absentmindedness becomes habitual, incidentals crowd out essentials. The French
painter Degas, tormented by lack of markets for his painting, and
laughed at by his contemporaries, finally submitted to the strain,
gave up the struggle, retreated to his rooms and to himself, forlorn, lonely, lost to the world of vigorous creation. And Cézanne,
sensitive to the misrepresentation of critics, unappreciated by the
academicians, a failure in his struggle for immediate distinction,
finding painting difficult, retired to his simple, semi-rural home in
Aix, there to live out his days painting vegetables and still-life at
which the surrounding yokels smiled and nudged each other.
Liszt, thwarted in his creative effort by the complications of certain love affairs, showed at one time in his life actual catatonic
symptoms so that a stupor into which he fell was mistaken for his
death, which was actually published, much to his later surprise.
Joseph M. W. Turner and Francis Thompson, temporarily baffled
in some task requiring months of extended effort, would disappear
entirely from the society of their normal acquaintances, retreat to
the lower levels of society, happy to be thus lost to the world,
counting for nothing. Michael Angelo and Benvenuto Cellini wrote
sonnets telling how wretched they were. The mystics know similar attitudes as the "dark night of the soul," self-depreciation and
the purgation of self-will. Read the records of such abnegations
and compare them with the effusions of the same minds when in
the flood tide of effective expression. There will then be no question about the reality of retreat, nor the pain of conflict. The world

of reality with its normalizing contacts, and its consistent balance ceases to exist. And when introversion reaches such a dominant stage, adjustment to that exacting world becomes difficult if not impossible—and again pathology results. Regression cuts off creation low down on the stem, so that future flowering is inhibited.

COMPENSATION

Still others violently *compensate* for their lack of progression in the chosen field of creative endeavor by the resumption of efforts in another—a point often emphasized by the theorists on genius. Over-compensation, they claim, is the mark of talent, distinguishing it from the degenerate, who, instead of vanquishing his inferiority, finally succumbs to it, escaping from it by a flight from reality. However that may be, men do build for themselves in the face of obstruction imaginative situations of successful character, bending all their energies toward the accomplishment of these revised goals. It is not so much the raw fact of their inferiority before the creative problem that fosters compensation, it is rather their *sense of inadequacy*, their *feeling of it,* that matters. Only men of supreme strength and daring can triumph magnificently over such attitudes. Daumier, perhaps the most outstanding French artist of the last century, renouncing the seduction of the Bohemian environment which rendered his contemporaries creatively impotent, was forced to work in slavish production in Paris for his living. Lacking early success in the contemporary mode of painting—that is, failing in the production of sweet sentimentalities for an already over-stocked market,—he set to interpreting the social environment, in all its pathos and brutality, with a passion that cost him dearly. But his energy carried him through to an eventual success which, as natural, he accepted with reservation at a time when he did not need it. His compensation, as usual in such cases, made achievement possible in a field allied to his earlier failure.

But compensation, though seen as a common reaction among men of ability, is only one of many possible turns which frustration may force upon the personality. It should not, therefore, be overemphasized, nor can a whole psychology of creative life be based upon it without serious injustice to the wider aspects of the field.

EMOTIONAL EXCESS

Again, emotional exaggeration, or indulgence, with its opposite extremes of anger and resignation, may be ways of relief. Instead of trying to shut off the responsibility for the creative undertaking by repressing and forgetting it; instead of retreating into a world of imagined success, divorced from reality; instead of laboring for a substitute goal or compensating victory, one may give free reign to the engendered emotions themselves. The endeavor to remove restraint by exaggerated muscular reactions, verbal outbursts, hyper-activity, gesturing, or doing violence to the environment, is matched at the other extreme by sloughing in stuporous immobile melancholy, irresponsive to environment, inaccessible in recoil from the outer world.

Such exaggeration of emotional response is a common symptom, forming the basis of the irritable and changing moods and of the extreme irascibility so often encountered in genius. It is an early and almost immediate response, the reaction often being out of all proportion to the apparent cause. The most insignificant difficulty in the undertaking, the most incidental matter seems to be the block on which the creator stumbles. His emotional outbursts, however, though intense, and associated with a variety of moods, are not of long duration. Indifference and depression, on the other hand, with their characteristic loss of the most lofty and complex sentiments toward the work, may last longer. The morbid disinterest in life is in fact usually conscious, definitely realized by the thinker as a harmful phenomenon. He senses his loss of feeling, deplores the fact that nothing will excite him or please him. He looks at his former effectiveness as at a far country, an attitude self-enriched as the frustration continues. Changes in other faculties are not necessarily proportional to those of his emotions. Good memory and lucid intelligence coexist with this type of ineffectiveness, though thought may introspectively appear slow, the will weak, moral values in abeyance, and anxiety common.

I have in mind a well known scientist, who, disappointed in the outcome of a complicated and well-planned chemical experiment, confessed that he was with difficulty restrained from destroying his apparatus. Consider even so competent an artist as Rodin, seizing his hammer and destroying a statue—really a precious bit—that belied his dreams. Consider Tschaikowsky tearing up and burning valuable score sheets in a fit of rage at his seeming failure; Shelley hiding his manuscripts so that no one would discover them; Hardy sensitively delaying publication for years. Such futility in creation is one of the hardest experiences to endure. It hurts the ego, crushes self respect, promises nothing but continued misery, is blind and suicidal. In reaction to it, therefore, it is no wonder that men become frantic, or hopeless, or both. Inherent in the very process of creation—inherent, that is, in the necessary delays, frustrations and ineptitudes of the Period of Renunciation—are the seeds of defeat and self-destruction. Suffering, the substance of all that is mentally injurious, is an almost inevitable prelude to success. But does this necessarily mean that mental disorder is a precondition of genius?

Creation and Mental Disorder

What of the relation of productive ability to "insanity"? If there are, as we have seen, psychoneurotic symptoms commonly manifest in the process of creation, is there not also severe psychosis—granted a genetic basis for the same? The question is a fair one, and the answer depends on how far the tendency to abnormal adjustment proceeds before it is arrested by *insight*.

It does little good, as Kretchmer, Lombroso, Hirsch and Nordau have done, to point out the coincidence of genius and abnormality based upon physical disability. Lange-Eichbaum estimates that in 90 per cent of all those who have been called genius one can demonstrate more or less severe psychopathic states; in 12 per cent one finds explicit psychoses. But it seems to me that such percentages have been wrongly interpreted to mean that genius is somehow dependent upon such severe disorder for its achievement. Of course there have been psychotic creators with every type of mental disorder, men of exalted but profoundly distorted mind: Rousseau, Nietzsche, Galton, Newton, Blucher, Tasso, Maupassant, Dostoievesky, Strindberg, Liszt, Schumann, Beethoven, Van Gogh —these to cap a long list. Owing to its sensitivity of response to the surrounding world, and its restricted energy available for adaptation to the excessively wide field envisaged for that purpose, genius is naturally the stuff of which over-effort and distraction is made. And if the desire for adaptation is made futile by circumstance, actual psychosis, as well as psychoneurosis, may develop.

But all such argument supports the point I have already made; —namely, that one phase of the creative process has inherent in it a potential pathology. It does not prove the reverse, that pathology holds responsibility for the productive output of genius. In fact, it strengthens still more the conviction that without a major degree of successful adaptation, presupposing an eventual equilibrium between rare positive talents striving toward the creative ideal and the actual powers of expression, there is no production which will stand the test of social evaluation. The essence of our question should be: is the man of genius a creator because he is a psychotic or neurotic or is he a neurotic because he cannot be fully a creator? Overlooked by the advocates of the genius-insanity theory is this: how much disorder is due to the frustrations of definite creative undertakings—that being the only source of maladjustment in the creative process—and how much of it is occasioned by frustration in the multitude of secondary pursuits which have little or nothing to do with the creative enterprise, or by hereditary predisposition?

Kretchmer says in his *Psychology of Men of Genius*:

"From all this we may be permitted to assert that mental disease of every kind leads in the overwhelming majority of cases merely to a diminution of mental power and to ineffectiveness in the social world; but that in a few exceptional cases of men of quite special mental construction and great talents, it leads to the activities of genius. And this stimulation to productive genius comes in the highest degree only in the initial stages, the mild borderline states of mental disease. . . .

"So we are forced to conclude that were we to remove the psychopathic inheritance, the demonic unrest and mental tension, from the constitution of the man of genius, nothing but an ordinary talented person would remain. The more one studies biographies, the more one is driven to the viewpoint that the psychopathic component is not merely a regrettable, non-essential accident of biologic structure, but an intrinsic and necessary part, an indispensable catalyst, perhaps, for every form of genius in the strict sense of the term."

For reasons which are largely familiar to the reader by this time I am inclined to disagree. Clearly enough Kretchmer admits that only the borderline states of mental disease, the psychoneurotic states, have much relation to production. And these, as we have already pointed out, are just the conditions most easily engendered by the long-continued difficulties, harassments and delays in creative accomplishment. It seems to me that the demonic unrest and mental tension of which he writes grows out of the fact that a balance cannot be effected between the intense and often over-ambitious creative drive and the rate of integration and accomplishment. It is the result of unfulfilled effort, not the cause of accomplishment. Whenever that balance is maintained, as it is in most cases, we find genius, aside from its hereditary incapacities, the forthright denial of pathology, the essence of health and effectiveness. And even in cases where the creator is actually mentally disordered, from causes which have little to do with his immediate ambitions, his significant work is done, not so much in periods of attack or obsession, as during intervals of lucidity.[3] Owing to the arrival of *insight,* owing, that is, to the new integration, the release of tension and free expression following the period of frustration, balance is restored by the completion of the creative—expressive —cycle, not destroyed by it; and that balance is maintained until symptoms of frustration are again brought into existence by some newly shouldered responsibility. Such a state, we grant, may be

[3] Note the history of Nietzsche, Compte, Maupassant, Van Gogh, Liszt, Blake, Thompson, and others in this connection.

frequent, and hence gives the impression of permanent maladjustment with attendant pathological symptoms. But in the long run the possibility of creation is the salvation of genius, the guarantee of health and effectiveness, not its undoing. That is what makes creative work with its developing interests and potential reeducation an indicated cure for certain types of psychoneurosis. It is only as one preserves the balance between frustrated desire and eventual attainment that unification of the personality and technical advance become real. Further research upon the psychical dispositions of the healthy creator instead of the inadequacies of the disordered, will, I think, support my point.

The point to remember is this: sooner or later in the case of genuine creative frustration some adjustment will take place, for the neuromuscular system inherently tends to protect itself against suffering. In general three things happen when nature takes its course: breakdown in various degrees of seriousness, abnormal behavior, neurosis, even psychosis if the strain is severe; redefinition of goals and the substitution of some alternate realizable aim; eventual solution of the problem as such, by way of *insight,* according to the integrative power of the individual. Nature is constructive as well as destructive—and under the same conditions of strain, depending upon the adaptability of the organism.

EFFECTIVE NORMAL ADJUSTMENT

The question now comes, is there no normal method of management of these persistent tensions engendered by creative effort which will insure the productive process against liability for the eventual breakdown of the personality? There is: and I suggest as the most effective way an acceptance of a period of renunciation or recession, a turning to unrelated interests, a purposive rejection of the problem from consciousness. The essential difficulty of the problem makes necessary its abandonment for the time being. William Butler Yeats says: "The actual idea for a work comes in a moment of unconsciousness or forgetfulness; *but the effort must be kept up until the strain produces what may be only a momentary passivity.*"

Such *suppression*, or laying aside of the problem, is to be distinguished from simple repression by its foresighted, voluntary, character. It is a deliberate attempt to systematize the creative process by setting aside the problem for a planned interval, with intentions of consciously resuming it at a specified later date. In the interim it may appear repeatedly in consciousness, no matter. If it causes day-dreaming, involuntary recall, no matter. The period given to renunciation is calculated to make room for such phenomena by resignation to desultory, or inconsequential mental activity. In a healthy revolt against all conventional thought, all social regulation, all deliberative work, the thinker effects a balance between the necessary intrusions of the problem upon consciousness, and the free time given to incidental matters. The insistence of the problem is not scorned; it is simply played off against a set of equally absorbing secondary concerns. It is not surprising, therefore, that at any time the mind may be recalled to the main problem by some apparently insignificant detail in this field of irrelevance which momentarily absorbs attention and occasions insight. It is no wonder either that would-be-artists have stressed unduly the unsystematic elements of this experience, thinking that in them alone lies the secret of originality.

SOCIAL UNCONVENTIONALITY VERSUS CREATIVE FREEDOM

In fact, it is exceedingly difficult not to mistake *social unconventionality* for such *creative freedom*. The Bohemianism of Paris, Greenwich Village, Provincetown, Hollywood, or of a hundred other artists' colonies, studios, and "workshops," is not the answer to the problem of finding such needed interludes. Nor is the necessary creative freedom clearly associated with them at all. Too often they represent the veriest surrender to a type of conformity as rigid in its way as that against which the whole of Bohemianism is thought to be a reaction. Creative freedom has meaning only in relation to the type of strain, and the pattern of reaction which the productive effort has hitherto engendered. Its application is always individual. For anyone who spends his time in systematic work, the release should perhaps involve unschematized diversion and spontaneous exercise of the imagination. Interest should be in attempts to express the self, to foster the deeper and more emotional levels of mental activity, to muse and dream, ponder and speculate, lest the work be interlined with purely surface considerations and platitudes. For anyone looking forward to the advent of insight, the diversion must be regulated according to the symptoms of frustration—voracious reading, organized selection of material, excursions into secondary fields, invigorating contact with objective life, quiet recreation, rest—anything to balance the possible introversion, regression, inferiority and continuous preoccupation with the self.

Periods of revolt and recusancy, or even of sheer idleness, can thus be justified. The snarling criticism levelled at the erratic working hours, the free time, the off-days of insightful minds is sometimes without point. And so the period of renunciation takes on a new significance. It is not opportunity to be lazy for its own sake; it is not liberty to be undisciplined, nor license to be self indulgent. Rather is it freedom for growth, autonomy of the creative self. And if the inherent responsibilities are properly shouldered, if the needs of the adjustment process are adequately met and balanced, the ethics of the period will take care of itself. The demands of such an ethics upon self-discipline, even though the discipline involves a measure of complete freedom from all customary responsibilities will be more severe than the Bohemians have ever realized. Bohemianism squanders its freedom, returns from its hours of dissipation less effective. Creative discipline conserves its leisure, returns refreshed, invigorated, eager. It does not sell its birthright to continued creation for temporary pottage.

In a society as full of enforced routine as is the massed, mechanized and intense American, it is often difficult to attain creative freedom of the sort we are here describing. *The attainment of it is, in fact, the hardest part of the creative discipline.* To work is easy; and it is easy to keep on working long after there is any appreciable value from the effort. So accustomed are we to the feverish pace, that we are actually afraid to stop lest we should lose something.

The cessation of effort for a time makes us neurotic. The research man in his commercial laboratory would be ashamed to be seen doing nothing, unaware, perhaps, that one really productive idea a week or a month is all he can deliver. Many an administrator who needs executive plans for his office next morning can with difficulty be persuaded that he will more readily formulate them if he takes a fling at his hobby. Great programs of living are made only by men who stand back and look over their universe as an artist retreats to look over his canvas. And from that point they know where the high lights are to be placed. There is nothing precious about it all, it is not the idleness of the indolent. It is a profound and rugged challenge to those who are tempted to wear out their strength in futility.

Conclusion

When the creative desire is active, intense, aroused, but for the time restricted in freedom of expression, the chief psychological symptom is tension. Such tension conditions in its own right various degrees of neuroticism. The symptoms show kinship with those universal characteristics which psychic frustration in any field produces. They may range from the slightest expression of annoyance to the fury of an artistic maniac. They may mean simply throwing an unsatisfactory sheet of manuscript into the wastebasket, abandoning a poor introduction, or smashing and tearing about like the elder J. P. Morgan, who, annoyed by an incorrectly reported item on the stock ticker, which thwarted his productive plans, wrenched the instrument from its moorings, carried it to the doorway of his office, and heaved it down the steps into Wall Street. All possible symptoms of repression, regression, compensation, and emotional instability crop out. The temperament, the so-called artistic temperament, has here its roots and its justification. Such temperament, however, is not "insanity." In the ablest minds, the tensions are not merely existent, they are properly managed. That method of management usually involves a conscious renunciation of the problem for a while, a resignation from the creative enterprise, a substitution of incidental or avocational interests until the appearance of insight. Then in a twinkling all is changed. The process which hitherto generated psychoneurotic symptoms now negates them, and if the creative drive has a firm grip on reality, carries the thinker well into a period of verified accomplishment. The creative process does have inherent in it the seeds of pathology. But owing to the fact of *insight*, those seeds flower—if conditions are just right —not in crippled deformity, but in vigorous achievement. The creative process at this second period in its cycle is, in short, an alternation or balance between tendencies toward maladjustment and the integrative processes making for insight.

THE NATURE OF INSIGHT

Eliot Dole Hutchinson

IN TWO previous articles,[1] I have set forth some conceptions concerning the nature of the creative cycle. We have seen that the scientist, the artist, the practical thinker—profession makes little difference—may have before him a problem involving some explicit production or decision in life situations. For months or years, it may be, this problem remains unsolved, this creative intention unfulfilled. Attempts at solution have ended only in bafflement. But suddenly, usually in a moment when the work has been temporarily abandoned, or when the attention is absorbed by irrelevant matters, comes an unpredicted *insight* into the solution, usually interpreted as a reorganization of the perceptual field, especially in regard to the relationship between means and end. As if "inspired," "given," arise ideas which constitute a real integration of previously accumulated experience—an answer, a brilliant hypothesis, a useful "hunch," forming, it seems, a short-cut to artistic or scientific advance. Exhilaration marks such moments of insight, a glow or elation goes with them, a feeling of adequacy, finality, accomplishment. The content of these insights is either lost at once through inattention, or if caught and held by explicit statement in consciousness, takes full form only in a later period of verification and criticism.

The solution of creative problems, in short, sometimes may be

[1] Hutchinson, Eliot Dole, Varieties of Insight in Humans. PSYCHIATRY (1939) 2:323-332. Hutchinson, Eliot Dole, The Period of Frustration in Creative Endeavor. PSYCHIATRY (1940) 3:351-359. [Editor's Note: Both articles are included in this volume.]

so difficult as to offer a positive block to further progress, defeating, for the moment at least, the most disciplined efforts toward accomplishment. Under such conditions activity tends to become random and effort may finally be given up—perhaps for a day, perhaps for years—until such time as solution or insight is attained. And with insight matured integrations of thought are released into consciousness, and the whole psychophysical organism enjoys new ease of expression.

Between the more systematic constructive processes on the one hand, and the insightful or intuitive, such as we have just sketched, on the other, exists a continuum representing all degrees of difference, the amount of psychic frustration being the differentiating factor. The logical, progressive, steadily integrating process of thought merges by imperceptible degrees into the intuitive, the suddenly integrating, the a-logical. The distinction has long been familiar to the philosophers who have disputed endlessly about the relative value of these two modes of thought—the systematic or dialectical, and the intuitive or mystical. From Socrates, Descartes, Bacon, Spinoza, Hegel, Dewey, and Russell on the one side, claiming that all truth may be founded upon an application of the rules of formal logic, to Plato, Augustine, Schopenhauer, Nietzsche, Fichte, Bergson, and Croce on the other, holding that moments of rare illumination add unexpected content to knowledge, the controversy has ranged up and down the byways of discussion until it has nearly lost itself in abstraction. Each proponent, convinced by his own psychological experience that his method is solely legitimate, has gone his own way secretly sure that his antagonist has no truth in him. It is only as the two modes of thought are seen to be extremes of the same process that any reconciliation is to be effected. I wish especially to emphasize the point that such insight or quick solution is not a compensatory measure, a substitute reaction which relies upon a radical redefinition of original goals. It is a direct solution of the problem as such, a specific key to a specific situation.

The creative cycle, then, as far as its intuitive aspects are concerned, consists of four phases: A Period of Preparation, Trial and Error Activity; A Period of Renunciation of the Problem during which effort is temporarily abandoned; A Period (or Moment) of Insight; and, A Period of Verification, Elaboration, or Evaluation.

It is to a discussion of the characteristics of the complex Period of Insight that we must now turn. The literature of psychology, philosophy, æsthetics, science, and religion touch generally upon insight from various angles. Yet curiously enough, aside from the Gestalt Psychologists and the religious mystics, few have carefully isolated the phenomenon or come to grips with it as such. Most expositors have contented themselves with vague and hyperbolic reference to it. Let us attempt to expose some of its essential psychology.

Specific Activities at the Moment of Insight

While it is difficult to systematize or classify in any way the occupations of creative thinkers at the time of insight, it is possible, I think, to add a note as to the function of their activities. Since in cases of genuine creative work one is usually dealing with the psychology of temporary frustration, he may expect that periods of illumination will be fostered best by those activities which relieve such conditions of tension. And since many, if not most, insights come when one is not consciously engaged upon the problem, the specific occupation of the individual at the moment of insight will have little to do with the strenuous, practical efforts at solution which have filled the earlier preparatory periods. On the surface these activities will appear casual, often apparently trivial, such as one performs almost automatically in moments of unrelieved strain; intermittent and often without apparent meaning. Let us inquire what they are, and then as to their function. Practical illustration will clarify the matter.

An English scientist, Mr. A. W. S. Briscoe, remarks:

Any ideas that matter usually arise when I have time to think, *i.e.*, in bed, during the 3-10 minutes before I sleep, in a train, while driving a car, or on a holiday.

All, note, activities dissociated from the work in hand.

Another scientist states:

The half drowsy moments of a lazy Sunday morning are as good a time as any in which to do real creative thinking. It is surprising how fertile the mind becomes when not interrupted, or restricted by criticism in the free and often fantastic expression of its ideas. The best moments are those, I find, in which I let the imaginative thought *become a game*.

Whiting Williams, industrialist and author, writes:

I have recently found it extremely valuable to organize my day for the furthering of concentrated thought in the morning. I even go so far as to enjoy the kick of my cold bath before shaving, because experience has shown the time of shaving to be highly valuable for the reception of fresh points of view regarding the work planned for the morning. I have certainly gained more from my day than ever before by postponing my activities along other lines into the afternoon.

It usually obstructs concentration to let the attention be diverted early in the day,

writes Samuel Merwin, well-known novelist.

The early part of a piece of work, always the hardest, I go straight at in the morning. After the story is built, the groundwork done, a reflective day, loafing, often leads to excellent work in the afternoon or evening.

The practice is strangely similar to Edison's frequent catnaps on the bench under his table, or of Echermann's quotation of Goethe as saying:

My counsel is to force nothing and rather to trifle and sleep away all unproductive intervening days and hours, than on such days to compose something that will afterwards give no pleasure.

William Butler Yeats writes:

All such efforts are to prolong the passive period in which the image, a birth following the impregnation of effort, can appear.

Aldous Huxley remarks:

Reading, especially of emotional literature, may produce a propitious mood. Smoking and walking about, calm restlessness, without taking the mind too far away from the main thought, helps.

Arnold Bennett says: "Only by seeing, hearing, and reading masterpieces in any art."

Vera Brittain, author of the autobiography *Testament of Youth*, writes:

I never have moments of sitting down and staring straight ahead, "stuck" for an idea, so to speak. When I feel one of those deadly blank moods coming on, I toss everything aside and walk and walk. That is one thing I miss here (in America). People are so very anxious to take me places in an automobile, that I don't get any chance for exercise. When I'm walking, I'm working, too, for the ideas come faster then. For real relaxation, though, there is nothing like travel—I mean the lovely, leisurely travel through France and Italy, where one can walk and climb hills and **all the rest.**

Through its power to create slight preoccupation or dissociation, music is often a help in fostering insight.

Whiting Williams continues:

I have recently come closer to enjoying a sort of chronic creative mood than ever before. For some months I have been working upon a book setting forth my philosophy of human relations in industry. I have noted this mood more than once at a symphony concert. Whereas previously I used to feel a sort of pain at my inability even to attempt such a masterwork as a symphony, I now find myself enjoying, in some slight measure, the feeling that I am in the midst of some such process as those composers must have gone through. I imagine, that is, that these men must have suffered from the same conflict—*the satisfaction of creation against the fear of total failure, tinged with the bold hope of achievement.* The music I like best, and that during which most ideas come to me, is that which best expresses this conflict.

Earl Marlatt, Boston poet and philosopher, remarks: "Music, or a train ride, are my best stimulants this side of Vienna."

Charles Hopkinson, artist, declares: "Music played while I am painting is stimulating." Many enjoy an undertone of soft radio music.

Cecelia H. Payne, astronomer, scientist, notes: "Music especially, not reading along similar lines, which is always depressing."

Samuel Merwin says: "Music and plays, seldom books, I feel a marked difficulty in surrendering my attention to another's fiction while absorbed in my own."

Although these occupations appear to be totally unrelated to the major purpose of furthering the creative undertaking, they are not so functionally. Insights, aside from those which appear while one is deliberately engaged upon the problem, come most frequently, I believe, under three preferred conditions: *during or just after periods of rest and relaxation; in periods characterized by a slight degree of mental dissociation; during periods of light physical activity, usually of a more or less repetitive and automatic character.*

Periods of rest and relaxation take many forms—the time just before falling asleep, or just upon waking, the mood of reverie or solitude, a quiet off-day, a vacation or pause in more pressing interests—any time when the intense compulsion of the creative drive is lessened for a while by the interpolation of other interests—there are a hundred special places and conditions!

Periods of mild dissociation are induced by any reverie invoking occupation—listening to music, reading emotional literature, quiet meditation, or listening to the radio. Commonly the element of dissociation is to be found in all three of these classes of activity, especially the last. Automatic muscular exercise, such as driving a car, walking, pacing up and down, and so forth, relieve psychic tension, at the same time leaving the thought processes free to make explicit whatever ideas may occur in connection with the problem. In other words, in order that such activities may reduce the insistent tensions of the period of frustration, they must either draw in a strongly motivated manner upon the attention and interest, or else furnish a lively employment of the muscles in a grosser way. It is little wonder that the stimulus to insight, appearing as it does within this field of general irrelevance and during these periods of preoccupation, seems to be largely an accident as far as its connection with the problem is concerned. But let us look at this matter more closely.

TYPES OF ACCIDENTAL STIMULUS

Two types of accidental stimulus have been distinguished: that in which the accidental idea is consciously related to the creative undertaking and its implications are at once incorporated as part of the work; that in which the accidental event is not used in the final product, but acts merely as a catalytic agent in the presence of which other ideas are fused into creative union. Several illustrations will make the point clear.

Type One. G. S. Fulcher, American research scientist, remarks:

The idea of electro-casting refractory blocks came to me accidentally after casually viewing a small furnace in which a test had been made, and while walking away to leave the room. It came with such a shock, that I can remember the exact position quite clearly. As far as I can remember I had not been concentrating upon the problem at the time.

Ian Hay (Beith) cites a personal example for such an occasion for insight:

I once read *by accident* a police report in a Paris newspaper about a poor old woman who had been convicted of stealing books from the second-hand book stalls on the *Rive Gauche*. She lived in great poverty in one small room, and as it happened, could neither read nor write. She had taken the books because their mere presence in her room gave her a certain literary prestige among her equally illiterate friends. Out of that paragraph I wrote a short story of about five thousand words. I made my central figure an old man instead of an old woman, and it was published both in England and in America. The idea had cost me exactly ten centimes.

Illustrations are innumerable. Franklin's chance perusal of DeFoe's *Essay on Projects,* influenced important decisions and writings of his life. The accidental reading of the *Lives of the Saints* incited

Loyola to create a new religious order, the Jesuits. LaFontaine read by chance a volume of Malherbe's poems, and ever after sought expression in that medium. Rousseau's genius was aroused by an advertisement for an essay, for which he won the prize. Dickens' *Pickwick Papers* were suggested by an accidental finding of some comic pictures in his publisher's possession. Scott as a boy chanced upon a copy of Percy's *Reliques of Ancient Poetry* which he read with eagerness, immediately set to imitating. The sight of the Porter suggested to Leonardo da Vinci his "Guida," and so on. It is clear that the accidental stimulus breaks some form of inhibition that has been withholding crystallization of the accumulating ideas, and that the elements of information contained in the accident are employed in part in the final product.

Type Two. Two examples of accidental stimulus will suffice to make the second distinction in type clear, the one historical, the other contemporary. Jacob Boehme, the late sixteenth and early seventeenth century German pietist, having wandered about Germany for three years as a journeyman cobbler, was in a state of deep doubt and perplexity occasioned by his inability to find peace within the church. Finally he experienced an insight into his difficulties, which formed the basis of his developing philosophy. The thing that interests us here was the manner of that illumination. His attention on one occasion seems to have been attracted and held by a shiny pewter dish which reflected the sun. In such a state of almost hypnotic abstraction the essence of his insight came to him. The division of mind apparently continued for some time, even though he went out into the open air. The dish was simply the occasion for a period of mild mental dissociation, furthered by the repressions of his earlier efforts, during which period his dominant interests crystallized.

The vagary of a misguided mystic, it might be argued, having nothing to do with sound creation! But compare the experience with the testimony of a modern research scientist—a chemist:

After twenty-five year's work on the mechanism of the sodium malonic reaction, and *after a month's vacation, I was dressing from a bath in the sea.* I said, "I have worked on this for twenty-five years and am no nearer the solution than when I started." Just then, the explanation, essentially complete, sprang into my head. This was the unconscious working out from new data obtained in an experiment tried that year. It was *afterward* proved to be correct.

Coleridge's mind frequently worked in such manner. Professor John Livingston Lowes, in his masterly volume, *The Road to Xanadu,* again and again shows how ideas gathered by Coleridge from the most varied sources, and apparently long since forgotten, fused in the presence of some momentarily compelling, auxiliary idea or event, which, accidentally hit upon in the course of his voluminous reading and conversation, was not itself employed in the final product—compare, the *dish,* and *bath in the sea* above—but acted merely as a catalytic agent, which almost disappeared as a traceable factor in the experience.

Further evidence of the fact that integrations of thought sometimes appear in moments of mental dissociation is to be seen in the occurrence of insight during sleep—a known period of such dissociation. Dreams may themselves be insights of real value, provided the motivation for them is strongly channelized by some pressing creative need. If their contents can be acquired by normal consciousness, and verified by subsequent investigation, they may even embody the definite solution to specific problems. The difficult task, as in all insight, is to arouse one's self sufficiently from such periods of dreaming to catch, in consciousness, the ideas that appear. If not recorded at the moment of their appearance, or at the moment of waking, such ideas are likely to be lost forever. The origin of insights in sleep is no guarantee and likewise no disparagement of their value. They may be the veritable debris of the unconscious, neurotic manifestation of the deepest sort, or they may be integrations of real power—Descartes, Coleridge, Klopstock, DeQuincy, Poe, Stevenson, Banting, Poincaré, Blake, Cooper, Hazlitt, Lamb, Hebbel, and so on—depending upon the explicitness and accessibility of their content. In objectifying the dream into actuality, a work of memory and translation is accomplished. Although it is too often seen as a poor and distant imitation of the seeming glory of the original vision, the work actually assures the practical acceptance of the dream. At any rate insight does appear in such periods of dissociation, though objectification of the insight is on that account all the more difficult.

What explanation can we give of the fact that insights come with such accidental stimulation and often under such conditions of mild dissociation?

The thinker, as we have already hinted, is often in a state of problem-generated "neurosis," or its lesser equivalent *tension*, owing to the block set to the immediate fulfillment of his creative desires. The constructive purposes may be in a state of suppression or even repression, intensified by the deliberate effort to turn away from them—a means of managing the tensions involved. The accident which occasions insight is an accident only by virtue of this distraction of interest from the main purpose; it is by no means an accident in function. Seeing a furnace, reading a newspaper, or picking up a book are truly chance events; but it certainly is no accident that those events happen to be related to a whole background of previous thought on the problem which has been waiting for just such a stimulus to integrate it into conscious productive accomplishment.

Now it is well known in psychoanalysis—which offers an analogous situation—that the pretext or occasion for the appearance of ideas related to any repressed system is the stimulus word or suggestion offered by the analyst to the patient and intentionally related both to the conscious thought-content of the moment, and to the unconscious and unresolved "complex" that is causing the neurosis.

So here, the occasion for insight, granted a similar state of suspension or repression of creative endeavor, is an accidental idea or event related both to the immediate preoccupation of the thinker and to his deeper problem motives. Such an idea forms just that unique addition to the dynamic and unconscious background that is needed to unite it with the element of consciousness in a new integration. In other words insights occur most frequently in periods of slight dissociation because only in such moments do levels of thought coalesce completely. In many cases the accidental idea forms part of the final integration, but in some, as in the cases of Boehme, Coleridge, and the chemist mentioned above, where the repression and hence possible dissociation are more marked, it furnishes merely the occasion in which the unification takes places, itself being overwhelmed and lost in the flood of more determinative ideas. At such time it is an auxiliary, merely, a strong and sudden absorption of attention, in the presence of which levels of mind coalesce in the period we have called *insight*, which state of intermediate awareness, as we shall see later, is but temporarily self-sustaining. The fact explains why the objectification of the ideas gained in insight is at times so difficult, and why amnesia attaches so readily to such creative periods. The potential organization of the major part of this work must, as it were, be just under the surface, volcanically ready to erupt, when some slight tremor of the crust cracks open a vent. And in the scoriac explosion one not only produces something; he reinvigorates his psychic constitution as well. Usually the symptoms of dissociation do not extend to the whole personality, but are confined largely to the problem area, the thinker being thus saved from tendencies toward possible hysteria which more severe and generalized division of consciousness in periods of conflict so often produces. And yet there is often psychoneurotic symptomatology. The act of creation is not complete, however, with the arrival of insight—not complete, that is, until the ideas captured in this fleeting period are secured for consciousness in some permanent or objectified form— written down, or made explicit in memory—and at length elaborated.

INTIMATION OF INSIGHT

Insight as we have seen is not itself a simple experience, but breaks up into separate elements each describable in relative isolation. The second of these to demand attention is a tenuous and fleeting *intimation* that insight is about to appear. Such premonition may occur any time after the problem is clearly established in mind, but is usually not far in advance of actual illumination. The annunciation of this implicit and dynamic activity in consciousness has no causation apparent to the experient. Its process is psychologically obscure; but what we know of it leads us to think of insights—intuitions—not as single ideas arriving alone in consciousness, but rather as we have seen, tied to whole systems of ideas, "complexes," that is, generated by the frustrations of the problem situation. At any rate, this convection of ideas attached to larger systems of unconscious thought, this evidence that some solution is maturing, that some integration is taking place, heralds itself by a certain emotional excitation, or satisfaction, often felt prior to the complete conscious realization of the full insight itself. There are, in short, gradations in our thinking, and we here refer to those ideomotor and organic responses which serve as an intermediary between deeply unconscious or implicit thinking on the one hand and the overt expression given to that thinking on the other.

An author remarks:

Insight is always unexpected with me in the sense that I can never say at nine o'clock that I am going to be effective in writing at nine-fifteen. Presumably so with everyone. *But sometimes I have a very strong suspicion that this is going to be a lucky day.* Under such circumstances the will or desire to work must be present first, and the problem long established in mind.

Graham Wallas, British political scientist, whose testimony, in view of his own book, *The Art of Thought,* is especially valuable, adds:

I begin the day by reading the newspaper. Here I sometimes mark significant passages, in bed and after breakfast. Soon I have a vague feeling that I ought to stop reading and sit down to work. It is usually bad for my work for me to be asked first to concentrate upon some practical problem—the answering of a business letter, etc. When I sit down to work, there is always a good deal to do in arranging and re-reading notes, etc. As that goes on, and as I start writing, or filling out the argument of a series of notes, I *become rather closely absorbed.* (Note again evidence for the fact that insight often involves a degree of dissociation from normal areas of awareness.) It must be remembered that a political scientist pieces together a number of points (apercus) each one of which has to be verified by reflection and criticism, and by special examination of evidence. He doesn't, or I don't, get the long succession of words which sometimes comes to the poet. But points, and sometimes a striking phrase, come to me at all times, often (during conversation) in the form of a sentence. I know by experience *that I must "let them come", and that the process of "letting them come"*, begins before the point is clear enough to set down.

Such intimation is evidence that somehow solutions to one's problems have matured or are developing though they have not as yet reached full conscious awareness. At times the experience is a vivid premonition; at times it is only a vaguely sensed impulsion. At times it contains a hint of the content of thought it is about to introduce; at other times it has no explicit meaning whatever. A strange ratification of mental events about to transpire, a warning or gesture toward the future, it is not itself the occasion for insight, though it foreruns that event; it is not a cause, but an effect.

THE MOMENT OF INSIGHT

When, after a period of nameless and frustrated waiting, the actual moment of insight does arrive, that moment often brings with it ideas in such profusion that one is not only astonished at their presence, not only startled by the vivid hallucinatory and automatic character of their appearance, but also largely at a loss to capture them. The hitherto casual and shifting attention must now be centered wholly upon the emerging ideas. The capacity of making them explicit in consciousness is rare. Hence genius is rare.

"The Moment of Insight is exciting, like quick motoring," says Bertrand Russell.

Tschaikowsky wrote:

I forget everything and behave like a madman. Everything within me starts pulsing and quivering; hardly have I begun the sketch, than one thought follows another with great rapidity. In the midst of the process it frequently happens that some external interruption *wakes me from my state* (note again the dissociative nature of the period)—a ring of the bell, the entrance of my servant, the striking of my clock, reminding me that it is time to leave off. Dreadful indeed are such interruptions. Sometimes they break the thread of thought for a long time, so that I have to seek it again.

Beethoven, as is commonly known, spoke of himself as experiencing a sort of rapture, or *Raptus*, as he called it. At such moments of release of ideas he became transformed. He no longer belonged properly to himself, being wholly absorbed and possessed by the musical idea. Every effort was made not to lose hold of it until it was wrestled out of obscurity and made explicit in consciousness— he did not always use the score sheet at once as his memory was remarkable. Nothing threw him aside from the pursuit of it. Conceived under such conditions, it is little wonder that Beethoven's work evokes an almost rapturous or hypnotic effect upon those who yield themselves to it. Poetry often has the same effect.

The eccentricity of genius—all of these examples, you may say! More than that! Probably the extreme limit of a process in which there is a momentary outpouring of the emotional and imaginative elements of mind, as well as the intellectual. The period continues, fosters and enlarges the mood set up by the event or accident which originally occasioned insight. W. B. Courtney, to use a modern parallel, one of the most prolific of writers, becomes wholly absorbed and practically unmanageable when once insight seizes him. Often he devotes a long time to one piece, in continuous, enthusiastic and unusually exhaustive labor.

The accompanying emotional transformation is at times almost miraculous. Joy, zest, gratification, elation, enthusiasm and, in the extreme, even rapture, replace the disruptive and disintegrative reactions of the period of frustration. It is in their description of this freedom, what to them is this ecstasy, that the mystics have exhausted the possibility of language. And it is in reference to this liberation that soberer minds use a vocabulary of enthusiasm. Upon certain outstanding characteristics of it they always insist: the energy, plenitude and exuberance of it; the renewed sense of a purpose to be fulfilled, and of the power to accomplish it; the abolition of a narrow-ranged consciousness and the substitution of a more integrated personality; the surge of self-confidence; the comprehension of the significance of the dreary periods of earlier effort; the occasional sense of impersonality, automatism and detachment; the tragedy of interference with the process. Rather than to elaborate the point, I think it is better simply to recognize that in this release of tension, this sudden reversal of the trends of past experience, we have one of the primary sources of emotional life, running in endless changes the gamut of all possible response. Artist and scientist, mystic and factualist tell of the same experience in different words. And in their disagreement lies a confirmation of the richness of the emotions involved. It is in this phase of the intuitive experience that the identity of the creative aspects of science and art is to be discovered. The preparatory techniques and later verifications differ endlessly; insights in both fields share in common.

THE FORMS OF EXPRESSION OF INSIGHT

Insight, as we have seen, is most commonly recognized in consciousness as a single, central idea to which adhere rapidly developing secondary elements; more rarely is it an organized system of ideas furnished complete to consciousness at one moment. And yet it is true that great principles, in either case, are usually in essence *simply stated*, achievements of remarkable verbal brevity, self-expanding in character. We may well ask why ideas come thus in short verbal forms, and then inquire further whether they are altogether limited to that mode of presentation in consciousness. Look first at some illustrations.

A mathematician avers: "The insight itself can usually be expressed in a single *sentence*."

G. Elliot Smith, British scientist, states: "It is the really important generalizations that are seen whole and at once, and verbally stated."

Graham Wallas writes:

Points and sometimes *striking phrases* come to me at all sorts of times, often, during conversation, in the form of a complete sentence. My main effort on such casual occasions is one of memory. I force myself to memorize the idea, often making it more explicit as I do so, and then perhaps on the top of an omnibus, or while walking, I write it down. I should suppose that about one third of my ideas come to me on such casual occasions, one third while reading, and one third while definitely writing and preparing lecture notes.

Cyril Burt, English educationalist, remarks: "Ideas come to me as a whole, *usually in verbal form, though I don't know them until I dictate at once either the plan or rough draft.*"

And Arthur Stanwood Pier, American novelist, adds: "Motive characters and setting are usually established in a *single sentence* expressed in my case *in concise verbal form.*"

Is it not strange that so many insights come in this more or less complete verbal form?

PSYCHOANALYSIS INADEQUATE

The psychoanalysts have given only a partial answer to this question. They point to a distinction between mental life as it exists in consciousness and as it appears in the unconscious mind. Further they insist, not altogether wrongly, that the contents of the unconscious cannot be raised by effort of will to the conscious except by the mediation of words. The material with which the unconscious has been stored exists largely in terms of *verbal imagery*, and most of consciousness is carried forward also in that medium. Language is, therefore, the property of both departments and becomes the agency by which transfer is made from one level to another. Moreover, they claim that it is the characteristic of such words, phrases, or sentences, to represent *symbolically*, and therefore, with brevity, the whole system of thwarted and perhaps repressed impulses which have been built up in reference to the problem. They are to those creative complexes what symbolic dreams and accidental slips of the tongue are to the more widely established inhibitions of daily life. They form a verbal concentration of great pith attached to wider systems of thought and are indicators of possible dissociation, and incitors to recurrent emotional dispositions.

So far the psychoanalysts have a point. Insights make themselves felt first in verbal form because the speech mechanism is the most universal and delicate instrument of expression in the organism, participating, as it does, in all levels of mental experience. The energy released by the new integration at the moment of insight, however that energy may have been dammed up, must deliver itself into some *motor channel,* speech the most ready in most thinkers. No wonder that in many cases insights are with difficulty expressible. There are various degrees of explicitness of verbal response, full expression not always being immediately attainable. But at this very point, also, the psychoanalysts are too limited in theory.

OTHER FORMS OF EXPRESSION

By no means all insights express themselves in *verbal* forms. The organism is capable of responding in many ways, and in many sense departments, to the cumulative energy which is set free. What shall we say of ideas which appear in other effector systems. To the pianist and sculptor, the instrumentalist, dancer, surgeon and skilled manual artizan, they burst upon awareness in kinæsthetic form; fingers "itch to play," music "flows from the hands," ideas "flow from the pen"—to use popular phraseology. Movement expresses the idea of the dancer, or orchestra conductor; the almost sensuous desire to model plastic form becomes compulsive in sculpture. A number of artists claim they cannot paint until they "feel it in their fingers." Moody you will say! Not at all! Work done at such times when the maturation of motor impulse is at its height is decidedly more efficient.

And what shall we say of musical ideas which sing their way into consciousness? To Tschaikowsky, as to Beethoven, melodies for themes come constantly through such insubstantial inner hearing. Wagner heard music spontaneously to the accompaniment of the visualized scenes of his operas. Brahms struck his themes accidentally, often when improvising—free association—and heard fragments of them in inner harmony. Berlioz tells how for a long time his muse was lazy. But during a stay in Rome, having sought for two months in vain for a theme for the piece "Armer Soldat," and having given up in despair—Renunciation—he was walking one day by the Tiber when suddenly *the phrase sang itself to him*—Insight. Thus not all intuitions are verbal. The effector components stimulated by them make it possible for them to monopolize any department.

Look closely at the following examples. They embody the same characteristics as the more spectacular theophonies with which history has long been astonished.

A research chemist writes:

After intense concentration and many vain efforts to overcome this difficulty (related to the determination of the successive ionization constants of the hydrogen of ortho- and pyrophosphoric acid) I reluctantly decided to abandon the method. I was tired, discouraged, and hungry. . . . Freeing my mind of all thought of the problem (Renunciation), I walked briskly down Tremont Street (Boston) when suddenly, at a definite spot which I can locate today, the idea came into my head (Insight) as emphatically as if a voice had shouted it in these words: "In pharmacy and industry we clarify emulsions by means of high speed centrifuge; such a method would be impractical in a thermostat. But if rapid whirling will do it for a brief time, why will not slow rotation for a longer time accomplish the same result?"

The rest of the verification need not concern us here. But note the auditory form of the insight.

VISUAL FORMS

E. Phillips Oppenheim writes:

The central figure or incident around which a story may be built comes to me with such force that I am unable to rest or do any other work until I have set down on paper the *visualized picture with which my mind is filled.*

L. Richter, German artist, gives a similar illustration:

Since now the twilight had come, I put aside the book and stepped to the somewhat darkened window. *My composition, about which I had not thought in the least,* appeared *definite and complete before me,* as if living in real form and color, so that I, entranced, grasped the charcoal, and in spite of the approaching darkness, sketched the whole thing on canvas at once.

Profound revolutions in mental state may so completely flood the neuro-muscular system with energy that any cortical area may apparently be stimulated. Are insights, therefore, akin to hallucinations?

INSIGHTS VERSUS HALLUCINATION

There is no question in my mind that insights involving these more exhaustive experiences are definitely similar in process to simple hallucinations. At least they have hallucinatory components. In incidence they are both uncommon, occurring only under conditions of profound psychic unrest. In both cases the interpretation of them is dependent less upon immediate objective factors than upon a knowledge of inner purposes and desires.

The emotional interest in the experience tends to be for the moment profound, and then progressively dwindling. In attitude the individual is generally surprised, even temporarily bewildered, the understanding of the meaning of the experience being for the most part but partial. Both are the symbolization of desires long disjoined from personal consciousness by continued conflict. Such simple hallucinatory experiences are often regarded as completely deceptive, maintained against the testimony of other senses, rarely seen through a screen of critical interest. When taken seriously both these experiences may exert a powerful influence upon subsequent thought.

WHAT IS HALLUCINATION?

It is an uncertain matter just how sensuous character can be given to mental content in any way but by the stimulation of the sense organs. Various theories have been proposed. Some authorities suggest a reflex action of the nerve current. The usual pathway of nerve conduction is from sense organ to sensory centers, and from there to the association centers. These investigators hold, however, that in very special circumstances, the nerve currents flow back from the ideational centers to the sensory ones, thus fostering the sensory components of hallucination. Still other investigators deny this retrogressive action of the nerve current as contrary to the theory that the transmission of the nerve current can be in only one direction, and locate the hallucination in some disorder of the sense organ, or of the sensory centers, the association centers being discounted in the process. A third group of researchers want

to do away with the distinction between centers altogether, and en-
visage the brain as functioning as a whole.

For neurological theory we must, then, be essentially silent; back
of it all stands a physiological process which is not yet completely
understood. In describing it we should normally expect to deal with
the facts which lie behind such terms as maturation of synaptic
connections, irradiation into adjacent pathways, psychic tension
and overloading, processes of inhibition, and so on. I suggest that
we take the fact of increased neural organization and growth in insight as a phenomenon, and deal with it phenomenologically until
we know more about it. It is almost impossible to picture what happens in the cortical psycho-sensory projection centers when the release of hitherto developed tension, however that tension may be
carried, frees neural energy, not only to make new neural connections, or to innervate a whole new set of responses, but also to irra-
diate into every phase of experience—sensory, motor, and emotional. But the fact that in sudden insight all these types of
experience occur, argues for the existence of the phenomenon.
Sensory experiences—non-recurrent visual and auditory hallucinations—in extreme cases are common. Men *see* a sketch of a completed picture, they see music written in scoresheets, and *hear*
themes in inner hearing. Moreover the seizure of the motor pathways, causing trembling, walking, pacing, jumping, vocalizing, is
likewise frequent. Men shout for joy, stand surprised at the hallucinatory vividness of their insights, rush to tell their friends of their
successes. And in addition the emotional life quickens indefinitely.
In short learning is instantaneous, and the experience opens the
way for new volitional possibilities which are a most important
consideration in education and ethics.

No Abnormality Involved

That there is anything abnormal about these experiences, is, I
think, to be denied. To call insights of the extreme type hallucinatory is simply to enlarge our concept of what is possible within the
range of normality. It seems to me that any mind, subject to the

rack of conflict between desire and its frustration, when suddenly reaching its goal, may experience such an overwhelmingly exhaustive crisis, that its sensory experiences are no more to be marvelled at than its emotional. And the mark of such problem-oriented hallucination is to be *specific* and *final,* never recurring again in the same field, in fact quickly lost to mind unless made immediately explicit. With the genuine psychopath, the hallucination is never integrated with, nor objectified into, the rest of behavior. His motivation, therefore, continues unaltered, the content becoming recurrent, or only slowly evolving. Most insights on the other hand, unless the experience is cultivated for its own sake as do some of the lesser religious mystics, are at once rationalized, and conjoined with concrete expression, thus satisfying the drive and encouraging their own natural termination.

But the whole process of recovering ideas at the moment of insight is also cumulative. Instead of confining expression to one sense department, or medium, the insight may encourage the use of several, thus opening channels of expression which drain the accumulated reserves with amazing rapidity. And no sooner are new thoughts fully made explicit than they draw other material from the region of mind that is directly amenable to normal associative stimulation. The heightened state of consciousness thus induced favors still more the recovery of material from the whole range of mental life, reaches further back into past experience, and deeper into the present for its sources; hence the creative vitality of insights. And upon this process one expends the closest *concentration.*

Whoever has himself been caught in such a period has probably in part shared the concentration of Conrad. You remember the General's daughter, "swinging her stick, who out of the warm, full sunshine of the Kentish fields walked in upon that grizzled exskipper as he 'blackened o'er' the sheets of paper that escaped from his desk and strewed the floor of the low room among the hopfields. There was a jar, as if of a 'terrible fall from a great height.' Conrad jumped from his chair; stunned and dazed, 'every nerve quivering with the pain of being uprooted out of one world and flung down into another.'"

There is nothing more mind-shaking, nothing that stirs thought up from the bottom quicker than such concentration. Only one or two ideas out of the mass may ever be rescued for use in the final product. But the surge is thrilling, incorporative and in no way indicative of the hours of consolidating labor that must follow. The period lasts for a moment, at most a few hours, isolating the thinker from his normal world. Living thus for one intense interlude exclusively in the present, he notes that his work takes the form not so much of consciously or logically compounding ideas, as of recording and verifying those self-forming ideas seeking expression. At that moment it is not work, it is listening; as Sibelius, the Finnish composer, claims in his symphonic field, the verification of inner music. And many a modern lyrist, composer, artist and research worker finds an echo of these experiences in his own life, attenuated, perhaps, but the same in process. It is more than the glow of close concentration, though that also is part of it. It is the outpouring and remodeling of past experience in a period of intense and fluid expression—partial or complete, accurate or fantastic depending on the nature of preparation, and the freedom of expression.

EMOTIONAL TRANSFERENCE

Under these circumstances it is no wonder that artists literally fall in love with their works, considering for the time being at least, that they have created a paragon, a masterpiece. Samuel Merwin, well-known author, writes: "I usually have to resist the impulse to rush up to strangers and tell them about it." And a scientist adds: "After I have been working upon a problem for a long time, and suddenly find its answer, I am so pleased with myself and with it, that I feel like rushing up to my friends and explaining it to them. To me the solution is perfect. It is usually simple, and in its simplicity lies its beauty. I always feel elated." Anyone who has experimented with the T-Puzzle, standard apparatus for the psychological laboratory, knows that when the subject attains the solution of the puzzle after some minutes of effort, that his overt behavior entails outbursts of laughter, a seeking for approval, and an immediate recurrence to the problem in pleased triumph. Animals solving similar puzzles, give evidence of much the same sort of behavior.

It is amazing how blind to the real evaluation of their work some artists become at such moments. To an outsider this amounts to conceit; but they are not conceited in the proper sense of the word. The feeling that has flooded into mind so enlarges the range of awareness that it seems to the creator that the whole objective world should be enthusiastic about his special product. Alas, it is usually indifferent! At any rate, after days of introversion and dogged effort he has at last attained a degree of effectiveness in that objective world and feels at one with it. This freedom of being again in contact with reality, again a wholly integrated and harmonious personality—if only until the assumption of the next problem, responsibility—shows how vivid and essential is the transfer of pent-up emotion upon the materializing ideal. Psychoanalysis deals widely with this phenomenon in regard to the patient-analyst relations. Here it is the creator-creative-product relation in similar setting.

Levels of Insight as a Key to Type of Interest

In the coalescence of materials which we call insight various mental elements predominate according to the extent of the concentration and absorption seen at the moment of insight. Persons vary in the freedom of expression they require depending upon the intensity and extent of the previous frustration. Accordingly insights vary in the liberation and drainage they give. If the requisitioning of past experience is only slight, the intellectual and rational elements of the intuition will naturally predominate. The thinker will never completely lose the critical control of his maturing thought processes. He will tend accordingly to turn to those creative disciplines where that form of thought is most useful—routine scientific work, or the more didactic and classical forms of literature and art. Except as an interest in technique, or in the programmatic, music will not absorb him, nor will he really understand its meaning. His capacity for feeling profoundly, for speaking with conviction, for emotionalizing others in the same field, for enjoying sheer imaginative activities as in art, for being wholeheartedly humble and honest in his work, will be limited.

If the recovery of material from the background of experience is more extensive, the *imaginative* and *emotional* elements will be more manifest. During the period of illumination the thinker removes himself farther from reality, enters more fully a world of relations as they exist in unconscious thought, a world of emotional rather than logical significances. He will therefore tend to occupy himself, as do the great originators in any field, with the speculative, the hypothetical, the symbolic. His insights will have the power to fire others, to send second-level men off on quests of research which are the stuff of detailed science. A certain breadth and resident richness of meaning, inherent vigor, will penetrate his thought. And if he is not tripped up and rejected by his occasional absurdities, he may continue his originality at the level which he has achieved. In science he will turn to the theoretical and the inventive, the cosmological; in poetry to the romantic, the lyric, the dramatic; in music to the profounder symphonies which he fully understands, the fugues and rhapsodies; in art to the symbolic, the ideal; in social life to the Utopian and the Unconventional. In his creative mood technicalities, while essential as grist, will be only accessory to his larger presentations.

As Shelley grew in maturity from his twenty-fourth year, at which time the body of his wife, Harriet Westbrook, was found in the Serpentine River, as he felt the shafts of pain at the loss of his children, the misery of poverty, the likelihood of his own death, his increasingly emotionalized thought shifted from prose, with which he had been intellectually and logically trying to reform the world, to poetry in which he found more liberation. That is, as he felt the need of expressing profounder levels of experience, his medium naturally changed to an emotionally more powerful one. And through his poetry he fired a world which had been largely deaf to him before.

Einstein's working procedure is said to be surprisingly like that of an artist. Once he has formulated the problem, the stages of his work are not slow and painful. He has a definite vision of the whole, and considers the best methods of realizing it. And when the work is finished, it represents not only an addition to scientific truth, but for him an æsthetic pleasure. He will exclaim at the beauty of solutions. There are no fixed hours, profound ideas have occurred even while he was ill in bed. He brings the addition of musical improvization to the productive period. And then a sudden breaking off and return to work. His mind flashes intermittently; in between is calm and quiet.

If one had the least vestige of superstition, it is easy to see how he might suppose himself to be merely the incarnation, merely the mouthpiece, merely the medium of higher forces. It is the impersonality and automatic production of such moments of inspiration that has led to endless theories of extra-personal revelation—from Socrates and his Daemon to the latest fundamentalist reiteration of literal biblical inspiration. But in truth it merely states the fact to say that one has revelation in the sense that suddenly, with genuine certainty and precision, some new truth, hypothesis or solution becomes realized which shakes one's psychic constitution to its foundation. One hears, as Nietzche says, one does not search; one receives, one does not ask who gives. Like lightning—and the hallucinatory components of many a historical insight are no mere accident—an idea flashes out, appearing as inevitable, necessary, without hesitation as to form. One never has a choice. And he not only produces something; he becomes something as well.

THERAPEUTIC INVESTIGATIONS IN SCHIZOPHRENIA *

Harry Stack Sullivan

I N INTRODUCING the following group of three papers concerned with the psychiatry of schizophrenic states, it seems meet that I comment on three outstanding considerations. The papers are reports of clinical research, about which in itself some words may be said. The papers are documents useful in the teaching of practical clinical psychiatry of the sort called intensive psychotherapy. Finally, the papers are in themselves contributions to the theory of psychiatry as the study of interpersonal relations, in these instances interpersonal relations which include schizophrenic and substitutive processes.

Clinical research has to be the principal tributary to the growth of psychiatry as a science and technology—in contrast with pseudoscientific and pseudopsychiatric "empiricism" and personal display for income and prestige. It is one of the, if not quite certainly *the,* most difficult fields of investigation with which man has concerned himself, perhaps, too, the most rewarding in terms of usefulness to the greatest number—a fact which is as yet chiefly unrecognized.

Clinical research is *participant observation* addressed to improving the living of the "patient" but also adequate enough, and well enough reported, to permit approximate repetition by others who find themeselves in significantly *similar* interpersonal situations.

* This paper has been somewhat expanded from remarks made at the time of presentation of the three succeeding papers.

The Foundation and its School which perpetuate the memory of the great teacher, William Alanson White, hold that psychiatry is the theory and practice of participant observation and interpersonal influence directed to uncovering difficulties in living in such a way that the patient's capacities can become more effective. Participant observation implies an ever-improving acumen "in" physician and patient for noticing what the patient "is doing" to the psychiatrist, and vice versa, along with but in ever more clearly recognized distinction to the more or less explicit "intentions" entertained by each.[1]

The momentary present of any interpersonal situation is the nexus of at least two duplex courses of events involving *recall* of the past and *foresight* of the at least closely neighboring future.

The duplex character of human events involved in the psychiatrist's work arises from the functional activity of the self-system with and in connection with *anxiety*. There are no people one is apt to encounter whose living is not strongly colored by recurrent experiences of anxiety and recurrent anxiety-avoiding or -minimizing performances.

The effectiveness of the psychiatrist as a worker in clinical re-research is in large measure a matter of his acquaintance with and facile recall of the security operations—the efforts to escape or to minimize anxiety—which he himself once lived and which now are being paralleled in the performances of the patient. His effectiveness increases in the measure that he is able correctly to foresee the anxiety-provoking aspects of his efforts at investigating, and thus to adjust his intervention towards optimum efficiency—with or without calling out anxiety "in" the patient but striving to learn from each instance of unexpected sensitivity, so that he does not twice evoke severe anxiety because he has "forgotten" what he had observed.

The idea that psychotherapy can proceed without a great many

[1] See, with reference to these culturally prescribed verbalisms, designed to avoid or minimize *anxiety* by claiming presumably esteemed motives, the discussion of the self-system in Sullivan's *Conceptions of Modern Psychiatry: The First William Alanson White Memorial Lectures* first printed in PSYCHIATRY and reprinted this year by the Foundation.

experiences of anxiety "in" the patient is utterly untenable. There is no credible basis for such an assumption, just as there is no justification for obtuse or indifferent blundering which calls out again and again such severe anxiety that it prevents the discovery of its particular interpersonal source.

It is necessary that the psychiatrist, as it were, map out the areas of the patient's living which are fraught with anxiety. He explores by participating in the occurrences of anxiety and participantly observing the security operations thereupon called out. This does not mean that he heedlessly stamps on the patient's self-respect, or kicks him again and again where he is tender. The fact that a distinguished research worker concluded that "any consultation with Sullivan is a stress interview" does not imply that the "victim" usually resents the experience. Had I not profited from some years of participating in stressful situations, it might be quite otherwise. Not but what there is still plenty to be learnt, but one hopes that even a surveyor shall not be content if he has to check up repeatedly on each numerical value produced by his exploration of a piece of ground.[2]

Clinical research calls for precise accuracy in observing the time order of events. As psychiatric events are both *covert*—subject to inference only—and *overt*—susceptible of notice by a perfectly unhampered participant—the impracticality of simple *correctness* has to be accepted along with the realization that unnecessary inaccuracy is prohibitive of any useful result. Without reasonably precise accuracy with respect to the time order of psychiatric events, most of the occurrences in the worker-patient relationship *cannot be interpreted usefully.* "Usefully" is the important word in this sentence. So-called interpretation, the sort of thing Johnny Jones does when you consult him about being beaten by your wife, or vice versa, is much easier if he knows only a few facts and nothing about the time order of your relationship. The whole numerically

[2] One of the usefully humbling observations of the writer's career is the fact that very few patients who suffer what is called "attacks of simple anxiety" ever return for a second interview. This observation, repeatedly documented, helpfully reminds one that he does not transmit in his views *the psychiatric word.* There is still plenty of room up front for (clinical) psychiatric research.

vast group of people who minimize or avoid anxiety by extraordinary recourse to "obsessive" or substitutive processes rather dote on "interpretations" based on inadequately observed and temporally confused courses of events. These so-called interpretations are interesting instances of success in *concealing* troubles; one might learn something—unhappily troublesome—of how to do it better.

Useful psychiatric interpretations essentially are statements of preferably alternative hypotheses *which in every case are to be scrutinized further.* The more useful of them are apt to appear slowly, to come into being only after the participant observation of numerous recurrences and congruencies in contexts much longer than a single interview. One hopes that after some years of training in psychiatry, one shall often be able, after two to nine hours of conference with a stranger, to present to him a meaningful statement about *some* important difficulty in his dealing with significant others. One is scarcely reasonable if he hopes at the same time to be certainly intelligible and significantly right in guessing (a) that this difficulty is *the* most important trouble the patient has in dealing with others or (b), even less probable, that the specified difficulty is the necessary outcome of sundry presumptively understood events in the patient's alleged personal history. The outcome of reckless enthusiasm is almost certain to make the psychiatrist and the patient feel foolish—except that such a psychiatrist cannot stand that degree of anxiety and often sacrifices the patient's progress to the protection of his own doubtful self-esteem, and the patient, as all too usual, cannot afford to judge correctly the psychiatrist's actual uselessness to him.

I must not take the time at this juncture to discuss the problem of *good clinical judgment.* I must instead emphasize that I mean more by precise accuracy in observing the time order of interpersonal events than an accurate recall of previous remarks on a particular subject. Not but what this is greatly desirable in a psychiatrist, but that which I have in mind—which is so nicely illustrated in these three contributions—is the gradual recognition of the dynamic interpersonal setting of recurrent, congruous details of interpersonal process in the long course of relationship with the patient, and the proper utilization of this data in interpretive questioning (see papers by Drs. Staveren and Cohen), *or* in exploratory alteration of the dynamic setting with keen observation of ensuing changes (see Dr. Tower's paper).

It is the psychiatrist's grasp on the longer contexts—the meaningful course of which can become clear to him while being concealed from the patient by the very processes for the relief of which he is undergoing treatment—that permits the type of intervention to which I have given the name, *psychotherapeutic operation.*

Moreover, the appearance of significant novelty in the doctor-patient relationship which, when reflected "to" the patient can be greatly revealing, is scarcely to be assessed accurately except on the basis of the longer contexts. The start of a complex process is often much easier to understand—and to make intelligible—than are its subsequent manifestations. Verbalisms and other devices to conceal, avoid, or minimize anxiety may take some time in being refined to the point where they successfully conceal the clues to dynamic significance of the change.

As to documents which are particularly useful in teaching practical clinical psychiatry, I would say that they are always accounts of participant observation which *start at the beginning* not of life but of the relevant data about which they indicate two categories of facts: those which might presumably have been observed by anyone of reasonable acumen and interest; and, carefully separated from these presumptively "objective" data, the facts of the observer's impressions about "his" and the "other fellow's" parts in the performance. Such documents proceed to recite the course of events, including the growing and changing impressions of the psychiatrist as participant observer, the hypotheses formed, and the steps used in testing the relevance and probability of these hypotheses. They culminate in demonstrating the relatively high probability of something of importance in terms of observation, experimental intervention, and explicit inference, capable of being followed by the reader and tested in significantly similar doctor-patient relationships.

I do not wish to seem to minimize the difficulty of *repeating* the interpersonal experiments from which psychiatric theory and technology derive their most valuable accessions. It is unlikely that the full long course of any instance of intensive psychotherapy or clinical research could ever be duplicated even approximately, even if such repetition were of some importance. The psychiatrist and his patient have in some measure *unique* career-lines. The measure of uniqueness is not apt to be anywhere near as great as the psychiatrist believes and the patient fears; but, much more important than this consideration, a great many of the significant events in their participation *could quite as well have occurred* in different personal contexts. These events may show fringes of insignificant uniqueness as do the physical attributes of one's pronunciation of a particular word on different occasions.

Some years ago, the young nephew of one of my friends was admitted to the Henry Phipps Psychiatric Clinic. The patient was suffering an acute schizophrenic disturbance, catatonic in type. He was placed under principal care of a close friend of mine, and I followed developments closely and saw the patient occasionally. As he became unmanageable, he was transferred to the Sheppard and Enoch Pratt Hospital, arriving there mute and requiring feeding by the nasal tube. He was extremely resistive to this feeding *unless* I did it, in which latter case he came to help with the insertion of the tube. I thoughtlessly took over on all these occasions and otherwise greatly interested myself in him. As he was convalescing quite nicely, he underwent what I call a malevolent transformation of interpersonal relations and became first mischievous and later definitely "hateful" on the ward. The outcome was a chronic dilapidating illness requiring State Hospital care.

From the few facts recited above and sundry other observations in my own and, mediately, other psychiatrists' work I inferred the theory of malevolent transformation of "personality," now taught in the Washington School of Psychiatry, after considerable supporting evidence as to its *current adequacy* had been derived from data on personality development.

In brief, this theory holds that if one progresses into a relatively enduring situation in which one's indicated needs for tenderness are customarily rebuffed, one comes to manifest malevolent behavior when one needs tenderness, in lieu of showing the need, and to expect—and by this pattern all but guarantee—an unfavorable attitude towards one in others.

The technological implication of the "case" and the theory as applied to my schizophrenic patient can be summarized for my present purpose as proving that a psychiatrist who collaborates with a patient in developing a relationship of extreme tenderness is undertaking a burden impossible to carry and thus assuring ultimate disaster—unfortunately to the patient only—by cultivating an expectation which is certain to be quite consistently rebuffed.

Some of you doubtless feel the need for a great deal more information about me and my patient, as you would say, to be sure I am right—as I would probably surmise, to be sure that there was nothing anxiety-provoking to you in me or the theory. Enough of those facts to establish either of these certainties would take a great many hours indeed for communicating, if actually you could seek and recognize these facts and remain intelligently "in touch" while suffering the strain to your self-esteem involved in discovering that psychiatry "makes sense"—is not solely a suave jargon with which to conceal ignorance profitably.

The contributions to the theory of psychiatry which I, under fortunate circumstances, can recognize are probable statements about how difficulties in living came into being, are maintained—continued—and may be remedied; these statements depend on accounts of courses of events in participant observation which demonstrate their inhering probability. As already suggested, these statements should be explicit enough to permit others to repeat approximately the psychiatrist's part in the therapeutic participation, or, if the outcome was disastrous as in my instance, to participate in a *significantly and explicitly different* experience.[3]

---

[3] This is not the occasion on which to set forth steps by which one could serve the administrative convenience of avoiding battles about "tube feeding" *without* encouraging an unearthly "dependency" by the patient on the psychiatrist's godlike special preoccupation with "being good to" the patient.

The three succeeding papers demonstrate with remarkable clearness the following rather important facts:

1. That the chronicity of a schizophrenic way of life does not preclude a collaboration with the patient important for psychiatry as clincial research *and* with benefit to the patient.[4]

2. That extraordinary use of obsessional substitutive processes is a feature of manifestly schizophrenic people—with the hint that schizophrenic states may prove to be the substitution of dreamlike referential processes for clarity about seemingly hopeless conflicts between needs and the avoidance of anxiety.

3. That the long context of the interpersonal relationship sheds useful light on the difficulties in living, while involvement in the obsessional content itself would get nowhere.

4. That this long-context approach is the prime function of the psychiatrist, because the patient's way of life precludes its appearance in easily recalled "free associations."

5. That the patient in this group has been denied much developmental opportunity, and that the handicap resulting from this must be remedied, at least initially, by *active* participation by the physician.

6. That "reassurance" is an intricate process depending chiefly on the patient's *inferences* from superficially unrelated remarks of the physician functioning as an *expert* in interpersonal relations.

7. That success in therapy and research is *basically* dependent on the physician's skill in handling the movements of anxiety in the patient.[5]

Besides these and many other important facts illuminated by these three papers, they show clearly some of the activities which

---

[4] This was long since demonstrated by Ernest E. Hadley in a study of "Chronic Hebephrenics" in St. Elizabeth's Hospital, never published because of the hesitancy of editors (including the writer) to violate the U. S. Postal Regulations and the investigator's—to me valid—idea that the purposes of psychiatric science were not served if meaningful data of research could be reported only after conversion into crude approximations in Latin.

[5] The term anxiety, as used here, is exceedingly easy to misunderstand. Some hints of the precise meaning here intended may be found in *Conceptions of Modern Psychiatry*, reference footnote 1.

are useful in improving the communication of patient and doctor, with increase in the significance of historical data obtained in showing us what does *not* work well in the evolution of personality.

Finally, I believe the thoughtful will obtain from a reading of these papers some highly probable information about "what ails" the schizophrenic way of life, notwithstanding many currently entertaining psychiatric fantasies.

SUGGESTED SPECIFICITY OF
CERTAIN DYNAMISMS IN A CASE
OF SCHIZOPHRENIA

Herbert Staveren

THE PATIENT is a 36-year-old unmarried woman whose home is in the West. Her overt illness probably began at the age of 13 or 14, shortly after she entered high school and began to menstruate. At that time a rather rapidly progressive withdrawal was noted, and there was a marked tendency to over-eat, with considerable increase in weight. At 16 she was sent to an eastern boarding school, where she was very unhappy and where she came to the attention of the principal who suggested to the parents that they consult a psychiatrist. The patient was seen by a psychiatrist, a diagnosis of schizophrenia was made, and she had a short period of office treatment. The parents made an attempt to have this only daughter go through the usual motions of acquiring an education, including trials at several colleges, but her difficulties continued to be marked and her discomfort with people remained so great that she led a very isolated existence. With her parents she remained uncommunicative and submissive.

When the patient was about 26, there occurred a noticeable improvement in the economic status of the parents. At the same time the patient had a rather long physical illness which led to considerable weight loss, following which she took an active interest in her appearance for the first time in her life. She began to dress well, used make-up, and on the whole affected a very brittle, excessively polite, superficial social manner. She went out a great deal, was flirtatious, talked excessively, and in her insistence in trying to solve other people's problems caused much embarrassment to herself and her parents. Rapidly her talking became more eccentric. She started smiling and laughing to herself and was found crying at times. When she was 31, the disturbance was so obvious that a friend of the parents, a psychiatrist, advised her hospitalization. She had a course of electric shock treatment without awareness as to what it was or as to the reasons for her hospitalization. There was a very brief period of improvement: she took a trip to Mexico with a friend of her parents and seemed to have a good time, but on her return developed the same difficulties as before. She was rehospitalized and this time received insulin shock, following which she became extremely resentful of the parents for consenting to treatment that the patient knew would not work. She developed delusions of persecution about the psychiatrist who had recommended hospitalization and mentioned several bizarre intentions of retaliation. She took a job as a waitress upon the urging of the local psychiatrist. This was her first work experience. She lasted for two weeks and was fired because of absent-mindedness and jumpiness. Matters became worse at home and she was committed. As a matter of last resort she was sent to this hospital.[1]

On admission she was an emaciated, frightened-looking woman, rather careless of her appearance. She talked incessantly, was extremely preoccupied and at times would talk to herself, smile and laugh, and frequently would burst out crying, unable to verbalize any reason for her crying. There was a complete disorganization of speech, ideas bursting forth at great speed and being interrupted continuously by any number of apparently unrelated thoughts. Answers to questions at times would begin by being relevant, but sentences were not finished, and there occurred frequent scatter. She felt that she had been very happy for five years, and perfectly all right, until her father decided that she was not to stay at home in idleness any longer, but that she should work; when she had not been able to get herself to work, he had had her treated with insulin shock and later committed. The patient also felt that she was a tramp or a WPA worker, which was the same as being insane, that life was hopeless, and that she would never be able to overcome

[1] Chestnut Lodge Sanitarium, Rockville, Md.

the blow of the treatment. She offered me five thousand dollars if I would smuggle her out. She thought the hospital was operated by a gang of racketeers who masqueraded as doctors, and that the real doctors were buried on the parking lot where, she felt, th name plates really were grave markers. She talked at great lengt and quite incomprehensibly about something that she called *The Line* which consisted of a series of significant statements and quotations. This *Line* was designed to improve relationships between people. It was preferable not to know about it at all; but if one did, one was obliged to memorize it accurately, in which job she had failed. One then was obliged to teach it to one's parents, and failure to do so successfully was likely to lead to commitment. Similarly, memorizing the *Line* incorrectly, or misquoting it, was dangerous and liable to lead to commitment. There was said to be something humorous in the *Line* which made one laugh to oneself and which people might mistake for insanity. Her difficulties, she stated, were largely due to her having been sloppy in the management of the *Line*. The attempt to quote "correctly" took up much of her time. She felt that grave danger attended slight changes in the wording, and for one's protection one must introduce the statements with phrases such as "They say" or "Some people say" or "There are some who." The same caution was observable in her speech in general, that is, questions about symptoms were usually introduced by "Have you ever seen patients who," and statements obviously referring to herself would be opened with "Aren't there some people who," and so on. It was very difficult to obtain samples of the content of the *Line*, as any knowledge of it, or getting mixed up with it might endanger me, but finally she consented to dictate a few statements:

They say there is something everyone should learn, that everyone should have a line on inferiority complexes. One should learn to be considerate of other people's feelings. That is the best approach to the subject. They say that many people have a little worry that they might wind up in an asylum, and needlessly probably. A *line* should be useful in this connection, but the subject is liable to become a diversion with some. They have a sort of liability which comes about through talking on inferiority complexes, that is the subject we are speaking about now. There is a false theory that people with inferiority complexes are crazy, or nearly so, or worse. This theory is involuntary, but they seem irresponsible at times. There is a flip expression "There's a bat in the belfry" which one should never take seriously, or seem to, even. This is the main thing. The most common explanation of this expression is that it is something that comes about through talking on inferiority complexes. It is nothing much and very common. They say you can't go crazy or not very, this way, but you might be surprised [laughter], 10 percent is the limit. There is a series of quotations. They are a curious phenomenon. These are the most likely to work out. [They were never mentioned.] Quotations coming out of a clear blue sky may be quite incomprehensible. There is not much wrong with "Tit for tat," or very, as long as it is not carried too far. The same holds for "An eye for an eye, an ear for an ear," the Mosaic law. It is legal precedent. These statements may sound a bit strong at times, almost vicious, but they aren't. The proper phrasing to use to keep out of difficulties is to say "Sometimes I am almost vindictive." This may be interpreted as a threat.

During the first few months, talk on the *Line* occupied probably 90 percent of all her verbalizations. Interspersed with this there occurred frequent mention of a doctor whose hand she would like to see cut off and whose eye she would like to see at the tip of a long knife. Also there occurred fairly frequent exclamations about "those five years when I was so happy." Relatively little was said about the family. It took several weeks to get a skeleton history from her, in the course of which considerable disorganization occurred every time resentment of her parents was mentioned by her.

The following gives a few necessary points of the history as obtained from the patient and her mother, mainly points which appear to have some bearing on the topic of this paper.

The patient is an only child, reluctantly conceived by the mother. The mother herself for many years suffered from fears concerning childbirth, from fears of cancer, and from the disgrace of her parents' divorce. She also felt chronically treated without consideration and respect, thought of herself as potentially a great artist had things been different with her parents, and apparently for years was determined that the patient fulfill her own lost ambitions, and so on. Her corrosive complaints choked off the patient's protests against discomfort and restriction. The patient's father came of a rural family and became a prominent attorney in the patient's home town. He failed to establish satisfying relationships with his wife and daughter and after a few years became engrossed in his work. He was depressed and alcoholic for a year just prior to a marked socio-economic betterment when the patient was about 26. At various times of his life the virtues of work formed the topic of his verbalized preoccupation.

During her first six years the patient was confined to the company of mother and grandmother. During the first few grades in school she was awkward, sullen, shy, without friends. Her attempts to make friends were discouraged by the mother. In the later grades she had one friend, a girl somewhat like herself, and at that time also her school work improved so that she graduated from grade school with very good grades. Between the ages of 12 and 14 the following events occurred: transfer to high school, menarche, death of grandmother, rapid weight gain, and withdrawal, marking the onset of her schizophrenic illness.

Two further items of the history may be significant here: with the cessation of parental pressure to force completion of a college career, there occurred a period of increased apathy, followed by almost a year of increased activity and apparently much improved socialization of a variety to be observed later in much more extreme form during the *Five Year Period*. The *Five Year Period* in turn was preceded by two stressful events: her inability to initiate any move to be of help to her father during his depression; and a rather autistic love affair which led to considerable humiliation.

I want to discuss the management within our therapeutic work over the course of two years of the following blocks of preoccupation: (1) the *Line;* (2) the *Psychiatrist* and the *Grave Markers;* (3) *Work;* and (4) the *Five Year Period*.

The course of therapy can be divided into several phases:

The first 4 to 5 months, during which I listened but could make out almost nothing. Attempts to learn to understand the meaning of the *Line* and of the *Psychiatrist* caused increased disorganization every time they were made.

The next 12 months, during which most of the pertinent data were established and during which were aroused in the patient the first suspicions that she was doing a number of things to escape or reduce anxiety. During this period I gave up trying to investigate the content of the major preoccupations, but attempted to discover at what points in our exchange they tended to appear in the discussion. This phase also marks the beginning of something getting established between us. The following incident occurred: The patient put a cigarette between her lips and held a match in her hand, about to light it. I struck a match and lit the cigarette for her, and she took a few puffs, and then proceeded to light her own match and relight the cigarette. I asked her to take time out and observe for a moment what had gone on. We were able to establish that though her senses had responded to my lighting her cigarette, there seemed to be no representation of that fact or of my person in her awareness. This made it possible for her to light the cigarette again herself, as if nothing had gone before. She summed this up by saying: "So, I'm talking out loud to myself rather than to you," and I tried to make the most of this by discussing this event as indicative of a lifetime of extreme isolation. This was followed by several weeks of increased disturbance and disorganization, at the end of which she suggested that her discussion of the *Line* was a ruse to evade treatment.

The last 6 months, during which she became progressively more often convinced that anxiety is due to things she does, thinks, feels. Also that certain "fixed ideas" (her own words) probably are not so but are held onto by her in order to avoid the kind of anxiety that leads to confusion.

As, during the second phase, her speech became clearer, there occurred some rather matter-of-fact statements about her life and her relationship with her parents and with a few other people. It then became possible to notice that a large cluster of ideas, apparently all charged with great anxiety, went into making up the *Line*. She had grave doubts about it herself, often started to question herself about its beginning, but never completely reported the

Line, nor did she ever get clear on its significance as long as we tried to understand it by content. Following her statement that it was a ruse to evade treatment, she could gradually be interested in the possibility of her *using* the *Line* at times when, for reasons of increased anxiety, it became necessary to slow down treatment. This made sense to her when I suggested that maybe her use of the *Line* was similar to her father's talk about work, which she felt occurred when he found himself stymied in his efforts to get somewhere with his family. At that time, when the *Line* did appear, it tended to stay 2 to 4 weeks, taking up by far the greater part of her hours.

After many months of working this topic over and over, it began to appear that the *Line* in some obscure way was saying something about her attitude towards the parents, and finally, when over the course of several weeks she had been growing more anxious and tense, she had a violent outburst of rage against the parents, pounded the chair, stamped her feet, and expressed a desire to torture them as she had been tortured by them. The next hour the *Line* was present in full force and remained with us for about two weeks. When relative calm had been restored we tried to establish what had happened. I had the impression that she saw that the *Line* had appeared as she became overwhelmed by anxiety following her outburst; but while we were still discussing this, the *Line* reappeared and continued for another week or 10 days. I did not again try to establish the connection with her. But when about a month later a similar outburst of vicious rage occurred, I said to her that in the past, following such explosions, we always had had the *Line* and asked whether she could interest herself in observing whether or not this time also the massive anxiety aroused by the outburst would lead to thoughts about the *Line.* The next hour she started off by stating that it was her own fault that she was in this predicament, for she had been warned when she learned the *Line,* and she had not heeded the warning. I stopped her and asked whether she remembered that at the end of the last hour we had predicted the return of the *Line.* There was some increase in tension, but then she did remember. We discussed for several hours her rage, the waves of massive anxiety following the rage, and her way of dealing with this by becoming preoccupied with the *Line*. That was the last of the *Line* in this form.

Once, about two months ago, following a prolonged expression of loathing and hatred for the mother over matters of sex, she said that she felt as if she were inclined to worry a little about that "ruse business." But she thought she knew that it was one of her crazy ideas which came when she got very nervous, and she thought that maybe she was quite a bit more nervous than usual at that moment. Since then she has begun to wonder whether the fact that during the *Five Year Period* she used to tell so many people about the *Line* meant that she really was being quite hostile; she felt that she must have been very uncomfortable with, and must have hated the people whom she associated with during that phase of her life.

We had a much harder time with the various paranoid notions that appeared here and there. There was, to begin with, the psychiatrist whose eye she wanted to see at the end of a knife. After she had been here for about a year, the father finally told us that this doctor had sent him several pamphlets on dementia præcox, all of them gloomy with bad prognosis. The father had carelessly left these booklets lying around the house and the patient had read them. He thought that not too much later the patient began to express persecutory ideas about the psychiatrist, insisting that he bore her father a grudge on the basis of some unsatisfactory business dealings he had had with the father many years ago and that he was trying to seek revenge by suggesting the patient's institutionalization, and so on. I made a number of attempts to deal with this topic factually and realistically, each time with increase in disturbance and hints that I probably was one of those who had it in for her.

Rather early in her stay here the *Psychiatrist* expanded into a larger paranoid system, for example, that the head of the sanitarium was the chief of a gang of racketeers who made it a business to smuggle committed patients out of the State in which they were committed and then blackmailed their families for years to come.

The entire staff was composed of racketeers masquerading as doctors; the doctors, whose places were now filled by the racketeers, had been killed and buried where the present staff parked its cars, and the name plates there were really the genuine doctors' grave markers. As time went on, the *Psychiatrist* merged more and more into and finally was entirely replaced by the *Grave Markers*. After our experience with the *Line*, I began to look for what preceded this topic of preoccupation. Gradually I thought I noticed that it followed expressions of shame and disgrace tied up with the fact that she had had a lunacy charge read to her and had been committed. I tried repeatedly to call to her attention the similarity of the appearance of this group of ideas to the general way in which the *Line* used to appear, but she could not see it that way. I did not realize at the time that she was correct and that I was wrong in drawing a parallel between the two preoccupations, as in *her* experience not only are the feelings arousing anxiety different, but particularly the ways of handling, or reducing, the anxiety are extremely different.

The next forward step occurred when she suggested that she might have some fixed ideas that were really quite crazy but that kept persisting, although in a way she seemed to know better. She thought she might discuss them, except that it was so very disturbing to her to think of herself as subject to fixed ideas. Eventually she did get around to stating her observation that when she was preoccupied with the *Grave Markers* and considered all the staff gangsters, this did not seem to interfere with her coming to her hours with me and at least trying to use me as a doctor now and then. She also noticed that she did not believe the *Grave Markers* all the time and that when she did, she was not as disturbed over the notion of being exploited and persecuted as that notion warrants. She thought that maybe there was something "paranoid" about the *Grave Markers,* and shortly after that insight she observed that the *Grave Markers* occurred whenever she got disturbed over the realization of the lunacy charge brought against her or when she thought about herself and her failure in moralistic terms such as shirking, laziness, tramp. After a while she extended this development and told me that at times she felt so ashamed of being such a "wash-out" that she could not bear the full realization of it; that when the true state of her affairs dawned on her at times, she became so anxious that she began to blame her present predicament on the fact that her parents had had her receive insulin treatments at a time when she was really quite well, that this treatment had made her so sick that she had to be committed, and that at that point she would get terribly confused, and she thought, would get preoccupied in a bewildered and harassed manner with the *Grave Markers*. This occurred about 5 months ago, and there has been no further mention of the *Grave Markers*.

The *Work* did not appear as a constellation used as an operation against anxiety, rather than as a communication, until after the patient had been in treatment for over a year. At that time, she was living in our open building, had full privileges—that is she could come and go as she pleased—and would occasionally go into Washington to do some shopping. She also rather frequently went to some of the local taverns for a few beers or wine fizzes. She apparently was able to make casual contacts with strangers and could tolerate contacts with nurses and attendants provided they took the initiative, but she could not tolerate contacts with other patients except at rare intervals and then only in small doses. At a time when the *Line* and the *Grave Markers* still appeared with considerable violence, she told me one day that she had gone into Washington and had answered an ad in a newspaper asking for a typist. The job was with an insurance company and it required some sort of an aptitude test. She had taken the test, but now she was not sure whether she had left her name and address. She had checked with a clerk at the desk and found out that it had taken her 10 minutes less than average time to complete the test, and she thought that she had answered all the questions. I showed considerable pleasure at this achievement, but suggested that she was not at all ready to go to work, since she had not even started to investigate why she still had to isolate herself to the extent she did. She became very disturbed and remained so for several days, accusing me of being like her mother and asking my permission to tell me to go to hell. She said that I made her very anxious, but could not discuss the matter any further at that time. She apparently achieved some calm by going rather lengthily into the matter of her mother's fear of cancer. After two or three weeks she told me that she had gone to the telephone company and asked for an application form for a typist's job. I again told her that I did not think she was ready to take a job, that I felt that she was capable of working, but that it would interfere with the treatment situation. She became very angry, threatened to leave the hospital, inquired about her legal rights, and so on.

When the upheaval had subsided somewhat, I asked her to get interested in the question of what was going on at the time she made these two attempts to secure work. She evaded for some time, talked about the necessity of work, and said that it was quite reasonable for her to feel that her self-esteem could not be restored until she had proved that she could work, and so on. I insisted that while this might be so, the problem of her relationships with people was a much greater one and would have to be solved before she could consider herself in shape for a job. Something in that seemed to make sense to her, and I reminded her again of what had happened with the other large groups of preoccupations. She got very busy working on that problem, and suddenly told me that while she did not like it, it was true nevertheless; that when she was 6, 8, or 10, she had serious difficulties with people, different in degree only from the ones she had now; and that at that age there certainly had been no issue about work and that as a matter of fact she had done rather well in school at that time. She then became curious about how she used the *Work* and thought that it had something to do with the realization that she was not just committed, but really mentally ill, which had frightening implications for her. She worked some more on this and concluded that the thing disturbing her most was the discovery of a *symptom* of mental illness. She apparently can talk about herself as mentally ill or as crazy without arousing much anxiety. The words themselves are detoxified. But the fact that she has fixed ideas, crazy notions, is disturbing. That is why the *Work* featured so prominently at the time she discussed "fixed ideas." A few weeks after the *Work* had given [way] to this extent, she said that she thought that there might be a possibility of her really getting well. While she had felt that she could only go so far—that is perhaps get a job, but have the misery continue inside—she had not been able to notice the extent to which she was sick and that is why she needed the *Work*. She felt now that if she did take a job at this time, it would mean cessation of treatment, although, of course, she would for some time go through the motions of having hours.

The last constellation, the *Five Year Period*, has become defined as a pattern only quite recently. It runs somewhat like this: "Once I was really happy, I had so much self-esteem, I felt I was good-looking, quite a charmer, I thought that I was interesting and popular and that people liked me and sought me out," and so on. If the patient is not interfered with, this has, during the last 6 to 8 months, tended to run into the following pattern: "Of course, if I had stopped to think I would have known all along that it wasn't so. I just ignored everything, my parents, my not working, my loneliness, and I kept building one illusion after another. I think I was awfully hard on people in those days. I would barge into them and sell them my ideas; I always insisted that I was being helpful, but I wasn't thinking about them, but only out to feel great and important," and so on. In spite of this insight the thing continued to appear. In recent months, however, there seemed to be more anxiety accompanying the *Five Year Period*. I did not think of the possibility that it too might be a preoccupation designed to deal with anxiety. During the last 12 to 15 hours, though, it has appeared to me that the *Five Year Period* is preceded by anxiety occurring with an accumulation of bits of evidence from various periods of her life, all indicating abysmally low self-esteem and almost complete lack of durable satisfactions. I have suggested this explanation to the patient a few times but have aroused so much anxiety as to permit her to deal with this in a dismissing manner. But indications are that the *Five Year Period* is some sort of an analgesic used on the sores of chronic frustration. Time will show whether this is the final answer or not. The fact that now and then she can discuss the *Five Year Period* in terms of a panic reaction set off by the humiliation entailed in her autistic love affair, rather than in terms of a period of mysterious recovery, suggests that she may be getting ready to deal with this anxiety in terms of the actual causes provoking it.

I do not know whether, at this time, there already are some large patterns of preoccupation similar to these, without my having been able to detect or define them.

It appears from what has been established so far that there may be a certain specificity of dynamism for certain areas in which anxiety is aroused, namely:

1. The *Line*, a predominantly obsessional process, occurred when anxiety was aroused by unmistakably hateful feelings expressed to me about the parents and recognized by the patient as such. She states that, as long as she can remember, she has been anxious or nervous whenever she has been angry at the parents. She feels that her mother's "corrosiveness"—I think she means her mother's way of throttling all protests by oblique blows aimed at the patient's self-esteem—has made it impossible for her to express what she felt, and that by the time she entered grade school she felt herself being "sucked into" a state of sullen gloom. It seems highly probable that she became addicted to obsessional substitutions for hateful feelings quite early in life, and the possibility suggests itself that the obsessional dynamism is the dynamism of preference for dealing with anxiety aroused by such hateful feelings.

2. The *Grave Markers*, unmistakably a paranoid system, occurred in relation to anxiety over the fact of overt mental illness. Mental illness became apparent in this patient around the time of her menarche, which was also the time when she began to realize that the best she could do in relationships at that time was a tepid friendship with a rather sick girl. There are some evidences of paranoid-

like explanations for her failure in relationships with other girls at the time, with much so far rather loose thinking about jealousy and envy, the objects being still rather hazy in the patient's mind. A problem for further study might be the question of specificity of this dynamism for anxieties aroused by conflicts—that is, being different and unfit for normal pre-adolescent relationships—which have their incipience at a stage of maturation when the personality also becomes capable of using the paranoid transfer of blame.

3. The *Work* appears to have obsessional as well as paranoid elements and seems to be somewhat less specific than the previous ones.

4. The *Five Year Period* has a strong manic-like coloring. It appears so far that the patient is handling the anxiety of complete despair by this manic-like dynamism, but there are not enough data about the manner in which this constellation is used by her to do more than to suggest a direction for study.

A few words about the patient's course since her admission to the hospital two years ago. She has remained extremely isolated. She still spends a great deal of time sitting on top of her bed, and when she is observed walking into town, and so on, she is obviously deeply preoccupied. But during the last six months she has now and then turned up with results after periods of deep preoccupation, and it has been mainly for this reason that the staff has not urged her very strongly into the usual hospital activities. Lately, there has been some inclination to make use of the nursing staff at times of increasing anxiety. In our relationship there has been considerably more freedom. She seems to be aware of my presence most of the time now, and our hours have assumed a very lively character with real give-and-take discussions. She has become aware of a need to argue and to fight, and she states that she finds herself again and again fighting for, or defending, an idea that she doesn't really believe in herself. This observation occurred somewhat concurrently with her discovery that she frequently feels a need to frustrate and to be "ornery," particularly with respect to her mother. She thinks that this originated when she entered high school and discovered that her mother had her life career all mapped out, that is, she was supposed to go to Vassar and later become a famous artist. She felt then that something irresistible was going on within her that made her weaker and more helpless all the time, and that now and then it would burst into awareness as a burning wish to defeat mother. She has become curious about the fact that the wish to frustrate mother seems to be greater by far than any striving for her own satisfaction, and she concluded that this may be due to her appallingly low self-esteem and her hopeless attitude as far as her own satisfactions are concerned.

A month ago she had a three weeks' visit from her mother, the first since her admission to the hospital. She made several discoveries in the course of this visit:

She realized that she did not particularly hate "this woman" who seemed to be rather old, pathetic, small, and much less frightening than the mother she had had all the trouble with before.

In spite of her realization that both mother and she have changed, she found herself wanting to be disagreeable to her mother. She thought that it was not entirely specific to mother, that she felt that way about most people, and that maybe some of her difficulties in treatment were due to the same motivation.

She noticed that many of the distressing patterns of dealing with people that she has become aware of in herself apparently are present in mother also.

She observed that something happened to her ability to give and accept affection, namely, when she was aware of her mother's friendly gesture she had to fight it and later minimize it in her own mind. At other times, when she was not too aware of what was going on, she later discovered that she had been quite capable of accepting affection from her mother and even of returning some.

On a few occasions she noticed that she suddenly again felt a little weak and helpless and then observed that she had not felt free to express some disagreement or protest against something her mother had said or done. She wondered later whether being weak and helpless was perhaps really a hateful act against the mother and whether perhaps most of her illness centered around that pattern.

The patient certainly is not at all near the end of treatment, but there seem to be ample indications that she is becoming progressively more able to tolerate rather massive anxiety associated with insight, provided she is permitted to move at her own speed. My impression at this time is that her outlook is rather favorable.

MANAGEMENT OF PARANOID TRENDS IN TREATMENT OF A POST-PSYCHOTIC OBSESSIONAL CONDITION

Sarah S. Tower

THIS PAPER will present the measures taken to avoid paranoid development in intensive treatment of an obsessionally defended person with a history of frank paranoid psychosis of brief duration.

The patient, Dr. B., is a 31-year-old man, born and raised in a small Southern town. His father is a carpenter. The patient is the elder of two siblings, having a sister four years younger. The parents are of old American Methodist stock, extremely narrow in outlook. Concerning the mother, the patient has been the only informant: Although the material presented has been scanty, she is clearly obsessional and sufficiently poorly adjusted to have had a menopausal depression. The father, by accounts both of the patient and of other persons, is a domineering and dependent person, also obsessive, and subject to recurring mild depressions. The sister is said by the patient to be also irritable, obsessive, and subject to depression.

After more than two years of treatment, I still know little about the patient's childhood, in part, apparently, because it is largely a history of non-occurrences, grim in its monotony, which the patient is exceedingly unwilling to recall or to recount. Under the operation of factors which are by no means yet clear, the patient led an increasingly isolated childhood and youth. By the age of eight or nine he had taken over, consciously, a habit of his mother's of categorizing the world about her into families better off or less well off than her own, an attitude which the patient had developed into

471

his chief orientation with respect to other persons: Are they "good," "better than I," "perfect," "to be associated with," or are they "bad," "having blemish," "to be dissociated from," or "like the man in the street"? When the patient presented himself for treatment, he had developed out of this trend an ego-ideal of being a "man of the world," a famous scientist, and mated in a "perfect marriage."

Dr. B's father had had an unfulfilled ambition to be a doctor which he transferred to the boy at an early age. The patient concurred in this plan through high school and college, with one tentative deviation, and then deflected his interest into medical research, partly, perhaps, in rebellion against the father, partly to build to a pinnacle a concept of himself as a "knower" which he had found useful in offsetting feelings of inadequacy at home and elsewhere. In consequence, he obtained a Ph.D. and was engaged in industrial research at the time of the outbreak of his acute illness.

This outbreak developed during the winter and early spring of 1942–43, when the patient was 27 years old. At that time he was working under pressure from an overbearing and neurotically anxious department head. And he found himself engaged to be married to a girl in a city at some distance. In midwinter the patient consulted a psychoanalyst, because of increasing tension and indecisiveness, and began treatment three times weekly. The indecisiveness applied to his full range of daily occupations, especially to those which involved meeting and talking with people, but applied most intensively to the problem of whether or not to marry. Was this the "perfect marriage"? By early spring the condition had flowered into a paranoid state with flamboyant delusions. He believed, for instance, that his office was a cell, that the people who walked up and down the corridor were guards or jailors; he heard others accusing him of homosexuality; and he had a "vision," possibly an hallucination, concerned with a cart like a tumbrel which was going to take him off to the State Hospital. Following a feeling in December 1942, that "something had snapped in his brain," he developed a preoccupation with the probable pathology of his own hypothalamus: Later developing suicidal thoughts were associated with this preoccupation in the notion of giving his brain to science for the study of schizophrenia, which he was then sure he had. In March of 1943, the psychoanalyst summoned the patient's parents and discussed with both of the parents the condition of the patient at that time. Hospitalization was arranged and the patient entered a mental hospital in March 1943.

On the patient's arrival at the hospital, the bizarre phenomena were again under cover, with depression and indecisiveness predominating. He expressed some fears of homosexuality and some suicidal notions, but rapidly reestablished his obsessive defenses. During his stay in the hospital, which was just short of one year, he had the benefit of intensive work with two able therapists, and enough was accomplished so that after nine months he could again take a position in industrial research.

Dr. B. was referred to me in September 1944. There was nothing unusual in the referral. However, other circumstances had established a complex situation between the patient and myself long antedating our first meeting. As it came to light in fragments, he traces his contacts with me back ten years, to a scientific meeting where he had heard me speak, and before that to being in college with my younger brother, and to a former contact, through a girl friend, with my sister—the whole integrated into a closely guarded fantasy which was uncovered, probably incompletely, only after a year and a half of treatment. Thus the treatment has been a problem in establishing and working through a real relationship as physician with an exceedingly rigid and uncommunicative man, in the face of this hidden fantasy stucture involving myself and tied in with the extensive fantasy which has always been for him a mode of living.

When Dr. B. presented himself for treatment, his chief complaint was "I feel the pull of people." As he illustrated this "pull" with banal incidents such as an invitation to dinner, a suggestion that he join the YMCA to play handball, a sailing expedition on which the skipper "ordered everyone around," the paranoid coloring of the complaint became unmistakable. The complaint has persisted to the present time, but the coloring has varied from paranoid exaggeration and justification, through acute resentment with anxiety, to querulous defensiveness of a no longer tenable position, and finally to an habitual mode of speaking in which he refers to the tension he feels in interpersonal relationships.

As I said, Dr. B. is an extraordinarily uncommunicative person. He forces his words out and at the same time blocks them, with an endless series of chokings, swallowings, wringing of the hands, clenching and beating of the fists, jerkings of the head, and movements of the body and legs. This ensures the expenditure of a large part of his time and energy, in and out of the treatment hours, in a performance by rote. The realization on his part of how this obstructs the treatment and the further interpretation, offered by himself, of the hostile nature of much of the feeling portrayed in this have had little ameliorating effect, as is the case with all verbalized understanding on his part.

The first two and one-half months of treatment went by in this lame fashion, with some clarification of history and with disturbing indications of an underlying process such as: "I have a feeling that everything you do or say has a superhuman validity." At the end of this period came an exceedingly halting hour in which the patient uncovered his need for perfection in me, his fear of finding a blemish. For the following two weeks, the patient ranged over his demands for perfection in himself and others, climaxing an involved eulogy of perfection with the statement, "If I felt I had a blemish, I could not exist." At the same time his feelings of being "pushed" by women, including myself, and "pulled" by men increased sharply in intensity. Pressed by the threat of paranoid development and remembering that the paranoid psychosis had flared up at about this point in his previous attempt at treatment, I was much concerned to counter this trend, but my efforts to make the patient aware of its fantastic quality only seemed to underwrite the movement.

In reviewing my handling of the case, an outstanding feature seemed to be the way in which increasingly I had coddled this patient, partly in an almost automatic—even physical—endeavor to facilitate his labored communication, partly from my original fear of the paranoid possibilities and increasing concern over them. I realized that my tone of voice especially had come as it were to woo his confidences, even though the content of my comments remained fairly objective. Clearly this was playing into his fantasy of being "pulled." Accordingly, an abrupt reversal of this attitude—accomplished largely by realization of what I was doing but evidenced again by change of voice, this time from concern to flat matter of factness—was followed by a "forgotten" appointment, a unique occurrence with this obsessional patient; this was rapidly followed by more down-to-earth talk of perfection, ending in painful disclosure of the patient's feelings that his mother is vulgar. For the five months following, until a three-month summer intermission, the work continued with—for this man—increasing productivity and spontaneity and with a steady broadening of the basis of the relationship between us. Throughout this period and to the end of the second year of treatment, I repeatedly and baldly stressed the professional nature and limitations of our relationship in an endeavor to counter his flamboyant fantasies of intimacy with me sufficiently so that the real intimacy of the physician-patient relationship might develop. Moreover, having seen the deflationary effect of a sharp, unsympathetic tone of voice on a paranoid process, under the pressure of my own disinclination to become involved in a paranoid twosome, I found that this verbal statement of non-intimacy was automatically backed up and made real in tone of voice in proportion to the paranoid coloring at any particular time. In sharp contrast, I tried to meet any offerings of simple real feeling, either friendly or hostile, with warmth and extreme simplicity and with a minimum of interpretation.

Throughout the second year, the patient made a steadily increasing investment of real experience in the analytic relationship, with a corresponding falling-off of reported outside experience. On the anniversary of beginning treatment, the patient volunteered: "Before going to bed last night, I had a flashing thought. It came to my mind that I didn't have to worry so much about these ideals of perfection. I can leave them to be worked out here. It's an idea that just came and went." The patient himself worked out the relationship between the loss of feeling which comes with isolating himself and his increasing "comfort," that is, relief from anxiety: Following this he was able to tolerate much more anxiety in the hours. By the new year the patient presented a fairly typical obsessional pattern of behavior, with the schizoid elements in the background and somewhat neutralized. With these changes in the patient, I, too, felt freer and more at ease in the treatment. In consequence, we were able to focus more clearly on the therapeutic relationship and work with its real and fantastic elements; this was still effected in considerable degree by living out situations with the patient, but increasingly also by considering and interpreting them, even though the patient's obsessional blurring continued to distort the focus.

As the therapeutic relationship thus took on real substance, instances of bizarre and frank paranoid process continued to occur. One such will illustrate. A picture of mountains had hung at the foot of my couch ever since the patient had been coming to see me. In February of this second year he brought this out: "For the past few days I have had a conviction that you hung that picture there to influence me in the direction of greater strength and masculinity." I met this with a flat—"You think that I would go about dealing with you that indirectly, by hanging a picture on the wall?" In this instance, my unreceptive stand—while it prevented exploration of the fantasy as such and kept me as a somewhat real figure out of paranoid involvement—also led to the patient's turning sheepishly to consider: "It seems I'm just beginning to learn what it is to be direct with people, you and others, in the last few weeks." Moreover, in bringing out this and other paranoid notions, the patient's attitude toward them had changed as compared with the earlier period. Although his attitude was still delusional in the instance described, as I evaluate it, he brought this and other paranoid processes out for consideration without expectation or apparent wish that I participate in them. On the contrary, I was established in my position as physician, to be used as such. It was at this point that the patient brought out for consideration the circumstances and fantasies relating to me which antedated our professional relationship by about ten years and sketched the bare outlines of the

elaborate fantasy underlying his initial approach to me. This disclosure, in the face of my deflationary attitude towards his fantasies,
amounted, in effect, to renunciation of the fantasy and put us in
a position, not to analyze the fantasies as such, but to attack their
use as a prime element in his defense, by isolation, against the
impinging demands of reality.

With the spring of the second year, we seemed to have established a sufficiently broad and real patient-physician relationship
to enable the patient to dispense with paranoid and other psychotic
defenses altogether. The most that I have heard since then has
been a tentative—and immediately discounted—suspicion that in
certain circumstances I might be testing him, followed usually by
sharp spontaneous discrimination on the patient's part between the
reality of my moves and his fantasy. At the outset of the third year
of treatment, the patient received an advantageous offer of a position in another city, which he accepted after some debate. After
a brief further period, treatment was brought to a close. Although
this brought out much hostility in the patient as well as much
passivity, there has been no recurrence so far of the paranoid
processes so readily evoked in this patient at a prior time.

Emphasis on reality with de-emphasis on fantasy is, of course,
a prime move in treatment of a basically psychotic condition such
as Dr. B. presented at the outset. But my bald—often rude—reception and handling of his fantasies, especially any with paranoid coloring, went beyond de-emphasis. This was, I believe, the important
step in avoiding paranoid development. It was effective, I believe,
not so much because it demonstrated my unwillingness to be involved or my disapproval of the process, as because it was present
proof that I was an unsuitable object, at least at the moment, for
that intimate relationship he had in mind—I was unsuited to share
his fantasy world. And this was brought home to him, not by
verbal statement, but by immediate experience, chiefly by my tone
of voice. I made these moves primarily for the patient's and my
own protection and to ensure my long-range usefulness to him,
sacrificing immediate closeness. I heard during this long period
much complaint from the patient, both direct and indirect, that he

could not get close to me. Yet this general deflationary working atmosphere gave to the rare—but increasingly frequent—occurrences of real, shared feeling a contrasting vividness. These, as I say, I endeavored to meet with tenderness—and any bits of genuinely spontaneous, free-flowing talk, with enthusiasm.

On first consideration, this active rejection of a transference relationship, the refusal to exploit it, appears to be contrary to the basic principle of psychoanalytic technique. Certainly, at these points, I did not analyze the patient's highly pathological mental and emotional processes. The procedures described belong to a process which must precede analysis in persons with as weak a grasp on reality as the patient—and to a greater extent with frank psychotics. This process is the establishment of—and education of the patient to—a real physician-patient relationship. In dealing with persons with a better grasp on realities, such as neurotics, this process may need little specific attention or run concurrently with transference analysis.

Since clarifying these essentials of management of paranoid trends with this case, I have had occasion to try them out in two other cases with somewhat similar, somewhat differing difficulties. Both of these were also young men who were university students. The one is a patient who has been under my care, first, for a year in a mental hospital and then for nearly three years since discharge. He was hospitalized with a schizophrenic reaction, presenting a delusion of body odor but no paranoid developments. However, during the three years he has been under treatment with me after discharge from the hospital, he has fallen back on paranoid defense whenever the problems of coping with a very difficult real situation threaten to overwhelm him. And repeatedly the paranoid process has begun to involve me. By resort to attitudes and procedures similar to those described, I have in each instance so far been able to extricate myself and help the patient to maintain his tenuous critique of reality. Currently this patient seems on the road to establishing a way of living in our culture, independent of me.

The second patient I saw at the onset of the incapacitating phase of a schizophrenic reaction. He was obviously in need of hospitalization, but his paranoid thinking made the consideration of that difficult. Again, in weekly sessions over a six weeks' period, very active utilization of the measures under discussion, far from alienating this suspicious and withdrawn young man, made him accessible to considering his real needs and willing to accept hospitalization.

THE MANAGEMENT OF ANXIETY
IN A CASE OF PARANOID
SCHIZOPHRENIA

Robert A. Cohen

IN THE YEAR before her transfer to Chestnut Lodge, the patient, a single woman in her late twenties, was admitted to two other mental hospitals. At the first hospital, she complained of easy fatigue, sensitivity to noises, a feeling that the lower part of her face was paralyzed, and fears that she might fall unconscious and bite her tongue. These difficulties had developed in the setting of an unhappy love affair in which she was rejected by the man to whom she was attracted; she is also said to have been "overworked" in her position at a public educational institution. She desired psychoanalytic treatment but her psychiatrist, who had diagnosed the condition as a mild anxiety state, advised against it. After a rapid superficial improvement, pressure was brought upon her by the psychiatrist to leave the hospital. This she would not do, despite his refusal to continue treatment. Six months after her admission, he is quoted as saying she was not sick enough to remain in a hospital. However, when she was transferred to a second hospital only five days later, she was withdrawn and indifferent; she smiled and giggled inappropriately; she described hallucinatory sensory experiences and expressed delusions of reference concerning her former physician who, she felt, had personally arranged for her transfer and for the many significant events which were happening to her. She remained remote and inaccessible. A diagnosis of dementia præcox was made, and when she showed no improvement in response to routine institutional management, it was recommended that she receive electric shock treatment. This advice was rejected by her family who were interested in securing analytic aid for her, and she was transferred to Chestnut Lodge. She was not informed of the transfer from the second hospital to Chestnut Lodge until the day it was to be made. At that time, her physician called her from the breakfast table, informed her she was to be transferred, gave her an injection of scopolamine, and escorted her to the car in which, accompanied by her father and eldest sister, she made the trip to Chestnut Lodge.

Ten days later I began seeing her four times weekly. At the time of our first interview, I found a fairly well developed girl so thin as to appear somewhat scrawny and taller than her 5 feet 6 inches. Her dark hair was roughly combed and hung down about her shoulders. She wore a particularly unattractive blanket bathrobe. Everything about her was hard and angular. Her facial expression was solemn and humorless. She was cold and remote in manner. She spoke only in response to questions, and her remarks were brief, laconic, and specific. She asserted that she felt fine except for fatigue, that she had come to the hospital only for a rest before taking a new job, and that there was nothing for us to discuss. On the ward she was polite when approached by hospital personnel and by other patients, but was so unresponsive as to discourage any friendly interest. She spent all of her time in her room, most of it in bed, apparently sleeping throughout the night and for many hours during the day. She occasionally read the newspapers and paged through the magazines. She showed no interest in the radio. Her appetite seemed poor, but it was noted that she ate everything from a box of fruit sent her from home. No hallucinations or delusions were elicited at this time, however. Her sensorium was clear; she appeared clinically to be of superior intelligence, and there was no obvious impairment of mentation. She was quiet but forceful in her denial of any manifestations of illness, emotional or otherwise.

This report deals only with the first year of treatment. She was on an open ward during the last seven months of this period, but there still remained much psychotherapy to be done. She is presented chiefly to demonstrate some of the methods employed in the management of anxiety in a paranoid schizophrenic.

FAMILY HISTORY

The patient is the youngest of three daughters of a retired educator who resumed teaching to pay for his daughter's treatment. The father is an extremely reserved, phlegmatic person with no capacity to express his emotions. Apparently, he tried to give his daughters some emotional support, but when he found himself unable to understand them, he withdrew entirely. During my only interview with him, he was extraordinarily ill-at-ease; he had absolutely no knowledge of his daughter's feelings and fearfully retreated from even the most superficial discussion of them. He was very close to and dependent upon his own mother until her death when he was 50 years old, a fact which may account for his marital difficulties. The patient's mother, in her sixties, is a self-centered, dominating person who has always been demanding and punctilious in the observance of social forms, but quite without interest in people as persons. Her own sister describes her as one who never faces facts, who puts up a false front, and who tries to make out that things are not what they seem. The parents have always been unhappy in their marriage, there have been frequent open quarrels in front of the children, and in recent years they have virtually separated.

The two sisters of the patient are regarded now as reasonably well adjusted. The eldest, 10 years the patient's senior, is a widow with one child. Her marriage was not a happy one. After her husband's death, she was quite troubled, went into analysis and now, after two years, is presumably more comfortable than ever before. Until she broke away from home, this daughter was the mother's favorite.

The second sister, six years older than the patient, was by far the most successful of the girls. She was an outstanding student and was popular with her colleagues withal. She married a brilliant educator. He also has been analyzed. This sister was the father's favorite, but she has now broken away from the parents, speaks bitterly of them, and tried to influence the patient to follow the same path. She was primarily responsible for the patient's transfer to Chestnut Lodge.

This family setting was not one calculated to provide any notable degree of emotional security for the patient. At the time of her birth, after some 12 years of marriage, the parents had given up hope of mutual happiness and had begun to drift their separate ways, their sole remaining bond being the recriminations cast chiefly by the mother. The mother apparently never had much interest in the patient. It was common knowledge in the family that she had wanted a son, if she had to have children at all, and the patient recalls that at the age of 6, she asked her mother if she would have preferred a boy and was told, "Well, it would have been nice." The father did afford her some support; she dimly recalls that he sang and read to her, that she enjoyed hearing him play the violin, and that he would take her sleighing on the steep hill in front of their home. But these moments of closeness grew infrequent, and except for the events during a trip to Europe when she was 10 years old, she grew progressively more lonely. She was separated from the rest of the family by physical as well as emotional space. The parents' bedroom and the rooms of the two elder daughters were on the second floor of the home, while the patient's room along with that of the maid was on the third floor. She recalls being excluded from her sisters' rooms, and once she broke a window in protest against this. But for the most part, she accepted her assigned status, played by herself in her room, and of course came to resent intrusion on her privacy by the others.

When the second sister went to France on her scholarship, the patient, age 12, was promoted to the vacant room on the second floor, and at the same time to the position of confidante of her 22-year-old sister on whom she developed a "crush." At that time the sister was in the midst of a quarrel with the father who did not approve of her artist friends; for five years the father and daughter lived in the same house and spoke to each other only when it was necessary. The sister weaned the patient away from any lingering attachment to the father by winning her sympathy in this quarrel.

The sister spoke of her boy friends, her hopes, and her dreams. She told of her dates. She talked of her plans for her future work. All this enchanted the patient, and for the ensuing year her happiness was bound up in this relationship. But then the sister went off to Europe to study art, and the patient was again left alone.

Meanwhile, her schooling had followed the family pattern. She attended a private coeducational school between the ages of 5 and 10. She remembers little of this period; she lived far from the school, felt isolated from her fellow students, and made few friends. She was a reserved and withdrawn child who spent much time daydreaming of becoming a famous aviatrix. Her grades at school were poor, she was generally moody, and even her pleasant fantasies did not prevent her from seriously contemplating suicide at the age of 10. One day she went so far as to climb out on the roof of their home but retreated to her room after an hour of indecision. She had no close friends at this time. There were a few girls in the neighborhood, but her mother disapproved of them as not having the proper background and effectively discouraged the development of any intimacy. At 10, the patient transferred to the private girls' prep school which had been attended by her mother and sisters and which was referred to by the sisters as a "snob factory." She welcomed this change, and during her first year her teacher reported that she was one of the more popular girls in her class. She feels that this was mainly because of her athletic prowess. In any event, she did not maintain her position but soon withdrew into her shell. This coincided with a period of much discord at home, and her suicidal thoughts were prominent at this period. In the ensuing years she became more moody and inarticulate. Her mother told her that her teachers did not consider her college material, and this confirmed her own feelings of inadequacy. She dropped the college preparatory course and was little interested in her work.

After graduation at 19, she was sent for her year in Europe. This was suggested by her mother shortly before the end of the school term, and was welcomed by the patient who had no other plans. Accompanied by her mother, she spent most of her time in Italy,

Switzerland, and southern France. On the whole, the trip was fairly pleasant. Away from her husband, the mother was no less bored with life, no less supercilious in attitude toward interests she considered "common," but at least she was less complaintive and less demanding. The patient was permitted to go about by herself during the day, made several friendly contacts with other tourists, and acquired some interest in the history of art and enough in herself to contemplate entering college. On her return to the United States, she attracted the favorable attention of several young men, two of whom continue to write her to this day.

She determined that she would attend the college where her sister had made such a brilliant record, but since she could not meet the entrance requirements, it was necessary first to go to another school to acquire sufficient credits. She went to a small state college for women and made a superior academic record, but remained isolated socially, partly because she considered it an inferior school and partly because she felt she could not compete successfully for men with her classmates. She then transferred to her sister's college where her grades dropped to place her in the middle of the class, but she did achieve a moderate social success. Her school life was clouded by frequent reports of serious difficulty between her parents. Their letters always carried their latest battle news and expressed little interest in her own activities. She was sufficiently disturbed about all this to consider consulting the school psychologist, but could not bring herself to do so—torn as she was by her desire to free herself from her parents, by her feeling that it was her duty not to do so, and by the fear that she could not support herself without their aid anyway.

As graduation approached, she found herself sorely troubled as to the future. She wished to go to Chicago and secure a job, but felt too insecure to face the prospect of searching for an acceptable opportunity. She did not wish to return home but felt that she could not ask her father to continue to support her away from home. A possible solution appeared in the offing when her brother-in-law died and her mother went West planning to remain with her eldest daughter for an indefinite period. The patient then decided she would go back to Cleveland, stay with her father, and try to get started on some type of career. But her mother returned in three weeks complaining bitterly about the sister, and then there commenced an unhappy period at home with the parents bickering, quarreling, or giving each other the silent treatment.

Meanwhile the patient found herself as unhappy in her work as she was at home. She took a voluntary assistantship at a public educational institution but found it uninspiring and left. She next did drafting work on a war project, understood that she had received a promotion, and then became bitterly resentful when the previous incumbent returned, presumably from vacation, causing her to be returned to student status. Instead of protesting, however, she took a two-week vacation without informing the authorities and returned to find herself released. She went back to the first job but without any better result. She finally persuaded her parents to let her move to a rooming house and then suffered agonies because she regarded the situation as so abnormal. She attended secretarial school but dropped out because of lack of interest. After a boring summer with her parents at their summer home in Michigan she decided to go to Chicago to become a teacher in a nursery school, but this, too, proved unsatisfying. She was lonely and miserable and made few social contacts, despite the fact that her second sister lived in the city and, in fact, sent her children to the school at which the patient was in training. This sister had a great interest in the Rorschach Test, and she sent the patient to have one. It was not interpreted at that time because of the death of the psychologist, but the protocol has since been reviewed and is reported as showing obvious anxiety, violent and uncontrolled emotional responses, and a tendency toward overt rebelliousness and explosiveness.

Three years after graduation, the patient managed to transfer from her lonely rented room to one in a college dormitory, and shortly thereafter secured a position as teaching aide in a public educational institution. These two events made a marked difference in her life. Her social opportunities increased, and for the first time since college she made one close girl friend and several good ones.

Although she took the place of a girl who had been an outstanding success on the job, she pitched into the work, mastered it, and displayed considerably ingenuity and originality in her class presentations. Nor were her efforts bent only to teaching; despite initial opposition, she proposed and carried through several time-saving and logical changes which conflicted with established routines.

Onset of Illness

At this time, she met a graduate student two years younger than herself. She recognized that he was diffident, prim, and somewhat effeminate as compared to the young men in whom she had been interested in the past, but nevertheless she found herself becoming more and more attached to him. Several embarrassing incidents did not cool her ardor. On one occasion, while they waited for a bus, she perched herself on the ledge of a bank window and kicked her legs only to be reproached for such an unseemly show. On another, she grasped his arm while they were walking, but he became so stolid and wooden that she turned into a store half a block away so that she might release him without too great a loss of self-esteem. When she took him to her sister's home, her brother-in-law not only displayed little interest in him but actually turned away in the midst of their visit to read a book, and the sister later criticized the young man for faults the patient herself could see. Nevertheless she thought herself in love with him, and was consoled by her mother's approval of her choice. It is difficult to say whether she ever had any reason to believe that her feelings were reciprocated, but in any event the man finally turned definitely to a younger, more vivacious woman who the patient thought was pursuing him. She became deeply depressed over this, refused to speak to him when he telephoned her, and was quite inconsolable. A vacation did not help.

She once more began to feel her old pangs of inadequacy. To complicate matters, she was forced to leave the dormitory, having long since lost her status as a student, and she could not make the effort to keep up her previous social contacts. She became preoccupied with her failure and discouraged about the future. She lost appetite and weight. Her sleep became restless. At first her work still held her interest and attention, but after a few months she felt she could no longer keep going. She sent a telegram to her father, who was at that time living alone, and went to stay with him before he could reply. She spent a month at the inn where he had rooms; most of the time she remained in bed, complaining of weakness and fatigue. She improved slightly, then went to visit her eldest sister. There she became more depressed, spoke of suicide, and was so preoccupied as to frighten the sister. However, it was on the patient's own initiative that she eventually consulted a physician and sought entrance to a sanitarium where she gave the complaints first described above.

Her psychiatrist diagnosed a mild anxiety neurosis, but I quote from her written description of her feelings:

> Alone on a cold, bleak, wind-swept plain
> Might as well die; no one would care
> No life, no love for me—this weird strange me
> Stripped of myself and clothed in gray
> Just a shell so empty and cold
> Nothing in me even to rattle
> Life seems a sham
> I've been pulled and flattened
> Squashed and squeezed,
> Pulverized to dust and hardened
> A new pattern takes shape, and I'm afraid
> What is this to be
> Such agony must bring some fruit
> Something beautiful might emerge
> Or will it be just void
> There seems to be only me
> I can't react to anyone
> But there were times when the pavement felt like clouds
> And life was blossoming
> Now the flower has withered
> And a new bud is growing.

Evidently her doctor had little time to spend with her, so he had her write her free associations down on paper. He would read